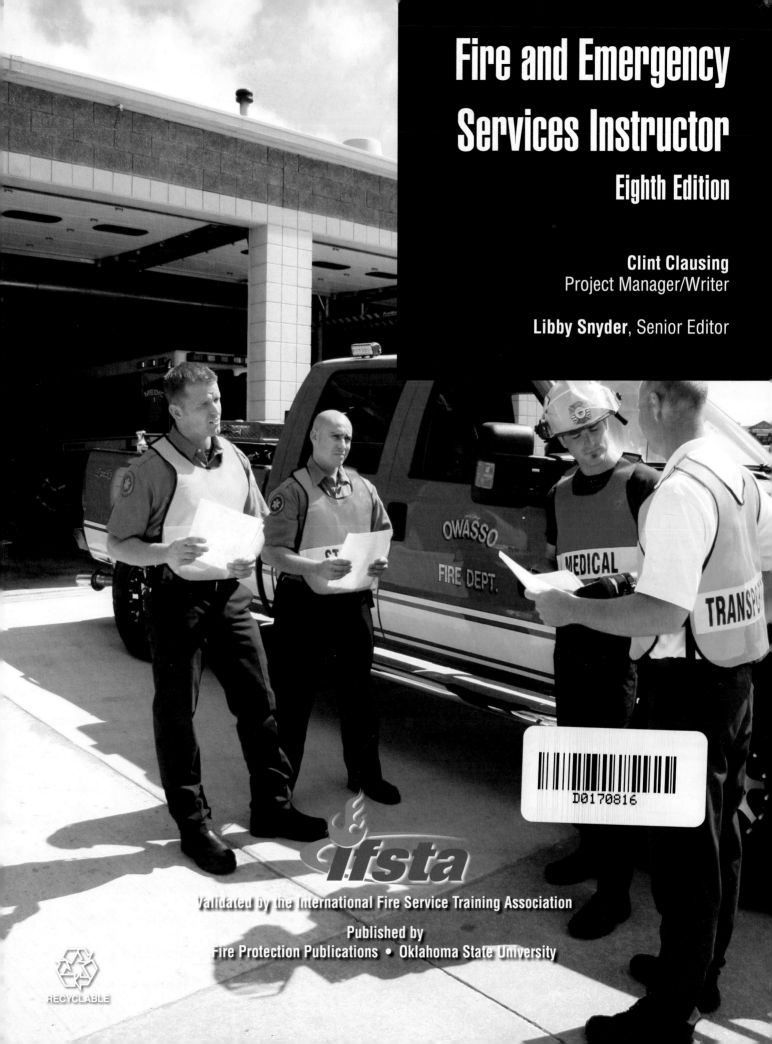

Fire and Emergency Services Instructor

Eighth Edition

Clint Clausing
Project Manager/Writer

Libby Snyder, Senior Editor

Validated by the International Fire Service Training Association

Published by
Fire Protection Publications • Oklahoma State University

RECYCLABLE

The International Fire Service Training Association

The International Fire Service Training Association (IFSTA) was established in 1934 as a *nonprofit educational association of fire fighting personnel who are dedicated to upgrading fire fighting techniques and safety through training*. To carry out the mission of IFSTA, Fire Protection Publications was established as an entity of Oklahoma State University. Fire Protection Publications' primary function is to publish and disseminate training texts as proposed and validated by IFSTA. As a secondary function, Fire Protection Publications researches, acquires, produces, and markets high-quality learning and teaching aids as consistent with IFSTA's mission.

The IFSTA Validation Conference is held the second full week in July. Committees of technical experts meet and work at the conference addressing the current standards of the National Fire Protection Association® and other standard-making groups as applicable. The Validation Conference brings together individuals from several related and allied fields, such as:

- Key fire department executives and training officers
- Educators from colleges and universities
- Representatives from governmental agencies
- Delegates of firefighter associations and industrial organizations

Committee members are not paid nor are they reimbursed for their expenses by IFSTA or Fire Protection Publications. They participate because of their commitment to the fire service and its future through training. Being on a committee is prestigious in the fire service community, and committee members are acknowledged leaders in their fields. This unique feature provides a close relationship between the International Fire Service Training Association and fire protection agencies, which helps to correlate the efforts of all concerned.

IFSTA manuals are now the official teaching texts of most of the states and provinces of North America. Additionally, numerous U.S. and Canadian government agencies as well as other English-speaking countries have officially accepted the IFSTA manuals.

ISBN 978-0-87939-441-7   Library of Congress Control Number: 2011944984

Eighth Edition, First Printing, January 2012   *Printed in the United States of America*

10   9   8   7   6   5   4   3

If you need additional information concerning the International Fire Service Training Association (IFSTA) or Fire Protection Publications, contact:

Customer Service, Fire Protection Publications, Oklahoma State University
930 North Willis, Stillwater, OK 74078-8045
800-654-4055   Fax: 405-744-8204

For assistance with training materials, to recommend material for inclusion in an IFSTA manual, or to ask questions or comment on manual content, contact:

Editorial Department, Fire Protection Publications, Oklahoma State University
930 North Willis, Stillwater, OK 74078-8045
405-744-4111   Fax: 405-744-4112   E-mail: editors@osufpp.org

Chapter Summary

Table of Contents

List of Tables

Preface

The eighth edition of the **Fire and Emergency Services Instructor** manual is designed to match NFPA® 1041.

Acknowledgement and special thanks are extended to the members of the IFSTA validating committee who contributed their time, wisdom, and knowledge to the development of this manual.

IFSTA Fire and Emergency Services Instructor
Eighth Edition Validation Committee

Chair
Randal E. Novak
Bureau Chief
Iowa Fire Service Training Bureau
Ames, IA

Vice Chair
Gary Wilson
Training Chief
Overland Park Fire Department
Overland Park, KS

Secretary
Anna Wieringa
Firefighter, Fire Instructor
Deadwood Volunteer Fire Department
Deadwood, SD

Committee Members

Gary Allen
Captain, Retired
Tampa Fire Rescue
Valrico, FL

Steven Edwards
Assistant Chief
Ingalls Fire District
Stillwater, OK

Assistant Chief David Fisher
Whiteman Fire Emergency Services
Whiteman AFB, MO

George A. Jamieson
Regional Training Coordinator
Fire Service Training
Oregon Department of Public Safety
     Standards & Training
Pendleton, OR

Captain Richard Llewellyn
Spokane Valley Fire Department
Spokane Valley, WA

Steven J. Martin
Deputy Director
Delaware State Fire School
Dover, DE

Brandon Poteet
Professor EMS Education
Grayson County College
Denison, TX

Bianca Thompson
Baltimore County Fire Department
Baltimore, MD

Much appreciation is given to the following individuals and organizations for contributing information, text, photos, photo shoots, or other contributions instrumental in the development of this manual:

Michael Boub, committee contrbutor

Wayne Chapdelaine, committee contributor

Tim Kreis, committee contributor

Lora Polson, College of Engineering, Architecture, and Technology, Oklahoma State University

Mandi Robedeaux, HES Academic Programs and Services, Oklahoma State University

Overland Park Fire Department, Overland Park, Kansas

Fire Service Training at Oklahoma State University

Jon Neely and the Edmond Fire Department, Edmond, Oklahoma

Owasso Fire Department, Owasso, Oklahoma

Spokane Valley Fire Department, Spokane, Washington

National Fire Protection Association® for use of annexed material from NFPA® 1403

Last, but certainly not least, gratitude is extended to the following members of the Fire Protection Publications staff whose contributions made the final publication of this manual possible.

Fire and Emergency Services Instructor, 8th Edition, Project Team

Project Manager/Writer
Clint Clausing, Senior Editor

Director of Fire Protection Publications
Craig Hannan

IFSTA/Curriculum Projects Coordinator
Ed Kirtley

Coordinator, Publications Production
Ann Moffat

Editor
Libby Snyder, Senior Editor

Illustrator and Layout Designer
Ruth Mudroch, Senior Graphic Designer

Curriculum Development
Andrea Haken, Curriculum Developer
Beth Ann Fulgenzi, Curriculum Developer

Photographer
Jeff Fortney, Senior Editor

Technical Reviewers
Kurt Glosser
Lieutenant
Savoy Fire Department
Savoy, IL

Ryan Scharnhorst
Deputy Chief
Pullman Fire Department
Pullman, Washington

Editorial Staff
Lynne Murnane, Senior Editor
Gabriel Ramirez, Research Technician
Chris Hayden, Graduate Assistant
Tara Gladden, Editorial Assistant

Indexer
Nancy Kopper, Kopper Indexing

The IFSTA Executive Board at the time of validation of the **Fire and Emergency Services Instructor, 8th Edition** manual was as follows:

IFSTA Executive Board

Executive Board Chair
Steve Ashbrock
Fire Chief
Madeira & Indian Hill Fire Department
Cincinnati, OH

Vice Chair
Bradd Clark
Fire Chief
Owasso Fire Department
Owasso, OK

Executive Director
Mike Wieder
Fire Protection Publications
Stillwater, Oklahoma

Board Members

Steve Austin
Past President
Cumberland Valley Volunteer FF Association
Newark, DE

Roxanne Bercik
Assistant Chief
Los Angeles Fire Department
Long Beach, CA

Mary Cameli
Assistant Chief
City of Mesa Fire Department
Mesa, AZ

Chief Dennis Compton
Chairman
National Fallen Firefighters Foundation
Mesa, AZ

John Cunningham
Executive Director
Nova Scotia Firefighter's School
Waverly, NS, Canada

George Dunkel
Consultant
Special Districts Association of Oregon
Scappoose, OR

John Hoglund
Director Emeritus
Maryland Fire & Rescue Institute
New Carrollton, MD

Wes Kitchel
Assistant Chief
Sonoma County Fire & Emergency Services
Cloverdale, CA

Brett Lacey
Fire Marshal
Colorado Springs Fire Department
Colorado Springs, CO

Ernest Mitchell
Fire Chief (Ret.)
Disaster Emergency Service
Cerritos, CA

Board Members (continued)

Introduction

Introduction Contents

Introduction

Fire and emergency services instructors train personnel on the skills they need to perform safely and effectively on the job. Training subjects include basic skills taught to entry-level personnel as well as specialist-level skills and in-service training for current personnel. The authority having jurisdiction (AHJ), which may include local, state/provincial, or national legislation or guidelines, usually mandates the level and type of skills-based training that is required. In addition, instructors today provide both vocational skills training and adult education for personnel of their organizations.

NFPA® 1041, *Standard for Fire Service Instructor Professional Qualifications* (2012), establishes widely accepted job performance requirements (JPRs) for fire and emergency instructors. NFPA® 1041 also supports the company-level training requirements of Fire Officer Level I in NFPA® 1021, *Standard for Fire Officer Professional Qualifications* (2009). The learning objectives included in this manual are written to reinforce NFPA® 1041. A correlation chart indicating the location of each JPR is addressed in the text in **Appendix A**.

Purpose and Scope

The purpose of **Fire and Emergency Services Instructor, 8th Edition**, is to provide personnel with basic information necessary to meet the JPRs of NFPA® 1041 for Instructor Levels I, II, and III. In addition, company officer candidates who wish to meet the JPRs of NFPA® 1021 Level I must also certify to Level I Instructor requirements.

The scope of the manual is to provide current fire and emergency services instructors and instructor candidates with basic instructional knowledge. This knowledge is necessary to develop skills for preparing and presenting training for personnel of fire and emergency services organizations through a variety of methods.

Book Organization

This book is organized according to the certification levels presented in NFPA® 1041. Chapters 1-9 present information for Instructor Level I. Chapters 10-14 present information for Instructor Level II. Finally, Chapters 15-17 present information for Instructor Level III. Each level has distinct duties and responsibilities as defined by NFPA® 1041, including the following:

- **Level I Instructor** — Delivers instruction from a prepared lesson plan. *Other responsibilities:*
  - Assembles course materials
  - Uses instructional aids and evaluation tools
  - Reviews and adapts lesson plans to meet the needs of individual students, groups, and the AHJ
  - Organizes the teaching environment to maximize the learning experience and provides a safe learning environment

— Presents a lesson from a prepared lesson plan, adjusting the presentation as required to ensure that objectives are attained

— Prepares and maintains training records in accordance with the requirements of the jurisdiction

- **Level II Instructor** — Satisfies the Instructor I professional qualifications and has the knowledge and ability to develop individual lesson plans for a specific topic, learning objectives, instructional aids, and evaluation instruments. *Other responsibilities:*

— Manages instructional resources, including facilities, personnel, time, funds, and records

— Schedules training sessions based on overall training requirements of the AHJ

— Supervises and coordinates the activities of other instructors

— Evaluates subordinate instructors

— Develops instructional materials, including the creation of new lesson plans and modification of existing lesson plans

— Develops student, course, and instructor evaluation instruments

— Analyzes the results of student evaluations to determine test validity

- **Level III Instructor** — Satisfies the Instructor II professional qualifications and has demonstrated the knowledge and ability to develop comprehensive training programs, curricula, and courses for use by single or multiple organizations. *Other responsibilities:*

— Administers organizational/agency policy and procedures

— Administers training records system

— Selects training staff

— Creates instructor evaluation plan

— Conducts organization needs analyses

— Develops training goals and implementation strategies

— Creates or modifies programs, curricula, and courses required to fulfill the organization's training needs

— Creates a program evaluation plan

Lastly, each Instructor level section in this text is organized around the Four-Step Model of Instruction presented in Chapter 6 as follows:

- **Preparation** — Planning instruction
- **Presentation** — Providing lecture, demonstrating psychomotor skills, imparting knowledge
- **Application** — Working with students to develop and practice skills
- **Evaluation** — Testing students, evaluating instructors, courses, and programs

With the exception of the *application* step in the Instructor III section, the chapters have been arranged to move the reader through these concepts in order.

Terminology

This manual is written with an international audience in mind. For this reason, it often uses general descriptive language in place of regional- or agency-specific terminology (often referred to as *jargon*). Additionally, in order to keep sentences uncluttered and easy to read, the word *state* is often used to represent both state and provincial level governments. This usage is applied to this manual for the purposes of brevity and is not intended to address or show preference for only one nation's method of identifying regional governments within its borders.

The glossary at the end of the manual will assist the reader in understanding words that may not have common usage in their experience prior to Instructor certification. The sources for the definitions of terms will be the *NFPA® Dictionary of Terms* and the IFSTA **Fire Service Orientation and Terminology** manual.

Additional Resources

The following additional educational resources to supplement this manual are available from IFSTA and Fire Protection Publications (FPP):

- The curriculum package includes the following items:
    — Lesson plans for each chapter
    — Digital presentations for each chapter
    — Tests and quizzes for each chapter
    — Plan of instruction and syllabus for teaching an entire course
    — Workbook in digital format
    — Clip art for the manual
- Study-guide in both digital and print format
- Online access to lesson plans and digital presentations

Key Information

Various types of information in this book are given in shaded boxes marked by the symbols or icons as follows:

Case History

A case history analyzes an event. It can describe incident development, action taken, investigation results, and lessons learned.

Safety Alert

Safety alert boxes are used to highlight information that is important for safety reasons. In the text, the title of safety alerts will change to reflect the content.

Information

Information boxes give facts that are complete in themselves but belong with the text discussion. This style of box provides information that needs more emphasis or separation. In the text, the title of information boxes will change to reflect the content.

What This Means to You

Information presented in the text and synthesized into an example of how the information is relevant to (or will be applied by) the intended audience, essentially answering the question, "What does this mean to you?"

A **key term** is designed to emphasize key concepts, technical terms, or ideas that the student needs to know. They are listed at the beginning of each chapter and the definition is placed in the margin for easy reference. An example of a key term is:

Reasonable Accommodation — Changes or adjustments in a work or school site, program, or job that makes it possible for an otherwise qualified employee or student with a disability to perform the duties or tasks required.

Two key signal words are found in the book: **CAUTION** and **NOTE**. Definitions and examples of each are as follows:

CAUTION
After an e-mail has been deleted, traces of the message still remain on the user's computer system.

- **CAUTION** indicates important information or data that the student needs to be aware of in order to perform his or her duties safely. See the following example:

- **NOTE** indicates important operational information that helps explain why a particular recommendation is given or describes optional methods for certain procedures. See the following example:

NOTE: If instructors are approached for information that might fall under privacy restrictions, they should consult their supervisor or agency counsel before releasing the information.

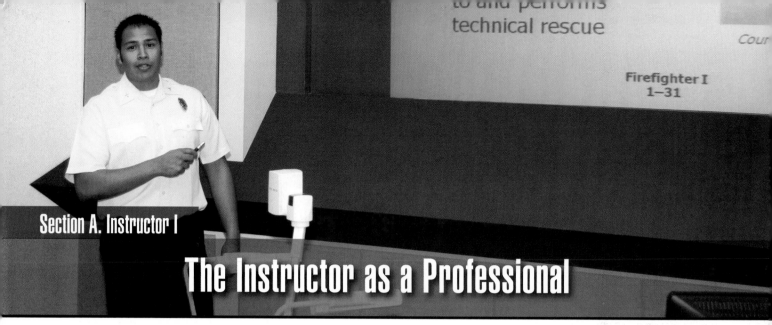

Firefighter I
1–31

Section A. Instructor I

The Instructor as a Professional

Chapter Contents

technical rescue

chapter 1

Key Terms

Job Performance Requirements

NFPA® 1041 Reference

4.5.2

The Instructor as a Professional

Learning Objectives

1. Explain the characteristics required of an effective fire and emergency services instructor.

2. Explain the term professional as it relates to the fire and emergency services instructor.

3. Summarize the instructor's obligations to the student, the organization, the profession, and themselves.

4. Summarize the challenges frequently faced by the instructor.

5. Explain local, state/provincial, and federal laws applicable to fire and emergency training. [NFPA® 1041, 4.5.2]

6. Differentiate between codes and standards.

7. Discuss ethical conduct as it relates to the fire and emergency services instructor.

Chapter 1
The Instructor as a Professional

Case History

After a class was over, several students were joking around with each other and the discussion got a little graphic on the subject of sex. On his way out, the instructor overheard the discussion and added a couple of comments of his own. No one seemed offended at the time, but several hours later the subject of the discussion reached the home of a young female student who was present at the discussion. The parents filed a formal complaint with the department, which eventually made a complaint against the instructor. A hearing was held and, as a result, the instructor was terminated for unprofessional conduct. Had the instructor chosen not to join the students' conversation or, better still, to have suggested that the students not be having those kinds of discussions after class, the outcome might have been different. Professional behavior means being a role model in these situations.

Training is vital to all fire and emergency services organizations. It ensures that all organization personnel conduct emergency and nonemergency operations in a safe, effective, efficient, and consistent manner. Ensuring that personnel attain the proper level of proficiency requires that they receive both education and training in their professions.

The terms **education** and **training** are often used interchangeably in fire and emergency services organizations; however, they have different meanings. Education is generally accepted as meaning the acquisition of knowledge, usually through academic means such as college or university courses. Training is primarily the transfer of knowledge regarding vocational or technical skills. Fire and emergency service training and education are usually provided by one of the following entities:

- Fire and emergency services organizations' training divisions
- State/provincial, regional, or national training academies
- Vocational/technical schools, community colleges, and universities
- Professional organizations and private training providers

Education — The acquisition of knowledge, usually through academic means such as college or university courses.

Training — The transfer of knowledge regarding vocational or technical skills.

Today's fire and emergency services instructors play multiple roles and must meet multiple obligations in their positions. This chapter discusses the following topics relevant to instructors at all levels:

- Characteristics of effective instructors
- Instructor obligations
- Instructor challenges
- Laws applicable to instructors
- Ethical conduct

Characteristics of Effective Instructors

By recognizing the characteristics of the teachers or instructors who were most effective in stimulating and facilitating students' personal learning experiences, new instructors can adopt those same qualities to develop or improve their own teaching skills. Some characteristics that effective instructors possess include the following:

- Desire to teach
- Motivation
- Subject and teaching competencies
- Leadership abilities
- Strong interpersonal skills **(Figure 1.1)**
- Preparation and organization
- Ingenuity, creativity, and flexibility
- Empathy
- Conflict-resolution skills
- Fairness
- Personal integrity
- Honesty
- Sincerity

Figure 1.1 Instructors must be able to interact well with students.

Desire to Teach

Without a desire to teach, no amount of knowledge and experience can create an effective instructor. Possessing a desire to teach affects performance and motivation, which contribute to success in the classroom and on the job.

A desire to teach generates enthusiasm in the instructor. Enthusiasm is contagious! Effective instructors strive to instill their level of vision and enthusiasm within the organization. Instructors can generate enthusiasm in both students and administrators alike when they show a high degree of interest in a subject, in students and their learning outcomes, and in the success of the training course. Student enthusiasm is fostered and maintained through the following expressions:

- Lively and varied vocal delivery
- High energy levels **(Figure 1.2)**
- Obvious love of teaching and the subject matter

Figure 1.2 An instructor sets an example for student behavior by exhibiting a high energy level while instructing.

When the educational experience becomes fun and exciting, students' willingness to participate increases and learning outcomes improve. As a result, administrators will be more supportive of instructor and curriculum needs.

Motivation

Instructors must have the motivation, desire, and determination to achieve goals and encourage that desire in their students. Instructors must show students that they are motivated to help each individual learn by giving each of them every opportunity to do so. Some of the ways instructors can motivate others are as follows:

- Clearly communicate what action must be performed and how it must be performed.

- Show students the importance of the presented information.

- Make the knowledge and skills easy to understand and learn.

- Allow for mistakes as students practice and improve.

- Encourage students as they attempt to learn.

- Reward successful attempts.

- Correct unsuccessful attempts without criticism.

Subject and Teaching Competencies

Instructors must have the background knowledge and experience to teach a subject and its skills, and they must have the ability to transfer that knowledge and experience to others. Because learning is a lifelong process, it does not stop with the end of a class or completion of a degree program. Instructors must continually seek to increase their knowledge and skills in technical subject matter and educational methodology. They must be open-minded and attempt to learn and understand alternative methods and ideas. It is important to maintain and add to skill ability and knowledge so that these concepts may be transmitted to students. Instructors can improve teaching skills only through experience, study, and professional development.

Leadership Abilities

Effective instructors must be effective leaders. An effective instructor leads or guides students through the requirements, knowledge, and skills of a class while ensuring that the needs of each student are met. An effective instructor provides appropriate learning opportunities, examples, and ideas and encourages students to discuss, think, and come to an appropriate conclusion. An instructor who is a good leader enables students to take the lead in appropriate learning situations.

Effective leaders are first effective followers. Instructors are followers within the organization. Although they may not have a direct influence on guiding policy-making decisions, instructors should follow the rules, regulations, policies, and procedures of the organization and apply them fairly and evenly to all students and other members of the organization.

Instructors should study various leadership models and determine the most appropriate model and methods for their own personal strengths, the instructional situation, and the students. Effective leaders know when to exhibit characteristics of different leadership models, recognizing times when they need to give instructions that are not up for debate or when they can allow students to make decisions for themselves.

Instructors lead by example; therefore, instructors never ask students to do anything that they themselves have not done or would not do. Decisions must be based on accurate information and able to withstand the application and scrutiny of logic.

Additional leadership qualities of an effective instructor include the following:

- **Self-confidence** — Develops through self-examination and having a clear appraisal of oneself.

- **Trustworthiness** — Develops over time based upon the leader's performance and the experience subordinates have had with the leader.

- **Consistency** — Make and maintain consistent decisions, actions, and relationships.

- **Responsibility** — Accept responsibility for both good and bad results from decisions.

- **Acceptance** — Realize that not all problems can be resolved to everyone's satisfaction; work within what is rather than complaining for what is not.

- **Expertise** — Teach only from developed skills and abilities based upon knowledge and experience.

Strong Interpersonal Skills

Instructors must have strong interpersonal skills that include clarity, sensitivity, and fairness. Clarity involves the ability to precisely and clearly explain concepts and processes through a systematic presentation of material. One standard method of presentation includes a brief outline/introduction of the material, followed by the main content. Each section is then concluded with a brief summarization. When students do not understand the material, the instructor must be able to restate the concept in a style that students will understand.

Sensitivity is the ability to view the learning environment from the students' perspective and recognize the barriers to learning and communication. Having a personal interest in students' successes and challenges will aid an instructor in providing meaningful instruction **(Figure 1.3)**.

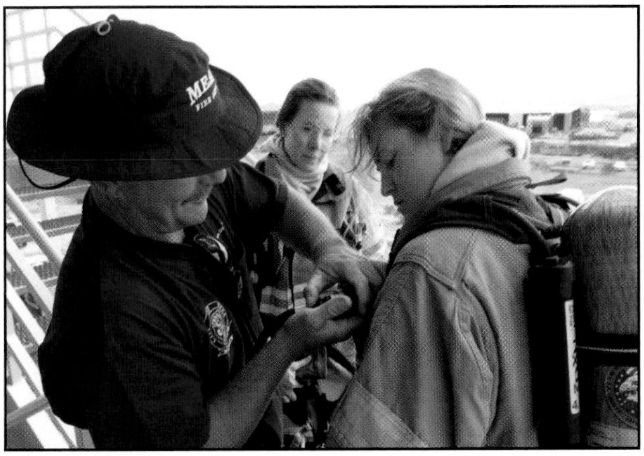

Instructors must be *fair and impartial* to all students, open-minded, and willing to hear, consider, and discuss ideas with them. In particular, instructors must be able to listen to and understand the needs of students.

Figure 1.3 An instructor who demonstrates interest in students' performance will benefit the entire class.

Instructors must also be able to apply interpersonal skills when dealing with other instructors, staff members, supervisors, and the public. These skills enable instructors to work well with other people. They must be able to develop relationships that are built on mutual respect, rapport, and confidence.

Preparation and Organization

Together these two elements, preparation and organization, are accomplished through detailed course outlines, established course objectives, defined evaluation procedures, and preparation for each class session. Before a class session, instructors prepare in the following ways:

- Assemble all materials, handouts, audio or visual materials, props, and equipment in the classroom or training area.

- Test equipment for proper operation, ensure that replacement parts (as needed) are available, and prepare alternative plans.

- Eliminate learning barriers such as audible and visual distractions, uncomfortable environmental temperatures, and poor lighting.

- Arrive an appropriate amount of time in advance of the training session.

Instructors must also practice their presentations to determine whether sufficient time and materials have been allocated for the topic **(Figure 1.4, p.14)**. A well-organized and prepared instructor is also one who can manage time efficiently. This requirement is particularly important when it is necessary to develop lesson plans for a new course or topic.

Ingenuity, Creativity, and Flexibility

An effective instructor understands that a teaching or learning technique suitable for one student or group of students may not be suitable for another. Instructors can demonstrate ingenuity and creativity by developing or using various training aids and supplemental materials and discovering and using innovative means of presenting information to meet the needs of every student. They must also be flexible and able to alter the training process quickly when there are changes in the environment, props, equipment, or size of the class.

Figure 1.4 Instructors must be organized and practice their lessons in order to use class time wisely.

Empathy

Empathy is the ability to understand the feelings and attitudes of another person. Instructors must be able understand the students' points of view, opinions, problems, or challenges. Empathetic instructors have a sincere desire to help individuals learn, are not condescending or punitive, and do not act superior or threatening. Having empathy is especially important when working with students who have learning difficulties.

Conflict-Resolution Skills

There are occasions when an instructor must act to resolve conflict between students and the organization and between students themselves **(Figure 1.5)**. Instructors may have to resolve disputes in the following situations:

- In the training environment
- On evaluations and tests
- With many types of personalities and responsibilities
- On a variety of other issues that may arise during the course

In these situations, an instructor listens to both sides and suggests solutions, and may have to assist both sides in formulating a solution without showing preference for a particular side of the issue. An instructor must work to create win-win situations and maintain positive relationships between all parties.

Fairness

Fairness means treating all students equally, providing the same learning opportunities, and evaluating their performance against an established objective

Figure 1.5 Disputes between students should be handled professionally and courteously.

standard and not against a subjective set of expectations. When students perceive that an instructor is biased against them or favors another student, the instructor's credibility will be damaged.

Personal Integrity

Personal integrity is based on the values and morals of the individual. It can be stated as a personal code of ethics that provides the instructor with specific guidelines for action and decisions. Personal integrity must also be consistently applied to all situations and people. Students will respect instructors who consistently follow their personal ethical codes. Student respect is easy to maintain when an instructor adheres to personal integrity but difficult to gain when that integrity is compromised or questioned.

Honesty

Instructors must always be truthful and honest. Students realize that an instructor may not know all the answers. Students want and expect honesty and prefer instructors who are willing to admit that they do not know but are willing to find the answers to questions. Instructors do not need to be embarrassed when they cannot answer a question during class. Instructors should be prepared to say, "I don't know the answer to that question, but I'll find out for you," or "Does someone in the class know the answer?" Instructors should not attempt to bluff their way through a question quickly because that can cost them their credibility with students.

Sincerity

Sincerity is the personal quality of being open and truthful. Sincere attitudes and responses that show an interest in helping students to learn are important traits for instructors to possess. Students react, respond, and cooperate more positively and willingly with instructors who demonstrate a concern for them.

Most instruction is based upon the instructor's ability to communicate information to students, both verbally and nonverbally. Communications that are not sincere, such as sarcastic remarks or offensive jokes, undermine an instructor's educational message and either distract students from their learning or put them on the defensive. The emotional reactions of the class may hinder effective communication.

Instructor Obligations

Fire and emergency services instructors are professionals who meet a standard that is based on a high level of personal performance. Instructors are providers of adult education and adult training. As members of the fire and emergency services profession, they must also be able to apply the same knowledge and skills that they teach to their students at emergency incidents on a daily basis. Like their students, instructors develop this knowledge and skill from practical experience with a variety of subjects related to fire and emergency services operations as well as keeping current on subjects through studying periodicals and journals and attending courses themselves **(Figure 1.6)**. As a result, instructors are both teacher and practitioner. This arrangement is a benefit to instructors because it increases the base knowledge that they teach from and their credibility with their students.

As both teacher and practitioner, instructors need to possess characteristics that are associated with both of these roles. They must understand the meaning of the term *profession*: calling or vocation that requires specialized knowledge and long, intense preparation that includes (1) learning scientific, historical, or scholarly principles that apply to specific skills, processes, and methods; (2) maintaining high standards of personal achievement and conduct; and (3) committing to continued study and educational advancement — all with the prime purpose of providing a public service.

Fire and emergency services instructors certainly meet these criteria for members of a profession. Along with the requirements inherent with the teaching profession, there are also obligations for instructors toward the following:

Figure 1.6 A good instructor works hard to remain current on instructional topics and professional skills.

- **The student** — Effective training ensures that students will perform their duties safely and skillfully in the fire and emergency services.

- **The organization** — An instructor provides training that supports the mission of his or her organization, through effective training that is in keeping with the training needs of the organization and its policies and procedures. The training should also meet all applicable federal, state/provincial, and local regulations and policies.

Figure 1.7 Wearing the same PPE that students wear during training is an example of how instructors model appropriate and safe behavior.

- **The profession** — An instructor provides an important link between the student and the fire and emergency services profession by providing a positive role model and effective leadership. Instructors are also role models for safe behavior in the fire and emergency services **(Figure 1.7)**.

- **Themselves** — An instructor has an obligation to continue professional development through the acquisition of knowledge and improvement of skills. Because the fire and emergency services profession is constantly changing, instructors must always be aware of new improvements or developments.

Ultimately, the instructor's role is to provide the most efficient and safest training opportunities possible for the student. By meeting these obligations effectively, instructors ensure that the public is served by the best trained fire and emergency services personnel.

Observe Other Instructors

At every opportunity, observe other instructors in their roles of planning, developing, teaching, and working with others. Ask questions of other instructors to discover why they use certain methods. Determine what methods of organization, persuasion, and teaching seem most effective after observing, questioning, and comparing many instructors, and then begin to adapt those methods.

Instructor Challenges

Challenges are a part of any profession just as they are in life. Managing those challenges is rewarding and an important skill for any instructor.

Besides the obligations that instructors have (to students, the organization, the profession, and themselves), the characteristics they must possess, and the traits they must exhibit in class, they must also be able to manage other challenges of the teaching environment. An instructor should apply knowledge gained from previous experiences and adapt to the environment. The inexperienced instructor should seek the advice of peers, supervisors, or other members of the teaching profession. Challenges the instructor may encounter include the following:

- **Familiarization with standards** — Instructors should be familiar with standards and regulations that may apply to the training that they provide. While these may or may not be required in their jurisdictions, the standards are

Figures 1.8 a-c Instructors may perform many additional duties, such as performing administrative tasks, developing additional curriculum, and providing demonstration.

Occupational Safety and Health Administration (OSHA) — U.S. federal agency that develops and enforces standards and regulations for occupational safety in the workplace.

generally intended to improve training safety. Some sources for these standards and regulations are the National Fire Protection Association® (NFPA®), the **Occupational Safety and Health Administration (OSHA)**, applicable EMS regulations (U.S. Department of Transportation [DOT], state/provincial, and jurisdictional).

- **Instructor priorities** — Instructors may perform multiple tasks within the organization such as administrative duties or health and safety officer duties. They may also be required to develop training curriculum in addition to delivering courses to students **(Figures 1.8 a-c)**.

- **Student priorities** — Instructors should be aware of time constraints and other outside influences on students' ability to train.

- **Student diversity** — Instructors must be prepared to teach students of both genders and a variety of races, ages, sexual preferences, and religious beliefs, treating all individuals in a fair and unbiased fashion.

- **Students with learning disabilities** — Instructors should be prepared to recognize students with learning disabilities and accommodate the needs of these individuals.

- **Organizational apathy** — Organizations sometimes have an apathetic attitude toward training especially when it comes to additional funding. Instructors should be champions of their roles and gain the respect of their organizations by providing thorough, safe, and effective training.

Figure 1.9 Developing relationships with other organizations will bring additional resources to the instructional process.

- **Changes in the profession** — Instructors must stay current on changes to the fire and emergency services profession and incorporate these changes in training.

- **Cooperative relationships** — Instructors must learn to cooperate with officials from other agencies and levels of government along with leaders in the private sector in both business and education **(Figure 1.9)**. Doing so provides additional resources to instructors and their organizations.

- **Organizational promotion** — Instructors must promote the benefits and assets of the organization and its training program to the public and other organizations and agencies that may send students as external customers. Instructors should assist the student with matching the student's training achievement with his or her professional advancement.

- **Management directives** — As subordinates, instructors must adhere to the management directives and mandates of the organization and its leaders. They should also be advocates for change when directives need to be updated, and work together with superiors to affect change within organizations.

- **Knowledge of instructional environment** — Instructors should have a working knowledge of instructional environments available to them for training. If these locations are not applicable to a planned lesson or training session, the instructor must seek out an appropriate environment.

- **Safe training environments** — Instructors must be familiar with local, state/provincial, and federal safety regulations as they apply to all fire and emergency services training. Students must be assured that safety is the primary concern of the organization.

Figure 1.10 Instructors should encourage students who show an aptitude for teaching.

- **Professional development** — Effective instructors continue to learn by taking advantage of continuing education and professional development opportunities.

- **Course schedules** — Instructors may be asked to take a role in planning and scheduling appropriate and required training sessions. They should be prepared to seek out any training formats that help to meet necessary training requirements for their organizations.

- **Funds and resources** — Instructors are obligated to use funds and resources effectively and efficiently. When organizational funding decreases, training programs may be the first to be affected. Lack of funding is not an excuse for lack of training. Instructors must seek out training opportunities that are in keeping with available funding and resources.

- **Qualified instructor recruitment** — Instructors should assist in locating and recruiting talented and knowledgeable personnel to fill instructor vacancies. They should also be involved in recommending individuals for training as instructors when those individuals show an aptitude for teaching **(Figure 1.10)**.

Laws Applicable to Instructors

Instructors must know and understand which laws apply to the fire and emergency services and be aware of alterations in those laws and the creation of new laws. There are federal, state/provincial, and local laws that apply to fire and emergency instruction as explained in the sections that follow.

NOTE: Other legal issues are included later in this manual. Information on copyright laws and infringement are included in Chapter 4, Instructional Materials and Equipment. Information on instructor liability is included in Chapter 7, Skills-Based Training beyond the Classroom.

Figure 1.11 Students who require additional assistance must receive reasonable accommodations such as having another student take a photo of notes on the board for a student who has difficulty taking notes.

Federal Laws

Some examples of federal laws that apply to instructors are as follows:

- **Title VII of the Civil Rights Act** — Prohibits employment practices that discriminate based on race, color, religion, sex, or national origin. The law also protects employees from physical, verbal, and **sexual harassment**. The Canadian equivalent of this law is the Canadian Human Rights Act.

- **Americans with Disabilities Act (ADA)** — Prohibits discrimination against a student with an identified disability. Instructors and training organizations must provide **reasonable accommodation** for students with documented disabilities **(Figure 1.11)**. For example, an individual with a *documented learning disability* might be given additional time on written exams. (See **Appendix B** for the formal, legal definition of ADA)

- **Privacy Act or Buckley Amendment** — Prohibits invasion of a person's right to privacy or unwanted publicity, restricts access to personal information such as personnel files and student grades, guarantees access to records only by the covered student or eligible parent or guardian, and prohibits disclosure of personal information without consent **(Figure 1.12)**. For example, releasing student grades to unauthorized individuals would be an infringement of student privacy.

NOTE: Instructors should seek a legal interpretation of the application of federal and state privacy acts on their organizations. The restrictions imposed by these acts may or may not apply to fire and emergency services training divisions based on that interpretation.

Harassment — A course of conduct directed at a specific person that causes substantial emotional distress in said person and serves no legitimate purpose.

Sexual Harassment — Superior offering advancement or special treatment in return for sexual favors from a subordinate; also may refer to any situation in which an employee, regardless of gender, believes that the workplace is a hostile environment because of sexually offensive or sexist behavior.

Reasonable Accommodation — Changes or adjustments in a work or school site, program, or job that makes it possible for an otherwise qualified employee or student with a disability to perform the duties or tasks required.

Learning Disability — Classification of a disorder in which a person has difficulty learning in a typical manner because of a problem with the brain's ability to receive and process information.

Figure 1.12 Instructors must protect privacy rights by sharing sensitive information only with the student.

Privacy as It Applies to Medical Records

In the event that a student is hurt or an EMS trainee is dealing with patients, students and instructors may have to maintain the privacy of medical records. Instructors should be knowledgeable of laws in their jurisdictions that apply to the release or privacy of medical records. One source for this information is the Health Insurance Portability Accountability Act (HIPAA). HIPAA outlines what medical information is public knowledge and what information is not. The HIPAA privacy rule is complicated and beyond the scope of this manual; however, instructors who may be required to access or handle medical records as part of their training should become familiar with HIPAA and how it is applied in their jurisdictions. HIPAA only applies as federal law in the United States.

State/Provincial Laws

States/Provinces also legislatively create laws. They may also authorize state/provincial agencies to review and adopt federal regulations and/or national standards. These agencies may enact state rules based upon these regulations and standards. These rules carry the force of law in that state/province and are known as administrative laws. State/Provincial laws and regulations vary dramatically among jurisdictions and are beyond the scope of this manual to explain in detail.

States/Provinces may adopt federal regulations and adapt them for use at the state/provincial level. For example, federal OSHA provides regulations for workplace safety. State agencies have the opportunity to enact these same regulations within their states or to create different regulations. This same process may occur in the legislature where OSHA regulations may be voted into law legislatively. Regardless of the method a state/province uses to adopt federal regulations or national standards, an instructor must take the time to learn which regulations and standards have been adopted and apply to their job functions.

Municipal, Departmental, and Organizational Laws

Municipal corporations, such as those formed by counties/parishes, cities, or townships, often have their own local needs and create laws (called **ordinances**) that address matters beyond federal or state/provincial laws. An ordinance is a local law that applies to persons, things, and activities in a jurisdiction and has the same force and effect as statutory law.

Local ordinances or regulations may impact certain training activities. Instructors should check with the **authority having jurisdiction (AHJ)** for any such local laws that apply to their training activities.

Departments and organizations in cities and towns create their own **regulations** to guide management and employee actions as they perform duties that must also comply with state/provincial and other regulations. Departments and organizations create their own regulations to address certain areas such as the following:

Ordinance — Local or municipal law that applies to persons and things of the local jurisdiction; a local agency act that has the force of a statute; different from law that is enacted by federal or state/provincial legislatures.

Authority Having Jurisdiction (AHJ) — Term used in codes and standards to identify the legal entity, such as a building or fire official, that has the statutory authority to enforce a code and to approve or require equipment; may be a unit of a local, state, or federal government, depending on where the work occurs. In the insurance industry it may refer to an insurance rating bureau or an insurance company inspection department.

Regulations — Rules or directives of administrative agencies that have authorization to issue them.

- Liability and personal insurance requirements
- Professional development and certification requirements
- Substance abuse testing
- Driver training, testing, and record policies
- Criminal record policies

Judicial Law

Judicial law (also known as judicial legislation or case law) is usually the result of a **legal precedent** or a judicial decision. For example, New York v. Baird, in which an assistant fire chief was found liable for the death of his trainee during a live-fire training exercise, creates a legal precedent for instructor liability. These decisions serve as rules for future determinations in similar cases, and these decisions may affect emergency responders almost immediately because there is usually no implementation period. Judicial decisions, if made at the federal level, can have a nationwide effect. Some case-law decisions can affect fire and emergency responders even though the original individual case did not involve emergency response personnel. See Chapter 7, Skills-Based training beyond the Classroom for more information.

Legal Precedent — The history of rulings made in courts of law that can be referenced and used to make court decisions in future cases or influence laws outside of the court system.

Codes — A body of laws arranged systematically usually pertaining to one subject area such as a mechanical code, a building code, an electrical code, or a fire code.

National Codes and Standards

National **codes** and **standards** are not laws unless adopted by the AHJ. They are, however, recognized and developed by experts in the fire and emergency services throughout the country. Instructors should recognize that just because the AHJ has not adopted a code or standard as law does not mean that an instructor may not be held accountable under that standard in a court of law. Legal precedent has been established that, because these codes and standards are developed by an instructor's peers, the code or standard should be taken under consideration even when it does not rise to the level of law.

NOTE: A list of NFPA® standards that apply to instructors can be found in Chapter 7, Skills-Based Training beyond the Classroom.

Standard — Criterion documents that are developed to serve as models or examples of desired performance or behaviors and that contain requirements and specifications outlining minimum levels of performance, protection, or construction. No one is required to meet the requirements set forth in standards unless those standards are legally adopted by the authority having jurisdiction, in which case they become law.

What This Means to You

As an instructor in the fire and emergency services, you will interact with students all the time. You will be partly responsible for their classroom success and fully responsible for their safety during skills training. Knowing the legal parameters for these interactions is essential to maintaining a good relationship with students while keeping them safe.

If you fail to stay current on the legal issues that apply to your position, you may find yourself in court for negligence, harassment, or civil rights violations. A good general rule is to treat everyone fairly. In social interactions with students, the instructor should be friendly, but maintain a professional level of decorum.

Finally, if you have any concern that you may be facing a legal issue, try to resolve the issue with the accusing party and begin documenting your interactions with that person. You may find that a little understanding and communication can prevent issues from escalating to legal conflicts.

Ethical Conduct

In order to be considered a professional, an instructor must follow ethical codes of conduct. In brief, a **code of ethics** is a statement of what is right and proper conduct for an individual in all relationships and activities within an organization or within society as a whole. This conduct may involve relationships with others, the decision-making process, or simply choosing between right and wrong. Few decisions are clear, and most involve many options that fall into the gray range between the two extremes of right and wrong. Situations that require a decision based on ethics:

- Sharing of exam papers between successive classes

- Allowing plagiarizing of material produced by others

- Allowing cheating on exams **(Figure 1.13)**

- Advancing students who have not received proper training or passed courses

Instructors will have to deal with ethical dilemmas. Students, eager for top scores or for promotional advancement, may put pressure on instructors to break their ethical codes to receive benefits that the student doesn't deserve or has not earned. Also, instructors must establish and promote an ethical code among students to minimize cheating, unwanted sharing of information, and plagiarism. Students may cheat or otherwise try to take shortcuts in their training. Instructors must be willing to stand by their ethics and not allow such behavior to become the norm of the training division. While ethical decisions can be difficult to make, instructors who establish codes of ethics for their students and adhere to them themselves are good role models and well respected professionals.

Figure 1.13 Permitting students to cheat would be an ethical violation.

One way to avoid making bad ethical judgments is to be aware of the common explanations individuals use when they attempt to justify wrong actions to themselves. Instructors who allow or engage in unethical behavior usually have a number of false justifications for their actions including the following:

- Pretending that the action is legal or ethical
- Believing that the action is really in the best interest of the organization or individual
- Believing that the action is okay because no one will ever discover it
- Expecting that the organization will support the action if it is ever discovered
- Believing that the action is acceptable because everyone else is doing it
- Believing that the end (result) justifies the means (method) even when the means are unethical

Once an instructor has justified one unethical action internally, then it becomes easier to repeat the initial action and may facilitate further unethical acts. To overcome these attitudes, an organization must create a culture that encourages and rewards ethical conduct and disciplines unethical conduct.

Ethics Program

The first step toward creating an ethical culture is the creation of an ethics program that includes an organizational and individual code of ethics. To ensure that the organization maintains an ethical culture, the ethics program should include a written code of ethics or ethics policy. Like the organization's mission statement, this code is a brief, one- or two-page statement of the values that govern the organization and the expectations desired in the actions of the management and membership.

Expressing the organization's code of ethics in written form provides the administration, members/employees, and the public with a visible standard to follow. The importance of a written code of ethics cannot be overemphasized because it has the following characteristics:

- Defines acceptable and unacceptable behaviors
- Promotes high standards of practice and fosters a strong ethical climate
- Provides a standard for individuals to judge themselves
- Establishes a framework for professional behavior and strengthens the organization's ethical climate
- Helps to enhance or establish an occupational identity
- Provides a mark of occupational maturity for the department, organization, or profession
- Establishes an environment in which open communication is expected, accepted, and protected
- Provides a clear and concise statement of the type of behavior that is expected from both management and members of the organization
- Establishes the basis for public opinion of the organization, its leaders, and its members

Personal Code of Ethics Example

This personal code of ethics is a public statement by fire and emergency services educators and instructors that establishes clear expectations and principles to guide practice and inspire professional excellence. It is the belief of fire and emergency services instructors that a commonly held set of moral principles and values can assist in the individual exercise of professional judgment.

These moral principles and values are the core values of the teaching profession as well as the fire and emergency services. The individual instructor should integrate these values into their professional and private lives to ensure the equity of their actions and decisions.

As a Fire and Emergency Services Instructor, I shall:

- Place the safety and learning of the student above all other concerns.
- Nurture the intellectual, physical, emotional, social, and civic potential of each student.
- Create, support, and maintain a challenging learning environment for all students.
- Apply my professional knowledge and skills to promote student learning at all times.
- Establish and maintain a clear set of standards for behavior and civility within the learning environment.
- Be a positive role model by displaying those habits of mind and work necessary to develop and apply knowledge while simultaneously displaying a curiosity and enthusiasm for learning.
- Strive to affirm the importance and the honor of my profession.
- Conduct both personal and official business in a manner that will inspire the confidence and respect of others.
- Never be disrespectful of others in public or private.
- Be committed to my own learning and professional growth in order to further develop in the teaching profession and the fire service.
- Collaborate with colleagues and other professionals in the interest of student learning.
- Recognize cultural and linguistic heritage, gender, family, community, ethnicity, and race and their influences on experience and learning.
- Make decisions and take all actions based on the moral and ethical values of this community and this organization.

Ethical Issues

The existence of a code of ethics strengthens the ethical culture of the organization but does not guarantee that ethical questions will not occur to challenge the organization or its employees. Training employees in the importance of making ethical decisions, how to make those decisions, and how to recognize and respond to unethical actions on the part of others provides valuable tools for resolving such issues.

However, instructors must be able to manage issues when they arise during training sessions. The use of logic and reasoning must be supplemented by the use of ethical decision-making. Organizations will have methods for assisting instructors in managing ethical problems.

Instructors are role models for their students and lead primarily by example. The most important example they can provide to their students, organization, and community is ethical decision-making and action. An organization's culture is only as sound as the example set by the officers of the organization. This simple fact means that instructors and administrators must establish and adhere to goals that are ethical. Those goals must be based on sound factual evidence and reasoning.

There are many models for working through ethical issues. The following steps are just one example of how an instructor can think through an ethical dilemma:

Step 1: **Recognize and define the situation** — Determine the answers to the following questions:

    — What is it?

    — What has caused it?

    — Who is involved?

    — What are the potential results?

Step 2: **Obtain all the facts surrounding the situation** — Conduct an objective investigation to gather the details of the event.

Step 3: **List all possible options necessary to respond to the situation** — Develop this list by brainstorming with other members of the organization when time allows. In emergency situations, an instructor may have to rely on personal experience to develop such a list.

Step 4: **Compare each option to established criteria** — Use benchmarks such as legality, morality, benefit, and justification as criteria.

Step 5: **Select the best option that meets the criteria** — Make the decision.

Step 6: **Double-check the decision** — Ask more subjective questions such as the following:

    — How would I feel if my family/spouse/friends discovered this?

    — How would I feel if this decision were reported in the local/national media?

Step 7: **Take action and implement the decision** — Ensure the factual foundation is firm, criteria are met, and potential for exposure is minimized. The correct decision is the result.

Chapter Summary

Fire and emergency services personnel who decide to become instructors must understand the obligations that they have to students, the organization, the profession, and themselves. They must have or be able to develop the characteristics normally associated with effective educators, the most important of which is the desire to teach. Instructor candidates must develop traits that provide a positive impression for students and create a professional image for the organization and the fire and emergency services profession in general.

Instructor candidates must have the knowledge and ability to accept the challenges that teaching affords and select the positive traits rather than the negative ones that some situations may create. They must be able to manage delicate situations that are created by diversity, legal requirements, and various training situations.

Finally, a fire and emergency services instructor must be aware of all the laws that apply to the training process. At the same time, an instructor must conform to an ethical code of conduct. The instructor who adheres to a solid ethical code of behavior not only provides students with a valuable role model but also finds it easier to remain within the legal constraints established by law.

Review Questions

1. What are the characteristics of an effective fire and emergency services instructor?

2. Why are fire and emergency services instructors considered members of a profession?

3. What are the instructor's obligations to the student, the organization, the profession, and themselves?

4. How can an instructor manage some of the challenges of the teaching environment?

5. What federal laws affect the fire and emergency services instructor?

6. When does a code or standard become law?

7. What are the characteristics of an effective ethics program?

Principles of Learning

Chapter Contents

Key Terms

Job Performance Requirements

NFPA® 1041 References

4.4.3

4.4.5

Principles of Learning

Learning Objectives

1. Summarize the foundations of learning. [NFPA® 1041, 4.4.3]

2. Explain the characteristics of adult learners. [NFPA® 1041, 4.4.3]

3. Explain the three domains of learning. [NFPA® 1041, 4.4.3]

4. Summarize the different styles of learning. [NFPA® 1041, 4.4.5]

5. Describe instructional strategies used in the fire and emergency services. [NFPA® 1041, 4.4.3]

6. Discuss motivation as it relates to students' success in an educational environment. [NFPA® 1041, 4.4.5]

Chapter 2
Principles of Learning

Case History

A firefighter was given a new piece of monitoring equipment with written instructions for its operation and maintenance. After several days of spending time trying to learn how to operate and maintain this device, the firefighter reluctantly reported to his officer that he was unable to understand how to operate and maintain the equipment. Surprised and somewhat angered, the Company Officer decided that possible disciplinary action should be taken towards the firefighter.

However, in reviewing the owner's manual, a Chief Officer noticed that a video version of the manual was available for a small fee. The Chief Officer purchased the video manual. A week later, the Chief Officer gave the video to the Company Officer and informed him to provide this to the firefighter. Within one shift, the firefighter learned the intricacies of the monitoring equipment. The CO was shocked. How did this happen? The firefighter admitted to his CO that he had a learning disability with word comprehension. He could read but had problems in translating what he read into performance. By providing a visual tutorial to the firefighter instead of a written manual, the CO created an environment in which the firefighter could learn successfully.

In order to become successful teachers, instructor candidates must also have an understanding of teaching methodology and the basic principles of learning. These principles and concepts are discussed in this chapter and include the following:

- Foundations of learning
- Characteristics of adult learners
- Domains of learning
- Styles and methods of learning
- Motivation

Instructor candidates should supplement the information in this manual with additional reading. Educational theories and methodology continue to evolve, and new information frequently becomes available. A Selected Readings list is located in **Appendix C**.

In addition, instructors may wish to participate in university-level courses in adult education and teaching methods. Other resources are available through the U.S. Fire Administration's National Fire Academy (NFA), state/provincial training agencies, libraries, and the Internet.

Foundations of Learning

Many educational psychologists have done extensive research on how humans learn and remember information. Their theories, research, and conclusions fill many textbooks. This section discusses a few areas of research that explain how methods and techniques of instruction can affect or influence learning.

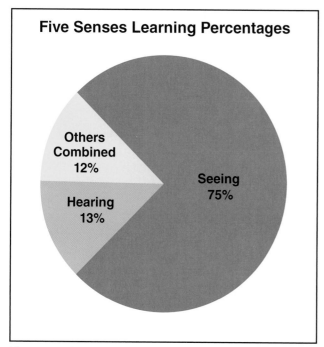

Figure 2.1 Students gather most of their information through sight, but other senses also play a part in learning. *D. Laird Approaches to Training and Development.*

Sensory Memory — Mental storage system for attention-getting sensory stimuli or input.

Cone of Learning — Visual representation that depicts the percentage of information humans retain using their senses individually and in combination.

Sensory-Stimulus Theory

Sensory-stimulus theory states that there is a lifelong reliance on the five senses as the primary tool set for learning. People can only change their behavior or base of knowledge by engaging the five senses. Those who promote the sensory-stimulus approach to learning emphasize that the sense of sight takes in the most information with hearing next. People learn very little through the remaining three senses, although those senses often stimulate memories **(Figure 2.1)**. Students pay more attention to sensory experiences than to mental processes or emotional involvement.

The mental storage system for attention-getting sensory stimuli or input (such as odors, sights, sounds, and sensations) is **sensory memory**. A sensory stimulus is either important enough to remember, so commonplace it is disregarded, or unimportant enough that it is forgotten. It is difficult to attend to more than one stimulus at a time and remember it well. In order to remember information, students must give an appropriate amount of attention time to the sensory stimuli they are receiving on the current information before they can attend to other stimuli on new information.

In the fire and emergency services, this sensory-stimulus approach has evolved and been more accurately defined using the **Cone of Learning (Figure 2.2)**. This cone illustrates that individuals retain approximately the following amounts of information:

- 10 percent of what they read
- 20 percent of what they hear
- 30 percent of what they see
- 50 percent of what they see and hear together
- 70 percent of what they say and repeat
- 90 percent of what they say while doing what they are talking about

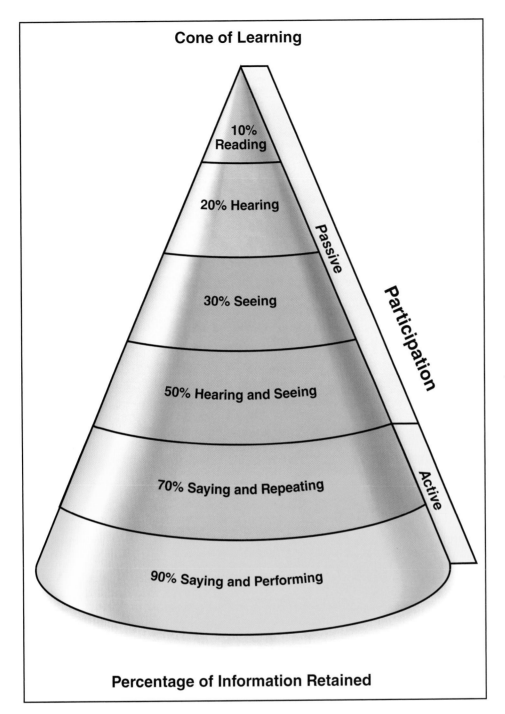

Cone of Learning

10% Reading

20% Hearing

30% Seeing

50% Hearing and Seeing

70% Saying and Repeating

90% Saying and Performing

Passive

Active

Participation

Percentage of Information Retained

Figure 2.2 The Cone of Learning illustrates the sensory-stimulus approach to learning. *Adapted from Edgar Dale's Cone of Experience.*

In addition, because people learn more as active participants than as passive ones, it becomes obvious that the most effective mode of learning is the one that includes receiving or learning a new idea by a combination of methods that causes individuals to be active or participate while learning.

As illustrated by the cone of learning, the highest level of remembering occurs when an individual performs a task while saying or describing that task. On the other hand, the cone illustrates that individuals recall very little from passive methods such as reading an assignment or listening to a lecture. The conclusion appears to be that the more senses used in the learning process, the more information that is remembered for later recall.

Knowles' Assumptions of Adult Learners

Dr. Malcolm Knowles, professor, researcher, and author, was among the first American theorists to use the term **andragogy** (an-druh-go-je), which refers to the art of teaching adults. It describes the characteristics of adult students and provides a set of assumptions for most effectively teaching adults. The theory of andragogy is now widely accepted and includes the following assumptions:

- **Self-concept** — Adults have a need to be self-directed while still relying on an instructor or training course to provide the knowledge they desire.

- **Experience** — Adults have accumulated extensive and varied quantities of experiences that serve as resources for them and to which they can relate new information. They also have more personal experiences to contribute to the learning process than children **(Figure 2.3)**.

- **Readiness to learn** — Adults are ready to learn whatever they need to know or do in order to meet job requirements or social roles.

- **Learning orientation** — Adults' orientation is problem-centered because they have specific purposes for learning and want skills or knowledge that can be applied to real-life problems or situations.

- **Motivation** — Adults have internal incentives or motivators. They are motivated to learn by such factors as increased self-esteem resulting from the successful completion of the learning process and the desire to attain a goal.

Figure 2.3 Experienced instructors have a great deal of information to share with students. Similarly, students can benefit from being grouped with other students of different experience levels.

Thorndike's Laws of Learning

The Laws of Learning, as theorized by Professor Edward L. Thorndike, suggest that there are certain laws or traits of adult learners that can be used to effectively instruct adult students. Instructors need to understand these laws in order to be prepared to lead adult education. The laws of adult learning – are as follows:

- **Readiness** — Readiness means a person is prepared to learn – not just ready and willing but also mentally and physically able to learn new knowledge or skills. In the fire and emergency services, adult students recognize that the information they will receive is necessary and important to them. There may be barriers to readiness such as attending a class after an all night shift; however, adult students still have to recognize the importance of learning.

- **Exercise** — Adults learn best when they are allowed to exercise skills; the more an act is practiced, the faster and surer the learning becomes **(Figure 2.4)**. Fire and emergency services instructors should, therefore, include as much time as possible for adult learners to practice concepts and skills. The amount of exercise required will vary among students.

- **Effect** — Adult learners need to see the positive effect of what they are learning. This effect could be the satisfaction of learning a new skill or the reward that accompanies mastery of new information. A good instructor continually reinforces why adult learners need to master the information or skills presented.

Figure 2.4 Students should practice the skills they learn in order to gain proficiency.

- **Disuse** — Among adult learners it can be assumed that habits and memories used repeatedly are strengthened, and habits not reinforced are weakened through disuse. Reviewing previously learned information at the beginning of a lesson is one way that instructors address disuse. The effects of disuse are the foundation of the argument for continued training and education. Follow-up practice at the company level reinforces skills learned during instruction.

- **Association** — Instructors can assume that adult learners tend to try to associate new information with information they have already learned. Creating association during instruction is very simple, such as expanding on prerequisite knowledge and adding another layer of information. Sometimes, information is wholly new to students. Instructors should still attempt to find associations for the information even though the connection to what students already know may take more advanced thought to discover.

- **Recency** — Skills and information practiced or learned most recently are also the best remembered. Adult learners, for example, who passed a certification test may not remember the information years later if they have not practiced or reviewed the information in the intervening years. Instructors need to recognize when skills or information have fallen into disuse so that they know when it is appropriate to review information that adult learners already know. Instructors should recognize that they need to include enough time to summarize the day's lesson in order for the information to be most recent in the students' minds when they leave.

- **Primacy** — Primacy is similar to recency. Primacy assumes that the first of a series of learned acts would be remembered better than others. Because of this, lessons should open with strong overviews including learning objectives and major concepts that will be presented.

- **Intensity** — The principle of intensity states that if a stimulus (experience) is vivid and real, it will more likely change or have an effect on the behavior (learning). For example, an instructor who demonstrates how to use a certain rescue tool or how to immobilize a trauma patient and involves students in the demonstration is providing an experience that is more likely to be remembered than a lecture or video recording on how to perform the skill **(Figure 2.5)**.

Certification vs. Qualification

Instructors may be certified to teach but may not have the knowledge or experience to be qualified to teach. Certification is based upon passing a written and/or practical exam. A certification may not rely upon keeping a skill up-to-date. Qualification means practicing and maintaining skill mastery for performance in real world situations. Qualification also applies to maintaining subject mastery on topics that do not have a skills component.

Instructors must recognize that they, too, may suffer the loss of skills due to disuse. Being qualified to teach something, especially fire and emergency services skills, requires continually maintaining mastery over the skills taught during training. When qualifications and certifications are in conflict, instructors must seek out opportunities to raise their qualifications before instruction begins.

Figure 2.5 Hands-on experience is an effective training tool.

Characteristics of Adult Learners

Personal characteristics and outside influences affect how students learn. Understanding the capabilities and limitations of adult learners makes learning more successful. Student characteristics include life experiences, motivation, time demands or adult responsibilities, confidence, and learning style variations.

Instructors have a challenge in meeting student needs and assisting diverse groups to find the most effective learning method. Knowing how and why individuals learn provides a foundation and direction for planning interesting and motivating lessons and matching learning and teaching styles effectively. The following are common characteristics of adult learners that instructors should take into consideration:

- **Life Experiences and Responsibilities** — Adult students possess a variety of life experiences that are gained through work, leisure, and family responsibilities **(Figure 2.6)**. Instructors should use discussion techniques to establish the relationships between adult students' past experiences and the new materials being taught. These discussions help to involve students in the learning process and allow the instructor to determine the gap between what students already know and what they need to know to fulfill the needs of their jobs or learn new skills **(Figure 2.7)**. Current life responsibilities may become a distraction and may not allow students to devote one hundred percent of their time and attention to a course. Instructors should take the time to get to know their students and become aware of other responsibilities that may hinder their success in a course.

Figure 2.6 Adult students bring their own experiences from the other parts of their lives to the classroom. These experiences influences how they learn.

- **Motivation** — Adults take classes for a variety of reasons. Sometimes they are motivated by an internal desire to gain knowledge or skills they believe will help them to be successful. At other times, they are in class because an employer or supervisor requires them to attend. In these latter instances the motivation is external and may be perceived as a negative requirement by the student. Whether internal or external, instructors should use these motivations to the advantage of effective instruction.

  NOTE: Motivation will be discussed further as part of the four-step method introduced in Chapter 6, Classroom Instruction.

- **Self-confidence** — Some students enter a course very confident about their ability to learn. Others may have low levels of confidence. For example, some students may have been away from the school environment for years or have little confidence in their abilities to be successful based upon prior, negative learning experiences. Regardless of how a student gained his or her level of confidence, instructors should be aware of potential challenges that students with low self-confidence face.

Figure 2.7 Informal discussions about students' personal experiences help instructors tailor instruction to their needs.

Adult learners are of different ages, sexes, cultural and ethnic origins, educational backgrounds, and sexual orientations, not to mention a broad range of other categories that are used to characterize people. In some cases, these factors are as much perceived as actual. Perceptions aside, the characteristics of North Americans are rapidly shifting. The population is becoming more diverse and better educated, and instructors will see an ever-increasing cultural diversity within their classes. Students should be respected for their abilities, experiences, and individuality. The value of student diversity is that it brings a diversity of thought to the instructional environment which in turn enhances learning. The sections that follow discuss some of the types of diversity instructors will encounter.

NOTE: Generalities based upon aspects of diversity may be inaccurate. Instructors are cautioned to avoid broad generalizations based upon any one aspect of diversity.

Age

Adults of different generations may have different experiences and skill sets that they bring to the classroom. A majority of one generation may generally have a more hands-on understanding of machinery, tools, and construction. Another generation may be more inclined toward emerging technologies and computers. Instructors should take these differences into account. For example, a class with younger students may require more time with practical skills training. Similarly, older students may prefer traditional instruction rather than web-based instruction. Instructors may pair a younger student with an older student during skills training and maintain the pairing when the students are working with computer simulations.

Gender

Both genders bring their own, unique experiences to the classroom and the training ground. In addition, students may also bring gender biases to the learning environment which may affect their relationship with the instructor, other students' perceptions of the instructor, and the learning process. Allowing gender biases to enter a classroom is disruptive to effective instruction. Gender issues during instruction may also have a negative effect on an organization as a whole.

NOTE: For the purposes of this discussion, the term gender has been used to refer to the differences between men and women.

Cultural and Ethnic Background

Individuals from different cultural and ethnic backgrounds bring unique customs, behaviors, attitudes, and values to the classroom. Instructors need to recognize and understand situations in which ethnic and cultural differences may have an effect on classroom instruction or student interaction. Because of the diverse group of individuals who participate in training courses, it is not always possible for instructors to be familiar with the customs of every culture and ethnic group. Instructors should take advantage of opportunities to attend cultural diversity training courses and should attend such training multiple times when different teachers or speakers are offering the training.

Generational Characteristics

The following are broadly worded generalizations about the generations that instructors will encounter in their classrooms:

Baby Boomers:

- Were born between 1946 and 1964
- Are typically idealistic
- Place a high value on fairness, equality, hard work, and competition
- Have a history of questioning authority and wanting to know why something is important
- Tend to place a high value on education, family, and personal leisure time

Gen-X:

- Were born between 1965 and 1980
- Require personal flexibility and thrive on feedback from instructors and supervisors
- Prefer to work independently with minimal supervision
- Seek a balance between work and leisure time in their lives
- Are accustomed to change
- May exhibit some qualities of the baby boomers (their parents) and some qualities of the millennials (their children)
- Referred to as the "baby bust" because their population is much smaller than that of their parents

Gen-Y, Dotcomers, Millenials, Nexters:

- Were born after 1980
- Use technology as part of their daily lives
- Use online social networks as a way of creating relationships and sharing information
- Are generally optimistic
- Appreciate diversity
- Demand instant gratification in the form of tangible results for their efforts
- Take a broad worldview
- Have high expectations for educational outcomes

What This Means to You

Student diversity basically means acknowledging that we are all human beings with unique backgrounds. Each of us brings something different to the classroom. Instructors are no different. You come to the classroom with your own experiences and biases as well.

While you use your experience to help students, you have an obligation not to let your biases influence how you treat students. Always remember that all students should be treated fairly. In addition, accommodations must be made for each student to be successful during fire and emergency services training. And above all, learn to embrace diversity in training. When you allow each individual to be unique and offer their particular experience to the training environment, all students benefit and the instructional environment is enhanced.

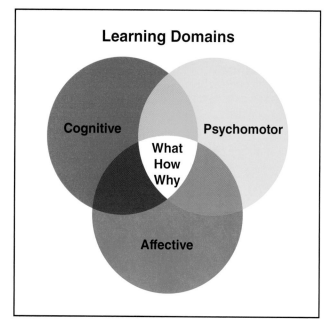

Learning Domains

Figure 2.8 The three Domains of Learning interact to indicate the what, how, and why of the learning process.

Domains of Learning — Areas of learning and classification of learning objectives; often referred to as cognitive (knowledge), affective (attitude), and psychomotor (skill performance) learning.

Cognition — Concept that refers to all forms of knowing, including perceiving, imagining, reasoning, and judging.

Domains of Learning

The three types or **domains of learning**, cognitive (knowledge), psychomotor (skills), and affective (attitude), are interrelated areas in which learning occurs rather than being independent areas of learning. Learning within the domains enables students to understand a concept, perform a task, or alter a behavior.

Having an understanding of these domains and how they interact will assist the instructor in presenting effective instruction. Through the cognitive domain, students gain understanding about a concept or topic. Through the psychomotor domain, students perform the skills associated with that concept or topic. Through the affective domain, students develop a willingness to perform the behavior correctly and safely. The cognitive, psychomotor, and affective domains are the what, how, and why of the learning process **(Figure 2.8)**.

Cognitive (Knowledge)

Cognition is a general concept that refers to all forms of knowing, including perceiving, imagining, reasoning, and judging. It is the foundation for the other two domains. Cognition enables a person to apply knowledge (what) to perform a task or skill (how) and understand and accept the reasoning (why) behind the basic concept.

Cognitive information is usually presented in a technical or factual presentation, usually in lecture and discussion form. With various techniques, instructors can prepare students to apply knowledge to skills (psychomotor domain) and understand and accept new ideas and methods (affective domain). To describe and illustrate cognitive material and make it interesting and dynamic, instructors may use the following techniques:

- Use audiovisual and training aids.
- Show models and other displays.
- Perform demonstrations.
- Involve students in application activities.

Psychomotor (Skills)

The psychomotor domain is typically referred to as hands-on training. Knowledge gained in the cognitive domain is transferred to physical movement. Learning is developed through repeated practice of the skill. Successful completion of the skill is measured in speed, precision, distance, techniques, or sequence of execution.

Through positive reinforcement (feedback) and continued practice, students develop correct techniques and become proficient so the skill becomes a habit that is performed automatically. With practice and experience, students modify actions or create new formats to fit other situations.

Instructors must be aware that students learn at different rates of speed and levels of ability. Students must be comfortable in one psychomotor level before advancing to the next. Some students may want to observe longer than others before they begin to practice. Others may want more guidance and coaching before feeling confident to work on their own.

Instructors must watch for and understand student abilities at each level and provide appropriate time and opportunity for learning. Studies of vocational training have indicated that providing an adequate amount of time to master each level is critical for the success of most students.

Affective (Attitude)

Affective learning involves how individuals deal with issues emotionally and includes the following traits:

- Individual awareness
- Attitudes
- Interests
- Appreciations
- Motivations
- Enthusiasm
- Values

Instructors influence students by providing positive attitudes toward authority, respect, responsibility, and safety (among other values). This attitude instills in students the same values that are demonstrated by instructors. At the same time, negative attitudes can result in students having a low regard for these values.

Learning outcomes of the affective domain take time to achieve and are not as readily observable as the results of the cognitive and psychomotor domains. While learning new cognitive information and performing new psychomotor skills, students may alter old attitudes, values, and beliefs. For example, a trainee may begin to value safety and demonstrate this by reporting hazards, wearing safety equipment, or following safety rules without being reminded **(Figure 2.9)**. Instructors should reinforce correct affective behaviors with positive feedback and not overlook the indicators of behavioral change.

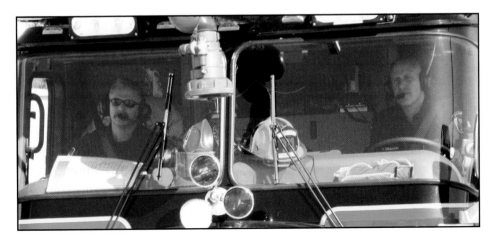

Figure 2.9 An instructor can teach students important safety behaviors by modeling the appropriate behaviors, such as wearing a safety belt when driving or riding in an apparatus.

Instructors' efforts in reinforcing correct affective behaviors will be most effective when students receive a consistent message from their supervisors and leaders. Instructors are often the first agents of affective behavioral change within an organization.

Learning Styles

A **learning style** is the consistent way a person gathers and processes information. Students in the classroom use sight, hearing, and touch to gather information. Students will favor one or a combination of these senses individually. Students may not be aware that they use any particular style to participate in learning nor that they may use different learning styles for different tasks or circumstances. But instructors can recognize different learning styles by making the following observations:

Learning Style — Learner's habitual manner of problem-solving, thinking, or learning, though the learner may not be conscious of his or her style and may adopt different styles for different learning tasks or circumstances.

● How individuals perceive, remember, and think about information and solve problems

● How individuals see and make sense of their world and attend to their environment

● How individuals attend to instruction and participate in activities

Figure 2.10 Many students will take notes during class lectures.

Instructors may notice that some students like to read assignments and take notes during lectures **(Figure 2.10)**. Other students may prefer to watch videos and demonstrations of skills. Instructors may also be able to identify those students who actively participate in discussions and physical activities. Instructors will notice that students show different degrees of attention, participation, and interest during presentations and class activities.

These differences are all representative of differing learning styles based on which sense or combination of senses provide students with the most accurate amount of information that is acceptable to them. To meet these different learning styles, instructors should plan a variety of teaching methods and learning activities in their lessons. Using a variety of methods helps instructors reach the many individual learning styles so that all students can participate in a style that enables them to learn.

In some situations, students will have developed learning styles that are not productive and can even contribute to their own failure. They are often not aware that their studying and learning habits are not working. Through the use of a variety of teaching strategies, an instructor can guide students into developing more effective learning styles.

Learning Styles Assessment

There are many learning style assessments that are very useful for instructors to assist students in discovering their learning styles. Through answering a series of questions, a student can discover what learning style he or she most likely uses during instruction.

Instructional Strategies

Instructional strategies are ways of organizing information that best fit the way students process information. Instructors can stimulate thinking processes by using a variety of activities that require students to select a performance, determine the logic of a procedure, draw conclusions, and determine outcomes. Most lesson plans in fire and emergency services classrooms use one of the following strategies:

- **Sequential or linear** — Using a step-by-step, orderly thinking process that has both a beginning and an end and includes the following processes:
  - Analyzing
  - Classifying
  - Reasoning
  - Tracking of times, dates, and events

- **Abstract or symbolic** — Recognizing common qualities in similar but different experiences. Students use written and spoken words and numbers to represent ideas or objects and use equations to express ideas. They also use gestures, postures, and facial expressions to represent feelings, ideas, or actions.

- **Concrete or real objects or items** — Preferring to manage items and work with facts instead of imagining outcomes or the feel of something. Students prefer seeing true-to-life visuals and demonstrations, hearing actual sounds, and touching textures and shapes.

- **Global or holistic** — Seeing the whole picture and forming relationships between concepts, events, or things. Students have an ability to gain insight from an overview or a picture and combine parts into a whole, form associations, make generalizations, and form theories from facts.

Motivation

Motivation is a key component to helping students to achieve their best and meet learning objectives. Instructors can use the following techniques to help motivate students:

- **Provide relevancy** — Tell students why the knowledge and skills they are learning are important and how they can be applied to real-life situations.

- **Set realistic and obtainable goals** — Identify criteria for successful completion of tasks, lessons, and courses.

- **Demonstrate enthusiasm** — Show as much interest in the course as that expected of students. Share ideas and receive positive comments or participate in reasonable debates.

- **Expect success and require outstanding performance** — Convince students that they are capable of mastering course goals. Encourage outstanding performance by guiding and coaching students to that level.

- **Incorporate motivators** — Make a conscious effort to determine student motivators. Provide external motivations such as rewards, recognition, and certificates that cause students to feel successful.

Figure 2.11 Good instructors should intersperse lectures with discussions that allow student participation.

- **Generate interest and participation** — Use activities that include discussions to develop thinking skills and provide opportunities for participation in activities that hold attention and interest, stimulate thinking, develop thinking skills, and develop relationships with others **(Figure 2.11)**.

- **Include instructional variety** — Use a variety of teaching strategies that match learning styles, abilities, and needs. Use visual aids and demonstrations that relate to job requirements. Promote team work to share tasks and learn from one another.

Chapter Summary

Effective instructors understand the principles of learning and use them to aid in their interpretation of lesson plans and preparations for classroom instruction. Instructors should understand what qualities apply to most adult learners such as readiness to learn. They should also be able to recognize how adult learners are unique as individuals and make differences a positive aspect of the learning environment. Effective instructors also understand that a variety of strategies and styles are needed to reach a diverse audience. Finally, instructors must realize that all their preparations and careful planning will not be enough in and of themselves to motivate students to learn. Enthusiasm, coaching techniques, motivational hooks, and a demand for excellence go hand-in-hand with well-prepared lessons.

Review Questions

1. What are Thorndike's Laws of Leaning?
2. What are common characteristics of adult learners?
3. What are the three domains of learning?
4. What should instructors do to address different learning styles?
5. What instructional strategies are used in fire and emergency services?
6. What motivational techniques can instructors use to help students succeed?

Instructional Planning

Chapter Contents

chapter 3

Key Terms

Job Performance Requirements

NFPA® 1041 References

4.2.3	4.4.3
4.3.3	4.4.4
4.4.2	

Instructional Planning

Learning Objectives

1. Describe the benefits of instructor organization. [NFPA® 1041, 4.3.3]

2. Explain the factors considered when selecting training aids for an assigned instructional lesson. [NFPA® 1041, 4.2.3, 4.4.3, 4.4.2]

3. Analyze potential events that can impact class continuity. [NFPA® 1041, 4.4.4]

4. Discuss the methods used to reduce the impact to class continuity by a change in instructors. [NFPA® 1041, 4.4.4]

5. Describe the aspects needed to achieve class consistency. [NFPA® 1041, 4.4.4]

Chapter 3
Instructional Planning

Case History

An instructor arrived at a permanent training facility prepared to teach techniques for advancing hose. The lesson began with a morning lecture session that included class discussion and was scheduled to take about an hour. After the lecture, the plan was to take the students to the outdoor training area to practice what had been explained during the lecture. The lecture portion of the instruction went well, but while the class continued to discuss tactics, it began to rain.

Because the instructor had planned the lessons for the course a few days in advance, he was able to move on to material that would be relevant in later lessons. The students, many of whom had traveled a good distance to attend the series of classes, were able to salvage the day's training even though they did not get to engage in practice.

The following day, the instructor arrived early to ensure that the training ground was safe after the rain. He had prepared a brief review on yesterday's lesson. After presenting the review, the class had plenty of time to practice advancing hose on the training ground.

A good instructor does not just appear in the classroom and begin teaching, just as good students do not just arrive for a class and begin learning. Both must prepare for the experience; both must have expectations and anticipations of what each wants to accomplish and how to accomplish it. Effective instructors take extensive preparatory steps to ensure that the learning experience is worthwhile, relevant, and interesting. Taking time to properly prepare before the presentation will result in a positive learning experience that motivates students to think, question, and become involved in the learning process.

This chapter discusses many important aspects of instructional preparation, including the following topics:

- **Instructor planning** — Preparing to teach and preparing students to learn

- **Training aid selection** — Choosing appropriate training aids for the information to be taught

- **Class continuity** — Tying each individual lesson plan together

- **Course consistency** — Presenting information that conforms to other information, standards, and accepted practices

Planning to Teach

Planning time spent outside class is crucial to instructor accomplishments inside class. If instructors do not plan ahead, then class time may not be used efficiently. As part of planning to teach, instructors must organize the learning materials, prepare for the class session, and ensure that all logistical needs are met.

Organization

Being organized leads to the success of any new fire and emergency services instructor. The use of good organizational skills can result in a variety of benefits such as the following:

- Increased instructor credibility

- Improved efficiency of classroom presentation

- More effective use of time, talent, and materials

- Reduced stress on the instructor

- Meeting legal requirements for record keeping (see Chapter 9, Reports, Records, and Scheduling)

Instructor organization begins with the physical organization of the instructor's office or work area as well as the training division's resources and training aids storage. Files, lesson plans, handouts, report forms, and ancillary materials should be neatly stored and easily accessed. Guidelines for the filing and storage of these materials may be formalized in the division's standard operating procedures or guidelines (SOPs or SOGs).

The new instructor should review these procedures or guidelines to determine the appropriate methods. When no procedures or guidelines exist, the instructor should find an organizational system that works best for him or her. Commonly used organizational systems can be found in numerous books, magazines, and websites. Any materials needed for a particular session should be organized and reviewed ahead of time and easily accessed when they are needed during class.

Session Preparation

Figure 3.1 An organization's standard lesson plan will serve as a good framework for the information that must be covered.

Instructors are often required to teach topics they have not taught before. Even a veteran instructor may be required to develop a presentation on a new topic. To prepare to teach a new topic, an instructor must first gain a thorough knowledge of the topic and ensure that he or she can perform the skills associated with the topic and answer any student questions. The instructor may already have this knowledge even if he or she has not taught the subject before. If the instructor has had absolutely no prior experience with the topic, it might be best to find another instructor or recognize that preparation to teach will take significantly more time.

Instructor Credibility

Assuming that an instructor is capable of teaching a topic when that is not the case can result in an embarrassing and potentially disastrous learning experience. However, circumstances may arise when qualified instructors find themselves unprepared. Instructors should never acknowledge that they are unprepared to teach a topic. Such a statement destroys student confidence, instructor credibility, and any opportunity to motivate students.

At the same time, an instructor who is unqualified to teach a topic should not attempt to teach it. Instructors lose respect and credibility when they are not forthright about their limitations. An unqualified instructor not only risks the safety of the students but also runs the risk of legal liability for providing incorrect or inaccurate information.

The most important session preparation tasks include the following:

- **Read the lesson objectives** — Become familiar with what the objectives require students to know and perform.

- **Review the lesson plan** — Use an organization's standard lesson plan to determine what material must be addressed, what time frame is required, and what assistance, materials, and equipment are needed **(Figure 3.1)**.

- **Check what equipment is needed** — Be familiar with training aids. Know how to operate and use various pieces of equipment for student activities.

- **Locate required equipment** — Arrange for additional equipment that will be necessary but is not already in the classroom or training area; find avenues within the organization to acquire what is needed.

- **Determine what skills must be taught** — Practice the skill steps, or at least review the steps mentally by looking at pictures, equipment, or handouts. Any instructor who lacks recent experience or practice in a skill must take time to review it or determine a method of presenting it so that the skill is understandable to students **(Figure 3.2)**. Ideally, the instructor presents a skill at mastery level.

Figure 3.2 Review step-by-step skills before teaching them to students.

- **Review required lesson audiovisuals** — Preview audiovisuals to prepare for engaging students in related discussions and applications. This step means being familiar with the lesson plan and knowing when and how audiovisuals are used.

- **Check documentation requirements** — Check on, arrange for, and have available and ready all handouts, rosters, and other reports and records before class begins.

The instructor must be familiar with the topic, familiar with the operation of all training aids, and be able to make logical, smooth transitions between sections of the material. For the new instructor, the best way to present an organized presentation is to practice the presentation. Making a practice presentation helps the instructor recognize any points where adjustments need to be made. It also helps to build personal confidence and create enthusiasm for the topic. Asking more experienced instructors how they approach teaching similar topics can be an excellent source of information for improvement.

Observe Other Instructors

When teaching for the first time or before teaching a new class or topic, purposefully observe the methods of several other instructors. Watch how others manage student groups, present information, and demonstrate skills. Look for advantages and disadvantages of their presentation methods.

Think about which methods accomplish learning objectives and which methods appear to create problems and cause disruptions in learning and lesson organization. Draw conclusions about what methods seem to work best, and adapt those as you develop your own teaching method and style.

Periodically, it may be necessary for an instructor to teach a class on short notice. For an experienced and well-organized instructor, this is generally not a problem. A new instructor, however, may feel the stress of having to adapt to a situation rapidly. The replacement instructor must make every effort to quickly prepare and deliver a lesson that makes the time in class worthwhile. The replacement instructor should attempt to apply the preparation steps mentioned before beginning the class.

As instructors gain experience in a subject in a familiar course, the time it takes to prepare decreases. In the beginning, it is not unusual to spend 1 to 3 hours of preparation time for every hour of delivery time. For some courses, preparation time can extend to more hours or even days of scheduling, coordinating, and confirming that class and teaching needs are met.

What This Means to You

You may sometimes be put into the position of walking into the classroom with little opportunity for preparation. One way to handle this situation is to make the class session a discovery zone where everyone learns something. This situation may mean using each learning objective as an overview point and proceeding from there. It may mean that the group learns or reviews the basic steps on whatever equipment or materials are available, such as getting sections of rope and practicing knots, or obtaining some manikins and practicing cardiopulmonary resuscitation (CPR).

Session Logistics

The term **logistics** as used in the fire and emergency services profession means the procurement, distribution, maintenance, and replacement of materials and personnel. Fire and emergency services organizations usually have a division or individual who manages logistics by providing the materials and equipment required to meet the mission of the organization and its various divisions. Within the training division, each instructor is usually responsible for acquiring the logistical support that the lesson plan requires.

Logistics — Process of managing the scheduling of limited materials and equipment to meet the multiple demands of training programs and instructors.

Logistics may also consume class time. The completion of some skills requires cleaning portions of the training area or restocking, refilling, or replacing certain items. The organization or the type of lesson plan may require that students perform some of the following duties:

● Cleaning a spill

● Returning the classroom to its pre-training arrangement

● Parking vehicles in designated locations **(Figure 3.3)**

● Cleaning manikins

● Refilling SCBA cylinders

● Reloading fire hose

● Restocking kits with supplies

● Recharging battery-operated equipment

● Cleaning fire hose

● Inspecting, cleaning, and replacing tools

Instructors must calculate the time it takes to perform these duties. Students should perform some of these duties during class time, as part of the required skills training; students should perform others after class time, so that the next class can begin promptly. Logistical needs may require several hours of preparation and restoration for classes with high equipment needs, such as live-fire training, EMT training, or driver training for groups of 25 to 30 students.

Figure 3.3 Returning apparatus to their starting placement may be a logistics task that needs to be performed so that another set of students can practice the lesson.

For many instructors, logistics means making arrangements to have the materials and support they need to deliver training. The instructor is responsible for ensuring that all materials and equipment needed are determined and arranged for before the beginning of class. Organized instructors will have a checklist of necessary materials and equipment to ensure that nothing is forgotten. This list can be retained as part of the lesson-plan documentation used for future class sessions **(Figure 3.4, p.56)**.

For those instructors who work in a training facility, there may be staff members to assist with maintenance, inventory control, and scheduling of equipment. But the final responsibility always rests with the instructor who must take the time to ask for assistance, to follow procedures when making requests or reservations, and to follow up on those requests. Arriving early to get or assemble equipment and materials gives an instructor the opportunity to perform the following steps:

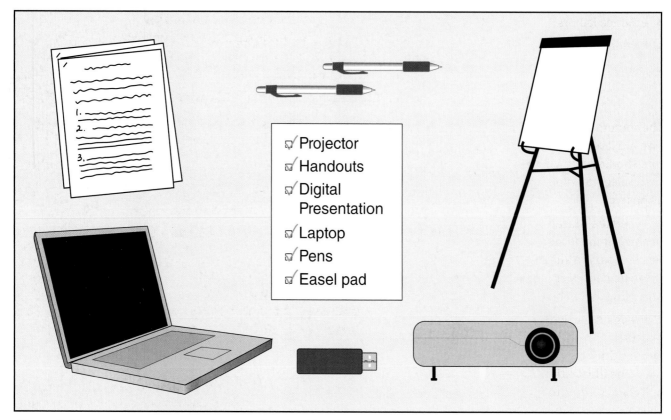

Figure 3.4 Instructors are encouraged to consult a checklist of materials and equipment that they need to conduct a class session.

Step 1: Check for missing items.

Step 2: Review operations.

Step 3: Arrange room layout.

Step 4: Find replacements or make repairs.

Step 5: Revert to a contingency plan (also known as Plan B). Instructors should always have at least one contingency plan per lesson.

Training Aid Selection

Instructor I candidates will usually be told in a lesson plan what **training aids** are required to teach a lesson. Procuring these aids is an important part of session logistics. However, there may be occasions when the training aid recommended in a lesson plan is not available. In these cases, instructors need to be able to adapt and select alternative training aids to meet the needs of the lesson plan.

Selecting the appropriate training aids to use with a lecture or demonstration requires planning in order to make them work with the learning objectives and lesson content and ensure that they have a purpose and are student-focused. Instructors should consider the following factors when selecting training aids or devices:

- Learning objectives and lesson content

- Required student performance

- Class size and interaction

- Pace of learning

Training Aids — Broad term referring to any audiovisual aids, reprinted materials, training props, or equipment used to supplement instruction.

- Practice factors
- Evaluative factors
- Budget limitations

Learning Objectives and Lesson Content

The content of any training aids that an instructor uses in a lecture or demonstration must reinforce the desired learning objectives and lesson content. Instructors should review the lesson plan, determine the content and objectives, and then select the type of training aid that will satisfy as many of the requirements as possible.

When the source for the training aid is a professionally produced curriculum or single item, it should be compared to the desired lesson plan outcome. It may be necessary to alter the training aid or use only the relevant portion of it. When the instructor does not have an existing training aid, it is then necessary to create one using the technology that is available.

For instance, when the lesson content concerns the behavior of fire and the learning objective is to understand the fire tetrahedron, then a simple digital image or a drawing on a dry erase board illustrating this theory would be appropriate. If the illustration is part of a longer video on fire development, the instructor can cue the video to the appropriate sequence before class, in order to maximize class time. If no image exists in the purchased curriculum, the instructor may look for an image elsewhere or create one.

Required Student Performance

Based on the lesson plan, an instructor should select training aids that most appropriately illustrate or demonstrate the knowledge that the student must possess when the course is completed. For instance, when a course is intended to help company officers become certified to command a multiple company operation, a computer-simulation program may be an effective training aid. When students are required to successfully perform patient ventilation, then manikins for training and evaluation are appropriate **(Figure 3.5)**.

Class Size and Interaction

Teaching situations where instructors want to encourage student participation and interaction can influence the choice of training aids. Class size and classroom arrangement may limit interaction with a large class to a question-and-answer period at the end of the presentation. Spontaneous diagrams on an easel pad or marker board can facilitate a highly participative coaching session in a small class.

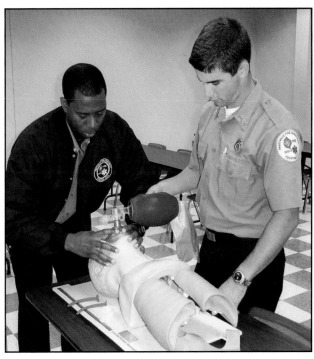

Figure 3.5 Training manikins can be used to teach a variety of skills such as patient ventilation.

It is also important to consider class size and seating arrangement when determining the image size of a training aid. Class size and seating arrangement have a direct relationship with the size of the image the class is expected to view. For example, using an easel pad in front of an audience of 200 people seated in a large auditorium would not be appropriate. A large projection screen would be a better choice. On the other hand, when debriefing a group of six trainees after a practical training evolution, an easel pad or marker board may be ideal.

Pace of Learning

Different training aids can be effective when applied in different instructional environments. One factor in the suitability of a training aid to the environment is the intended pace of learning. When the expected pace of learning is high, training aids can be integrated into the lesson plan to allow a class to move quickly through the information. For example, a video can quickly review the basics of an incident command system at the beginning of a lesson on the responsibilities of the division or group supervisor.

When the content of the lesson is primarily unfamiliar to students, training aids that allow an instructor to proceed at a slower pace are more appropriate. One strategy for teaching new material is to assign outside reading assignments from textbooks or self-study guides for completion before the beginning of class. Guided discussions using marker boards, easel pads, or large illustrations used in class can reinforce new material. Students can then view a video for review and reinforcement.

When students represent a variety of knowledge levels or experiences, a student-centered strategy can include a mixture of the two scenarios. Those students who are not yet at the required learning level can have access to self-study materials before joining the more advanced students at the appropriate time.

Practice Factors

It is always important to give students an opportunity to apply new knowledge and skills. To make the new application meaningful, practice time should be included in the lesson plan along with the training aids or props needed **(Figure 3.6)**. In order to apply the knowledge and skills obtained from a lesson on tying knots or operating a power tool, for example, the students need the equipment and props so they can execute the steps.

Figure 3.6 Time to practice using the correct equipment is key to any course.

The training aids required to apply nonphysical concepts or skills such as incident management, accident investigation, personnel supervision, problem solving, or fire investigation may be more difficult to select. Training aids for prospective incident managers can include practice scenarios using the following methods or devices:

- Paper, marker boards, or easel pads
- Tabletop models
- Technology-based training (TBT)
- Interactive and virtual reality equipment

Similarly, investigation skills can be applied by using case studies on paper, using computer-based scenarios, using structures (acquired or purpose-built) for practical evolutions, or staging an accident or incident scene for the student to physically investigate. Each of these examples requires that instructors carefully plan the use of training aids into the lesson in order to give students meaningful application of their new knowledge and skills.

Evaluative Factors

A further consideration when selecting the appropriate training aid is how a student's knowledge will be evaluated at the end of the course. The training aid used during the lecture may also be used as a testing tool. For example, the same CPR manikin is usually used for the initial demonstration, student practice, and final evaluation. In a command course, the TBT simulation (or a similar one) can be used for both training and testing.

Using the same training aid throughout a course ensures that the student is familiar with the prop or item during the skills evaluation. However, an instructor must ensure that the continuous use of a specific training aid promotes overall skill development, not just familiarity with that particular training aid.

Budget Limitations

Training aid devices should also be cost-effective; that is, the benefit to the student and instructor must be greater than the purchase cost of the device, cost of upkeep and storage, and cost in time to develop the training aid. Generally, instructors overlook the cost of developing training aids when they are preparing a slide presentation or creating a video. They may invest many hours in the creation of a presentation to illustrate a concept that is more easily understood through an oral presentation. The lack of funding or time may automatically prohibit the purchase or development of a training aid. But when the benefit to student understanding of the subject is increased, then a means of overcoming the costs should be determined. If training aids must be purchased, the instructor should follow the SOPs established by his or her AHJ.

Class Continuity

Continuity ensures that presented information flows in a logical and understandable stream. Many factors can affect **class continuity**, but instructors can take steps to reduce their effects. Most of the steps can be included in the processes of session scheduling, preparation, and logistics. Instructors should always anticipate problems and prepare contingency plans for potential events such as the following:

- Instructor changes
- Weather variations
- Equipment and material variations and failures
- Instructional resource variations
- Differences in learning styles
- Differences in learning knowledge levels

Class Continuity — Principle of instruction that states that all information throughout a course should be presented in a logical, understandable pattern.

Instructor Changes

There are times when an instructor is not available to teach a scheduled class. Ideally, that instructor or the instructor's supervisor contacts someone familiar with and experienced in teaching the lesson. Every time a different instructor teaches, it causes some amount of discontinuity in the class.

Another instance that causes discontinuity occurs when additional instructors must assist the lead course instructor in teaching a skills session. All instructors have their own personal perceptions, views, beliefs, and methods of teaching. It is possible that their ideas and methods may be different from those of the lead course instructor. The lead course instructor should maintain continuity by following these suggestions:

- **Know fellow instructors** — One of the many benefits of in-service training, meetings, conferences, and seminars is that instructors meet, exchange ideas with, and make assessments of each other. If an instructor must call on another to substitute or assist in teaching a class, it should be someone whom the instructor knows and trusts, who has similar ideas and methods, and who has similar or better experience.

- **Prepare the students** — Ideal situations do not always occur, and the desired instructor substitute or assistant may not be available. Students become dependent on and familiar with the methods, attitudes, and personalities of their instructors and may not relate as well to a different one. Instructors should tell students in advance to prepare for what may be a different teaching style than that to which they are accustomed.

- **Meet with substitute instructors or assistants to prepare for the class** — Every instructor involved in teaching a class must prepare for it. The lead course instructor who arranges for a substitute or for assistants should meet with the substitute or assistants and perform the following activities **(Figures 3.7 a-c)**:

  — Outline the learning objectives and what must be accomplished in the lesson.

  — Assign specific duties or skills.

  — Show and orient each person to the teaching area or classroom.

  — Provide directions or assistance in locating and assembling equipment.

  — Coordinate rest break and cleanup times.

  — Perform any other duties needed to ensure a successful lesson.

Practicing these activities regularly also has the benefit of providing continuity in instructor preparation and delivery: classes run more smoothly, instructors perform more effectively, and students have the continuity they need to participate successfully in the learning process.

Preparing Students for a New Instructor

Whenever possible, the lead instructor should do the following when another instructor is conducting the lesson:

- Give students some background on the additional or substitute instructor's experiences, knowledge, and teaching methods.

- Introduce the additional or substitute instructor to the class when the person arrives or the day before he or she is going to teach a lesson.

- Describe the lesson plan that a guest or substitute instructor will be teaching so that the students know what to expect.

Figures 3.7 a-c The lead instructor should ensure that the other instructors involved in a class are prepared for their tasks, introduce those instructors to the class, and share necessary information with them.

Weather Variations

Weather changes can have an adverse effect on training activities and schedules. Instructors must build flexibility into courses that are scheduled during times of the year when inclement weather is possible. Extreme weather conditions may challenge a course's continuity as instructors attempt to teach the same skills during the summer heat and winter cold. They must be able to adapt the skills to the existing weather while still remaining faithful to the specific skill requirements.

Instructors should not expect their students to learn skills effectively in any extreme weather conditions. When teaching psychomotor skills, the learning environment should not distract students from attending to the objectives of the lesson. Even though students may later have to perform the same skills under severe conditions on the job, these conditions are not conducive to learning the skill.

Instructors may decide to train in inclement weather conditions for the sole purpose of preparing students for facing those conditions on the job. Personnel safety becomes even more of a priority in inclement weather. Students must be provided with the appropriate equipment, rehabilitation, and safety instruction that are applicable to the weather conditions.

NOTE: Instructors should be aware that in some jurisdictions and situations there might be specific policies or labor/management contract provisions regarding weather conditions and training. In Florida, for instance, labor/management contracts have heat index provisions that limit training to days that have a heat index less than 100°F (38°C).

Rescheduling Because of Unsafe Conditions

Instructors should understand that there are conditions, such as those presented with ice or snow, where some evolutions cannot be safely performed. Even though the skills being taught in the evolution might have to be performed in a real emergency response mode under similarly adverse conditions, they do not have to be performed under those conditions while in training mode. If the instructor requires that the students perform such evolutions under unsafe conditions while in training mode, it could create liability issues for the instructor if a student gets injured. Sometimes it is best to postpone the class in the interest of safety.

Equipment and Material Variations

When scheduling equipment, an important factor in maintaining the continuity of the course is using the same type of equipment in the learning sessions that is used in the testing session and on the job. When a group will be tested on tying knots using a certain type and size of rope, for example, students should also practice with that type and size of rope. When students use a certain type of SCBA on the job, they should also be trained on the same or generically similar equipment **(Figure 3.8)**. This procedure is not only fair, but it also makes testing valid and reliable.

Instructional Resource Variations

Instructional resources used in training include the information, product data, skills sheets, and references required to meet the lesson plan requirements. Instructors can maintain continuity when this information is available to all course instructors during the planning of their course presentations.

Course materials may also be substantially different from the latest training material being published in the fire and emergency services. The Level I Instructor should, whenever possible, verify that the information he or she is using for instruction is the most current information available. If the instructor discovers that updates to materials are necessary, he or she should consult with the individual responsible for purchasing and updating materials.

Figure 3.8 Standardizing equipment will help students learn to perform tasks using the same equipment they will use during an incident.

Differences in Learning Styles

Differences in learning styles can create a challenge to instructors who are attempting to maintain class continuity. To maintain continuity, an instructor has to be flexible and adaptable within the structure of the course in order to appeal to the learning styles of all the students. Ideally, instructors adapt lessons that include a variety of teaching methodologies so that all types of students have the opportunity to learn through their preferred learning styles. This makes it more likely that students will gain the appropriate knowledge and skills and meet the lesson objectives.

Many students do not know that there is more than one way to learn, and they may not learn successfully by using the only way they know. By using a variety of teaching methods, instructors expose students to different and possibly more successful ways of learning.

Traditional teaching styles used by many training organizations have historically depended on a lecture-style format to provide cognitive information. Asking questions or using short written quizzes was generally used to check student understanding of the lectures or reading assignments. Students were expected to listen carefully to the instructor and take notes.

In order to enhance the learning process, instructors added visual aids to lectures to include the sense of sight in the learning process. Even though addressing the visual sense has greatly improved learning, some students still do not learn best using even the illustrated lecture format (See Chapter 6, Classroom Instruction). When teaching individuals who learn best by doing, changing to a demonstration or skill practice format works best (See Chapter 7, Skills-Based Training beyond the Classroom).

In addition to the situations described in the preceding paragraphs, there are also occasions when the abilities of students do not match the level to which the training material was written. Students may be either ahead of the material or not ready for it. Instructors should begin their course preparation by assessing their students' abilities and adjusting course materials accordingly.

Differences in Knowledge Level

Instructors may discover that their students are less knowledgeable (remedial) or more knowledgeable (advanced) about the topic for a daily lesson or for a course. The instructor should be prepared to make adjustments in order to provide a successful learning environment for both remedial and advanced students.

Remedial Knowledge Level

When the knowledge base of a student or a group of students is lower than the level of the course material, instructors have to adjust the teaching pace and expectation. It may be necessary to spend more time on review or practice. Students may need a review of basic skills or knowledge before they are ready to progress to the new material in the lesson. Reviewing previous material or skills may initially delay the lesson agenda or course time frame but can allow students to feel more comfortable with their knowledge and abilities so that they feel ready to proceed. Assigning additional reading or study assignments for students to accomplish outside the class period may also help them advance in the class.

Advanced Knowledge Level

When the knowledge base of a student or a group of students is more advanced than the material, instructors should review the material with students, and then assign problems or exercises at the advanced level. When the lesson includes some form of evaluation such as a test or demonstration of skills, instructors should have the students act as test evaluators or skills demonstrators. When there is still time available, instructors have the following options:

- Preview the next lesson and involve students in discussions or exercises to determine their levels of readiness.

- Have the group create exercises or scenarios and plan for the equipment they need to perform the exercises in the next lesson. Then arrange to have that equipment available for the next lesson. This option is available when it is not possible to move on to the next lesson because of equipment limitations.

- Have participants work together in groups to create test questions, complete with answer keys and text references. These tests can be used for study, debate, and discussion.

What This Means to You

Part of maintaining class continuity is having contingency plans. You will, at some point, be faced with a situation where the equipment for a lesson will be suddenly unavailable or where a student's learning style will be discovered part way through a course. Having a "Plan B" is important to address these situations and also to address unforeseen circumstances at the time of instruction. For example, the weather conditions could change on the day that a training evolution is planned. Students may have made special arrangements with their departments to be at the training or they may have traveled some distance to be there. Having a Plan B for such an occasion prevents the loss of a training day.

Course Consistency

Course consistency means presenting information that is always accurate and maintaining the same learning level throughout. Instructors and the training division lose credibility when the information has not been checked for accuracy and consistency. The following aspects of instruction should remain consistent throughout a course:

- Safety factors
- Training materials
- Resource materials
- Approaches to teaching
- Skill performances

Safety Factors

Safety is the primary responsibility of instructors and students who are engaged in training exercises. Both instructors and students must consistently adhere to safety policies and procedures. Instructors must continuously demonstrate by example every safety feature, every time, and under every condition if they want

Course Consistency — Principle of instruction that states that information throughout a course should have the same level of accuracy, be presented with the same equipment and training aids, and maintain a similar level of learning.

students to learn and perform every safety practice. They must be consistent in their use of safety equipment and procedures to ensure that the safety message is apparent to students.

Instructors should recognize and teach any safety issues that are appropriate to a lesson. When the lesson requires that students wear a protective hood during live-fire training, then all instructors involved in teaching live-fire training must also wear one. This rule also applies to all other PPE. When instructors or standards require that students wear PPE on the fireground, then students need to wear it when they train **(Figure 3.9)**.

Figure 3.9 During training, students must wear the appropriate PPE for the skills that they are simulating.

Skills and activities should be planned around the safest way of performing them. Instructors must inspect training classrooms and outdoor sites and then eliminate or reduce all potential hazards. In addition, students should be encouraged to identify and report any safety concerns as soon as they are noticed. Students must be taught to perform psychomotor skills in a safe manner. Consistent repetition of skills in a safe manner helps create a safety-conscious behavior pattern that students will continue to use after training is complete.

Types of Training Materials

Consistency in the types of materials used in training is also necessary. Fire-extinguishing agents, medical supplies, respiratory-protection equipment, and decontamination products should be identical to the types used in everyday and emergency activities. This consistency gives students the knowledge of how the product or material works and how it is packaged and looks.

Consistency also extends to the way that equipment and material is stored on the apparatus. Students perform more efficiently when they are familiar with a standard method of storing and accessing the equipment.

Resource Materials

Instructors draw on a variety of resources for their course materials, such as trade journals, the Internet, conferences, other training courses, and other instructors. When using these types of information and materials, instructors must ensure that all sources can be cited to the appropriate credible resource or standard and are accepted by the sponsoring training organization. To ensure course consistency, the resources should support the learning objectives of the course and should not contradict each other.

Approaches to Teaching

Consistency must also exist among the instructors who are teaching the course. When instructors disagree on a particular fact, they should resolve it during planning meetings and not in front of students.

When the inconsistency is a matter of personal preference, instructors should decide which approach to use with students. When two conflicting opinions are equally valid, instructors should present them at the same time, explain the advantages and weaknesses of each opinion, and allow students to draw their own conclusions. This method provides an excellent teaching opportunity that demonstrates the wide variety of approaches to some topics.

Skill Performances

When a jurisdiction has strict procedures/guidelines for performing a particular skill, it is even more important to ensure that lessons consistently comply with those guidelines. Although there may be multiple ways to perform a particular skill, such as raising a 24-foot (7.2 m) extension ladder for climbing, local SOPs/SOGs or state/provincial performance objectives may be very specific in how the skill will be performed. In these situations, consistency is essential.

Chapter Summary

Effective instructors must be prepared to teach before entering the training ground or classroom. This preparation to teach is one part of planning instruction. Choosing appropriate training aids is also important to instructional planning. Aids must, first and foremost, meet the needs of learning objectives and expected course goals.

In addition, instructors should plan ahead for the variations that occur during the course of a class. This type of planning ensures class continuity and consistency.

Review Questions

1. What are the keys to a successful teaching experience for instructors?

2. What factors should instructors consider when selecting training aids?

3. How can instructors prepare students for a change in instructors?

4. When can class continuity be affected?

5. In what areas can course consistency be an issue?

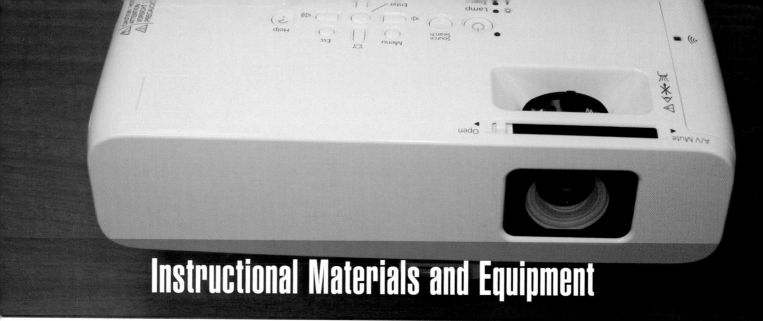

Instructional Materials and Equipment

Chapter Contents

chapter 4

Key Terms

Job Performance Requirements

NFPA® 1041 References

4.2.2	4.4.3
4.2.3	4.4.6
4.3.3	4.4.7
4.3.2	
4.4.2	

Learning Objectives

1. Identify the components of a lesson plan. [NFPA® 1041, 4.2.2, 4.3.3, 4.4.3]

2. Explain the benefits of outside resource materials. [NFPA® 1041, 4.2.3, 4.3.2]

3. Discuss copyright laws and permissions involved with instructional materials.

4. Describe the variety of training aids that an instructor may use in both the classroom and training environments. [NFPA® 1041, 4.4.6, 4.4.7]

5. Summarize the benefits of using training aids in the classroom environment. [NFPA® 1041, 4.4.2]

Chapter 4
Instructional Materials and Equipment

Case History

A populous county had its own photo lab and print shop. Fire and governmental departments used these facilities to reproduce materials for training purposes. Many of the materials reproduced were copyrighted and warning information concerning unauthorized reproduction was printed in the books, articles, and media materials being used for teaching classes. The county did not provide any guidance or training in the reproduction of materials. The written request for reproduction work did not require the authorization or a release signed by the writer or producer of the materials. A concerned employee knew about the reproduction of the material and that copyright violations were occurring. He contacted the local FBI office and informed them of the situation.

An FBI Special Agent investigated and found the facts were correct. The county was instructed to have all departments complete a form stating what information they had copied for the past three years, to sign an affidavit that all copied materials had been destroyed, and sign an affidavit that they had read the copyright laws and would abide by them. No further action would be taken if these conditions were met.

Compliance with the request was completed within the 30 day period stated in the agreement. The county and the individuals involved were fortunate that this incident occurred before someone filed against them for copyright violation, which could have resulted in criminal charges and/or civil penalties.

In theory, the training organization will provide an Instructor I with a prepared lesson plan that includes a list of any additional materials or equipment that may be needed to teach the lesson. Instructors need to understand the components of this prepared lesson plan and how to apply them to a training or classroom session. Also, instructors should be familiar with the equipment they may be required to use to assist in teaching prepared lessons. This chapter discusses the various materials that instructors will typically use in the classroom.

Lesson Plans

Basic to all teaching is the lesson plan, a road map that guides the instructor through the topic and the instructional methods used to teach the topic.

Instructors should never just walk into a classroom and begin teaching without some plan as to what they will do, where they will go with the information, and how they will get there. Teaching without a plan gives no guarantee that course objectives will be met or that students will actually learn what is required by the course outcomes or NFPA® job performance requirements (JPRs).

Using a lesson plan does not ensure fulfillment of objectives either, but it increases the likelihood of success. Without planning the lesson ahead of time, instructors may find that they are lacking important support equipment or supplemental materials, which means that they cannot teach or demonstrate information. The result for both instructors and students is that time is wasted because appropriate teaching and learning could not take place. The sections that follow elaborate upon the following topics:

- Purposes and benefits of lesson plans
- Components of lessons plans
- Lesson outlines and learning objectives

Purposes and Benefits of Lesson Plans

Lesson plans have multiple purposes and benefits to students, instructors, and administrators including:

- Providing uniformity by standardizing the instruction and enabling instructors to provide the same information in a similar format each time the lesson is taught, which makes teaching easier. Lesson uniformity also assists with the administration of a cadre of employees who perform consistently and meet the requirements of the job.

- Giving a clear path for both instructors and students to follow. Sequential, orderly instruction makes learning interesting and worthwhile.

- Helping create consistency when more than one instructor must teach from them. Establish consistency through appropriate sequences in the following ways:
  — Introduce the material.
  — Guide students through practical training evolutions to meet performance objectives.
  — Guide students through a summary of the key learning objectives.

- Providing documentation for the training division and the organization's administration in the following ways:
  — Indicate teaching/learning information, methods and activities, and time frames for lessons.
  — Provide documentation of the amount and type of materials, equipment, and other resources needed to teach the lesson, which in turn provides justification for budget requests involving material and equipment purchases.

- Providing a document for developing test and evaluation requirements in the following ways:
  — Establish the testing criteria.
  — Show the material that was taught (based on the objectives).
  — Verify that the information presented is appropriate for testing.

Lesson Plan Components

In the most basic format, lesson plans consist of the following components:

- **Job or topic** — Short descriptive title of the information covered. The title briefly describes or gives an indication of the lesson content. Topic titles usually come directly from the course outline.

- **Time frame** — Estimated time it takes to teach the lesson. Lesson planners may set a time frame for each lesson objective so that the instructor has a better idea of how to set the pace of the lesson.

- **Level of instruction** — Desired learning level that students will reach by the end of the lesson, which may be based on NFPA® JPRs or an academically established taxonomy related to the appropriate learning domain.

- **Learning objectives** — Description of the minimum acceptable behaviors that students must display by the end of an instructional period.

- **Resources/materials needed** — List of all items needed to teach the number of students in the course. This section of the lesson plan also includes any preparation, planning, or activities that an instructor needs to complete before delivering the lesson, such as the following:

  — Determining the appropriate training site and seating arrangement

  — Arranging for audiovisual equipment, training aids, props, and devices

  — Reproducing handouts

  — Acquiring tools, apparatus, and other equipment

  — Contacting guest speakers

  — Listing lesson resources; Include information on the following items:

    - Instructor qualifications

    - Textbooks and other instructional materials

    - Special equipment needs

  — Determining specific instructional methods and learning activities required to meet objectives.

  — Selecting topic-specific training locations or changing training locations to meet the requirements of the topic being taught.

- **Prerequisites** — List of information, skills, or previous requirements that students must have completed or mastered before entering this course or starting this lesson.

- **References** — List of specific references and resources (textbooks and other instructional materials) on the lesson plan, along with page numbers to refer to and review. References allow instructors to provide additional material to enhance a lesson.

- **Lesson summary** — Restatement or reemphasis of the key points of the lesson to clarify variables, prevent misconceptions, increase learning, and improve retention.

- **Assignments** — Readings, practice, research, or other outside-of-class requirements for students.

- **Lesson outline** — Summary of the information to be taught. It may use the four-step instructional method that is described in the following section.

- **Evaluations** — Type of evaluation instrument the instructor will use to determine whether students have met lesson objectives.

Lesson Outlines and Learning Objectives

So far in this chapter, it has been assumed that a Level I Instructor will be provided with a prepared lesson plan to guide instruction. While this is normally true, Level I Instructors may find themselves in situations where they have to create training exercises without the benefit of previously developed lesson plans. In these situations, instructors should realize that they do not need to produce formal lesson plans and curriculum like certified Level II and III Instructors might do. However, the ability to briefly outline a lesson with learning objectives as a road map for a lesson is a useful skill for a Level I Instructor. Whenever possible, the most experienced available Instructor I should be responsible for creating any needed lesson outlines.

Basics of Learning Objectives

When writing a basic lesson outline, the instructor should first consider the intended outcome of the lesson. This **learning outcome** determines both what will introduce the lesson to the students and the direction that the lesson will take. Learning objectives are the stepping stones the instructor needs to address in order to reach the learning outcome. Each objective should contain an action and either a knowledge or skill. For example, a good objective might be, "The student will identify a patient's pulse at three different locations on the patient." Some appropriate action verbs for use in learning objectives include those in **Table 4.1**.

Learning Outcome — Statement that broadly specifies what students will know or be able to do once learning is complete.

Table 4.1 Common Action Verbs for Learning Objectives		
Recognize	Identify	Design
State	Locate	Manage
Select	Explain	Estimate
Compare	Demonstrate	Evaluate
Determine	Analyze	Measure

One of the most widely used models was developed by Robert F. Mager in the early 1960s and continues to help define the role of learning objectives in training. According to Mager, learning objective statements should contain the following three components:

- **Performance (behavior) statement** — Identify what the student is expected to do. The behavior must be stated in observable terms and use a clear action verb such as recall, identify, list, label, describe, or state. Examples:

  — **Learning objective:** Describe the safety precautions used when ventilating a pitched roof with a power saw.

  — **Cognitive performance/behavior:** The student lists the safety precautions for ventilating a roof.

- **Conditions description** — Describe the situation, tools, or materials required for a student to perform a specific action or behavior. Example:

  — **Learning objective:** Given an adult cardiopulmonary resuscitation (CPR) training manikin, administer CPR.

  — **Condition:** An appropriate CPR training manikin must be available and in good repair for the performance of administering CPR.

  — **Psychomotor performance/behavior:** The student will accurately perform CPR.

- **Standards criteria** — State the acceptable level of student performance. Standards provide measurable criteria for evaluating student performance and may include a statement about the degree of required accuracy or a time limit for completion. Example:

  — **Learning objective:** Given photos of extrication tools, identify (label) 90 percent of the tools accurately.

  — **Criterion:** The standard requires 90 percent accuracy.

Comparing Job Performance Requirements (JPRs) to Learning Objectives

Fire and emergency services instructors who administer NFPA® professional qualifications standards are familiar with job performance requirements (JPRs). They describe the performances required for a specific job and are grouped according to the duties of a job. The complete list of JPRs for each duty defines what an individual should be able to do in order to successfully perform that duty. Together, the duties and their JPRs define the job parameters; that is, the professional qualification standard as a whole is a description of a job.

Annex C of NFPA® 1041, *Standard for Fire Service Instructor Professional Qualifications*, explains the components of the JPRs and how to write them. The three critical components of JPRs are as follows:

1. Task to be performed

2. Tools, equipment, or materials required to perform and complete the task

3. Expected performance outcome

These components are essentially the same as the following ones found in the Mager Model for learning objectives:

- Performance (behavior)

- Conditions

- Criteria

Using the example found in Annex C, which contains the 3 components of a JPR and components of the Mager Model, the following comparison between JPRs and learning objectives can be made:

Ventilate a pitched roof (performance), given an ax, a pike pole, an extension ladder, and a roof ladder (conditions), so that a 4-foot × 4-foot (1.22 m by 1.22 m) hole is created, all ventilation barriers are removed, ladders are properly positioned for ventilation, and ventilation holes are correctly placed (criteria).

Brief learning objectives generally describe what performance is required of the students. If the instructor can pinpoint this piece of information, he or she can move on to outlining how to construct a basic lesson to guide students to the learning objectives.

Lesson Outlines

A lesson outline should not be confused with a lesson plan. An outline is a basic roadmap designed to lead students through a single lesson, while a lesson plan is usually developed in relation to a larger course or curriculum. A lesson outline is useful when training needs to continue but may not be occurring as part of a larger course curriculum or at a formal training facility. When creating the outline, the instructor should begin with the learning objectives, then consider, in sequence, what points or steps should be followed to guide students toward meeting the objectives.

A variety of formats can be used to write a lesson outline. Three that may be suited to fire and emergency service instructors are as follows:

- **Outline major points** — Includes only the major statements or concepts that apply to the learning objectives. The instructor uses these bullet points as guideposts and relies on teaching and field experience to fill in the gaps. This format is best used for very experienced instructors who have a wealth of knowledge regarding the topic and extensive teaching experience. It may not serve inexperienced instructors or Level I Instructors as well if they do not have a lot of knowledge in the subject matter **(Figure 4.1)**.

- **Detailed outline** — Paragraph format that includes complete, detailed, "word-for-word" written information instead of the short statements of keywords. It may be a distraction for experienced instructors because they do not need this much information and may consider this style too complicated or distracting to teach from this type of outline. However, it may be an advantage to inexperienced instructors who need additional information in the lesson plan **(Figure 4.2, p.78-79)**. Instructors using a detailed outline are cautioned not to simply read the information to students. Simply reading the presentation in paragraph form limits or eliminates any feedback and interaction with students.

- **Major points with explanatory material** — Presents the lesson in a two-column format with major points discussed in one column and explanatory information in the other column, which may be more of the information found in the detailed outline. The outline is not a "word-for-word" description of the lesson, but goes beyond a simple list of key terminology. This type of lesson outline can serve both experienced and inexperienced instructors because all of the information is present **(Figure 4.3, p.80)**.

Fire Instructor **Student Lesson 7**

3 min. Lecture/ Discussion	**I.**	**Preparation**		
		A.	Administrative Details	
			1.	Fire alarm.
			2.	Exits from the classroom.
			3.	Student roster.
		B.	Instructor Introduction	
Easel			1.	Name of instructor.
			2.	Experience in the fire service.
			3.	Experience with the use of fire hoses.
			4.	Training and certifications.
		C.	Motivation of Students	
			1.	The most common hose roll is the straight roll. Every fire fighter will have to perform the roll following incidents, training exercises, testing hose, etc.
			2.	A fire fighter must be able to perform the roll so the hose is rolled evenly, without kinking, and with the correct coupling on the outside of the roll.
		D.	Lesson Goal	
			1.	At the end of the lesson, the recruit fire fighter will be able to successfully perform a straight hose roll.
		E.	Learning Objectives	
			1.	Describe the purpose of the straight roll.
			2.	Demonstrate the straight hose roll.

Oklahoma State University Fire Service Training Page 1 of 1
9/2004

Figure 4.1 A major points outline will work best for an experienced instructor.

Fire Instructor **Student Lesson 7**

3 min.
Lecture/
Discussion

I. Preparation

A. Administrative Details

1. Fire alarm.
2. Exits from the classroom.
3. Student roster.

B. Instructor Introduction

Easel

> Print your name and contact information on an easel. Reveal the sheet during your introduction so that students will have the correct spelling of your name and your contact information in case they need assistance following the lesson.

1. Name of instructor.
2. Experience in the fire service.
3. Experience with the use of fire hoses.
4. Training and certifications.

C. Motivation of Students

> It is critical that the students understand and appreciate the need to be able to properly roll a joint of hose using a straight roll. Review the following key points about performing a straight hose roll. If possible, share a personal experience or an anecdote that illustrates the importance of being able to safely and quickly roll a joint of hose.

Oklahoma State University Fire Service Training
9/2004

Page 1 of 2

Figure 4.2 A detailed outline provides "word-for-word" information an instructor will need to deliver a lesson; typically intended for less-experienced instructors.

1.   The most common hose roll is the straight roll. Every fire fighter will have to perform the roll following incidents, training exercises, testing hose, etc.

2.   A fire fighter must be able to perform the roll so the hose is rolled evenly, without kinking, and with the correct coupling on the outside of the roll.

D.   Lesson Goal

> **Lesson 7 Goal**
>
> The recruit fire fighter will be able to successfully perform a straight hose roll.
>
> OSU/FST Fire Instructor I – Student Lesson 7   SL 1

1.   At the end of the lesson, the recruit fire fighter will be able to successfully perform a straight hose roll.

E.   Learning Objectives

1.   Describe the purpose of the straight roll.

> **Learning Objectives**
> - Describe the purpose of the straight hose roll.
> - Demonstrate the straight hose roll.
>
> OSU/FST Fire Instructor I – Student Lesson 7   SL 2

2.   Demonstrate the straight hose roll.

ASK: Are there any questions about the learning objectives or the goal of the lesson?
Answer any questions or concerns. Once any questions have been addressed proceed to Section II.

I. Preparation

    A. Administrative Details

        1. Fire Alarm

        2. Classroom exits

        3. Student Roster

Easel

    B. Instructor introduction

        1. Name of instructor

        2. Fire Service Experience

        3. Experience with the use of Fire hoses.

        4. Training and certifications

> Print your name and contact information on an easel. Reveal the sheet during your introduction so that students will have the correct spelling of your name and your contact information in case they need assistance following the lesson.

    C. Student motivation

        1. The most common hose roll is the straight roll. Every fire fighter will have to perform the roll following incidents, training exercises, testing hose, etc.

        2. A fire fighter must be able to perform the roll so the hose is rolled evenly, without kinking, and with the correct coupling on the outside of the roll.

> It is critical that the students understand and appreciate the need to be able to properly roll a joint of hose using a straight roll. Review the following key points about performing a straight hose roll. If possible, share a personal experience or an anecdote that illustrates the importance of being able to safely and quickly roll a joint of hose.

Data Projector PowerPoint Slide

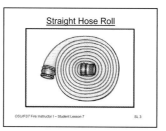

Straight Hose Roll

OSU/FST Fire Instructor I – Student Lesson 7   SL 3

II. Presentation

    A. Purpose of a Straight Hose Roll

Figure 4.3 An outline that shows major points with explanatory material enables instructors of varying levels of experience to use key words as a guide.

Resource Materials

Prepared lesson plans and basic outlines may not provide enough information to adequately teach a topic or course. Good instructors often search for additional resources to reinforce information provided in lesson plans. While lesson plans generally outline the abstract concepts and key points of a topic, outside resource materials can provide real world examples of lesson topics in practice. There are numerous sources for resource materials. Some of the more common sources for fire and emergency instructors include, but are not limited to, the following:

- **National Institute of Science and Technology (NIST) reports** — NIST produces research reports discussing emerging technologies in the fire service and new information about fire and explosion science.

- **National Institute for Occupational Safety and Health (NIOSH) reports** — NIOSH produces incident reports that describe fire and emergency service accident and fatality incidents, which also include information on how procedures and policies could have been better followed to prevent the incident.

- **User-generated video** — Numerous websites afford users the opportunity to upload video that they have taken. Fire and emergency services organizations sometimes upload video of their training to such sites. Eyewitnesses may also take video of accident and fire scenes and make this video public.

- **Supplementary texts** — Fire and emergency service periodicals and journals can be sources for articles that reinforce daily lessons. Book publications can also provide information or additional reading sources for students in courses.

- **Fire and emergency services related websites** — There are many websites dedicated to the fire and emergency services community. Many feature community forums, blogs written by experts in the field, and articles that may or may not be duplicated in print publications.

Copyright Laws and Permissions

Whenever an instructor moves outside the provided materials, he or she must consider what is and is not permissible when using and distributing additional training materials. *Copyright laws* have been established to provide the legal guidelines for the use of training materials.

Copyright laws protect the works of artists, photographers, and authors and give them exclusive rights to publish their works or determine who may publish or reproduce them. Since the *Copyright Act of 1976* was passed, the majority of U.S. copyright laws are governed by federal statute and include the following provisions:

- All works published in the U.S. before 1923 are considered **public domain** (subject to appropriation by anyone).

- Works published between 1923 and 1977 are protected for 95 years from the date of publication.

- When the work was created but not published before 1978, the copyright lasts for the life of the artist, photographer, or author plus 70 years.

- For works published after 1977, the copyright lasts for the life of the artist, photographer, or author plus 70 years.

NOTE: A copyright holder can renew the copyright on material that he or she owns. Just because something has been around long enough to be in the public domain, doesn't necessarily mean that it is.

Public Domain — Works of artists, photographers, and authors that were published before 1923 or are no longer covered by any copyright ownership.

Unauthorized use of copyrighted materials is considered infringement on the rights of artists, photographers, or authors. Infringement gives them a right to recover damages or gain profits from the use of their works.

Copyright may apply to some portions of a work but not to others, even though all the portions are part of one whole. Instructors need to be aware that even though they have access to materials in the public domain, for example, there may be copyrighted material that they do not have permission to reproduce within the public domain material. For instance, the National Fire Academy (NFA) gains copyright permission to use certain materials in their courses. The course materials are in the public domain; however, copyrighted portions of those course materials are not in the public domain. Only the NFA gained permission to use them. The instructor would have to seek out the same copyright permissions that the NFA did in order to reproduce the material.

Instructors and students often copy materials from texts, journals, periodicals, and the Internet for use in class. Whether this copying is copyright infringement depends on how the material is used. The **fair use** doctrine of the *Copyright Act* grants the privilege of copying materials to persons other than the owner of the copyright without consent when the material is used in a reasonable manner. Section 107 of the *Copyright Act* lists the privileges or factors to consider when determining whether the use of copyright materials is fair use.

A few of the fair use guidelines are as follows:

- Instructors may make single copies of the following for scholarly research or when preparing to teach a class:
  - Chapter from a book
  - Article from a periodical, newspaper, or Internet
  - Short story, essay, or poem
  - Chart, graph, diagram, drawing, cartoon, or picture from a book, periodical, or newspaper
  - Video recordings of a television broadcast
- Teachers may make multiple copies of items for their students to use in class provided that the copied material is brief and the idea to copy an item is spontaneous because it is currently appropriate to the day's lesson. Copying must be for the particular class being taught at the time and *not cumulative* or copied repeatedly for subsequent classes.
- Copying shall *not* substitute for buying books, publisher's reprints, or periodicals. Students *cannot* be charged for copied materials beyond the cost of photocopying **(Figure 4.4)**

Instructors must use proper citations when copying, downloading electronically, or using any materials, regardless of copyright. It is recommended that instructors familiarize themselves with the applicable copyright laws regarding copying print, audio, video, or electronic

Fair Use — Doctrine of the *Copyright Act* that grants the privilege of copying materials to persons other than the owner of the copyright, without consent, when the material is used in a reasonable manner.

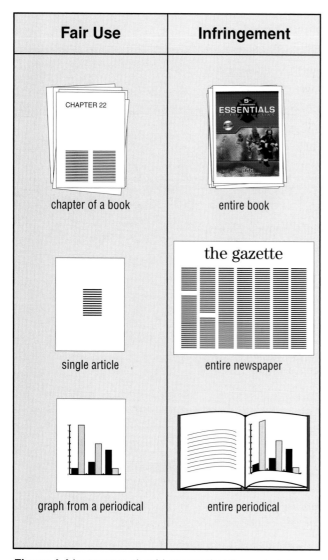

Fair Use	Infringement
chapter of a book	entire book
single article	entire newspaper
graph from a periodical	entire periodical

Figure 4.4 Instructors should ensure that the materials they reproduce are fair use and take extra care to avoid infringement.

materials for use in class. Because copyright laws that apply to the Internet or digitally reproduced material are constantly evolving, instructors must monitor those changes. In some cases, digital media may have its own laws that are separate from copyright laws that apply to traditional print media.

Many instructors are tempted to search the Internet for supplementary material and reproduce that material for classroom use. When doing so, instructors are assuming that materials on the Internet are public domain (free for anyone to use regardless of copyright). However, materials on the Internet may be copyrighted even without notice. The rules of fair use apply to such materials as do the copyright laws governing printed materials.

Instructors can provide a sense of reality in their instructional methods by using photographs and video recordings taken at emergency incidents. But when fire and emergency services personnel take photographs or video recordings at a scene, they may be invading the privacy of the individuals or victims involved in the incident. **Invasion of privacy** is the wrongful intrusion into a person's private activities by the government or other individuals.

> **Invasion of Privacy** — Wrongful intrusion into a person's private activities by the government or other individuals.

Individuals have the right to control the use of pictures of themselves and their property. An instructor or organization that uses these pictures or films may be sued for invasion of privacy or libel if permission is *not* obtained. The legality and success of lawsuits to protect the right of privacy depend on several factors, such as the following:

- **Where and who** — Where the photograph or film/video was made and who was photographed or recorded are both important to document. Events that are newsworthy and photographed or recorded for the public interest take precedence over the right of privacy. Details:

  — Using photographs or recordings a month after an incident has lost its public appeal and is no longer newsworthy steps over the line of privacy.

  — Images that are retained as *file photos* and used in conjunction with a story of continuing interest may *not* be subject to the privacy requirements.

  — Taking photographs or recordings is allowed when the setting is a public place rather than an individual's private residence.

  — The law allows for photographing and video recording publicly famous individuals who are seen in public.

  — It may still be considered an invasion of privacy when any ordinary citizen, celebrity, or criminal is photographed or filmed on a public highway stripped of clothing and dignity and having emergency procedures performed while being rescued from a serious accident.

  — Extreme care must be taken when images are made of severely injured victims or fatalities to *not* infringe on the rights of victims or their families.

- **Permissions** — Because of potentially serious legal and professional consequences, organizations must always make arrangements in advance to obtain permissions in writing (called **model releases**) from individuals to take photographs or films/videos of events and use them after events. **Appendix D** has an example of a generic model release form that instructors can use.

> **Model Release** — Legal document that grants permission to use a person's image or voice in photos or recordings.

- **Restrictions** — Organizations must also explain the purpose of intended use so that individuals can make an informed decision or restrict use to a specific form only, such as training. Photographic images, and audio and video recordings of students participating in training classes require written permission before the material is published or used by the organization in the following situations:

— In training sessions

— On departmental/organizational web sites

— On closed circuit or public broadcasts of organizational-sponsored television programs

NOTE: Additional limitations are placed on the length of time that a copy of an on-air broadcast can be retained and used. Permission to record a broadcast should be obtained from the producer of the material, and the proper length of time that it may be used should be determined.

- **Rights of individuals** — Individuals must be given the opportunity to preview pictures or recordings and make a decision before they are used. Individuals may also require that an organization maintain their anonymity while showing the photograph or recording, which is usually accomplished by blocking faces with graphic overlays or showing them in shadows and altering voices on films/videos.

Training Aids

It is unlikely that a single training division or agency will possess all types of training aids that are currently on the market. Many types perform similar functions, and some are economically out of reach of small training organizations. However, instructors should be familiar with the various types and their uses. Instructors who may be required to teach in facilities provided by other jurisdictions or organizations will have the opportunity to come into contact with some or all of these training aid types.

The sections that follow categorize training aids and devices as nonprojected types, projected types, simulators, and training props. Each category has several types of devices or equipment that are described. Also discussed are the cleaning and maintenance care for these training aids.

Nonprojected Training Aids

Nonprojected training aids offer several major advantages over projected aids. Nonprojected training aids do not depend on high levels of technology or technical skill. As a result, they are easier to use and less likely to malfunction during presentations. Generally, nonprojection-type equipment also costs less to purchase, is easy to create illustrations for, and is easy to maintain. Some training aids that use popular and easy-to-use nonprojected equipment include the following:

- Chalkboards, marker boards, and easel pads
- Interactive boards
- Illustration or diagram displays
- Duplicated materials
- Models
- Audio recordings
- Casualty simulations

Chalkboards, Marker Boards, and Easel Pads

The easiest, most frequently used, and most versatile nonprojection-type equipment is a marker board (chalkboard, dry-erase marker board, or easel pad). These items may be fixed or mounted to a wall, movable (on wheels or stands), or portable (folding and compact for travel). Instructors find these training aid devices useful for numerous instructional activities and rely on them as supplements and backup when more technical or complex training aid equipment fails.

Using Marker Boards

- Lightly write any easily misspelled words or technical terms or lightly draw diagrams and other similar material on your easel-pad paper or chalkboard in advance with a pencil. The pencil marks are visible to the instructor standing at the front of the class but not to students. Quickly trace over the pencil marks with chalk or marker. This technique ensures accuracy and quick reproduction of material in class.

- Draw complex or detailed diagrams in advance. Mark prepared material with instructions not to disturb if the classroom is to be used by other instructors in the interim. Keep diagrams covered until needed in order to avoid distracting the class. Use one of the following methods:

  — Cover material with a sliding section of a chalkboard or marker board.

  — Tape paper across material on boards.

  — Cover material on an easel pad with blank sheets or title sheets.

- Avoid speaking when facing boards or easel pads. Develop the skill of pausing your speech when you have turned away from the students to write.

- Write only what is necessary. It is rarely necessary to transcribe verbatim every spoken word of a lesson. Using concise points minimizes the time needed to write while maximizing the space available.

- Use chalk or marker pen colors that contrast with the background. Contrasting colors means using light colors of chalk and dark colors of markers. For example, the use of yellow or light orange markers in a large classroom is not recommended because those colors are difficult to see.

- Write letters large enough to be seen at the back of the room. Experiment with letter size in advance. Remember that some students may be ten or twenty times further from the board or easel pad than the instructor.

- Bring chalk and marker pens of several colors when scheduled to teach in an unfamiliar location.

- Use manuscript (print) instead of cursive (written) letters.

Illustration or Diagram Displays

Instructors can create interesting and informative lectures by displaying topical illustrations or diagrams that they have purchased or prepared in advance. Illustrations or diagrams that are prepared in advance save class time and provide consistency between similar class sessions. Illustrations and diagrams also address a variety of learning styles beyond those addressed by written or spoken words. Some examples of illustrations and display boards are as follows:

- Technical diagrams such as mechanical or electrical schematics illustrate and help explain troubleshooting or repair procedures.

- Maps or plan diagrams illustrate routes, aid in preplanning, and/or assist in debriefing incidents.

- Anatomical charts assist in explaining human anatomy and physiology in emergency medical services (EMS) classes.

- Flowcharts help explain processes or procedures.

- Data charts such as pie charts or bar graphs illustrate common causes of injury, response types, or other statistical data.

- Photographs of incident scenes are invaluable in illustrating proper procedures.

Illustrations can be mounted or created on poster board. The boards are available in all colors and sizes up to 36 × 48 inches (914 mm by 1 219 mm). Maps may be mounted on rollers or hung flat from clips on chalkboards. Easels may also be used to support the mounted illustrations.

When displaying any of these types of training aids, it is important to remember the ability of such items to distract students. Avoid leaving illustrations and diagrams in view when they are not in use or relevant. Instructors should not attempt to hold illustrations in front of themselves while describing them. This practice is distracting and changes an instructor into an expensive easel. Also, before using these aids, instructors should view them from the point of view of the students to ensure that everyone in the class will be able to see them.

Duplicated Materials

Duplicated materials (handouts) include any printed matter that instructors distribute before, during, or at the end of a class. Instructors should remember the copyright laws explained earlier in this chapter and apply them appropriately. As with other training aids, instructors must strategically plan their use in the lesson to gain maximum benefits. Examples of their suggested uses include the following:

- Distribute handouts of lecture material at the end of a presentation unless it is necessary for students to refer to or take notes on them during the class.

- Consider using handouts as precourse material when they contain the same material as the presentation. This method of early distribution has the additional advantage of advancing the achievable learning level of the class.

- Give self-study guides to students to assist them in working through textbooks or other learning materials at their own pace.

- Give assignments to students for completion within the class.

- Give activities such as research projects, practice applications of theory learned in class, or reviews of material presented by the instructor as take-home assignments.

- Provide note guides with an outline of the lesson for students to fill with notes during class. As students write they must be attentive to the lesson's major points.

Models

A model is an excellent tool for illustrating mechanical or spatial concepts. Students can clearly observe the types of relationships between parts of a model as they watch it function or manipulate it. Instructors can obtain many types of models or construct them at low cost, but some types (depending on their size and complexity) require a large investment of time and money. Some examples of models that are used as training aids include the following:

- **Tabletop miniatures** — Tabletop models allow participants to enact a simulated incident in compressed time (for example, 5 minutes of simulation can represent 1 hour); may allow for video monitoring from another location, simulated fires, or changing scenarios **(Figure 4.5)**.

Figure 4.5 Tabletop models offer flexibility in simulated training scenarios.

- **Cutaway models** — These models are of great value when students are learning the inner workings of mechanical systems such as valves or pumps. Instructors can often obtain cutaways at little or no cost by dismantling obsolete or surplus equipment. Some manufacturers may also have cutaway training models available **(Figure 4.6, p.88)**.

Figure 4.6 Cutaway models are useful for demonstrating how a piece of equipment functions.

Figure 4.7 A moulage kit allows instructors to simulate an injury using realistic effects.

- **Anatomical models** — These models are available in three dimensions, some of which have cutaway or take-apart features. These models benefit students who are developing their EMS skills and knowledge in such areas as the mechanisms of internal injuries. A life-size or even small-scale skeleton is also a good anatomical model.

- **Replicas or miniatures** — Replicas can demonstrate how actual equipment or devices are used. Examples are various types of cribbing and shoring assemblies based on actual designs. Students can see how the components are assembled and used before a practical training evolution is conducted.

- **Actual tools and equipment** — Actual equipment can also be used for demonstrations. For instance, an actual self-contained breathing apparatus (SCBA) is a better training aid to show key components than a transparency of the SCBA.

Audio Recordings

In order to add a level of realism to lessons, instructors may wish to include sounds that relate to the lesson. Some examples of sounds that can be played for use in the classroom include the following:

- Engine and pump sounds (for problem identification, such as pump cavitation)

- Dispatch radio traffic (for telecommunicator training or postincident critique)

- Heart, breathing, or blood-pressure sounds (for EMS training)

Instructors may record these sounds themselves on cassette tape or as Mp3 recordings. These recordings may also be available on compact disc or playback from digital computer files, such as Mp3s. These digital files are also easy to transfer to a student's personal music device or computer for listening outside of class, if this does not infringe upon copyright.

Casualty Simulations

Any teaching aid that increases the realism of a simulation increases its value. Simulated casualties provide tremendous benefits by increasing the realism of hands-on EMS training. Instructors can simulate injuries using commercially available **moulage kits** and prostheses, or by applying Plasticine® modeling paste, wax, and makeup **(Figure 4.7)**.

Moulage kits typically contain plastic wounds that instructors can apply to a simulated casualty. Prostheses such as simulated amputated limbs, devices to simulate arterial bleeding, and other lifelike injury effects are also available. Minimal training is required to use moulage kits. The plastic wounds also have the advantage of being relatively quick to prepare and apply.

When a very realistic simulation is required, instructors can arrange to use personnel who are qualified as casualty simulators. Casualty simulators are typically EMS instructors who have been trained to use Plasticine®, mortician's wax, makeup, prostheses, and simulated blood to produce very realistic wounds and other effects. The preparation process is more time-consuming than moulage but results in a higher degree of realism. For practical examinations or when when filming simulations for later use, the time invested is worthwhile.

Projected Training Aids

Standard practice in today's fire and emergency services is to use projected training aids such as **computer-generated slide presentations** of the lesson. Projected training aids offer many advantages: Images are vivid, multicolored, and visible to a large audience. Most educational materials provided to Level I Instructors come with projected training aids such as computer-generated slides, photographs in electronic format, or training videos. Instructors should use these training aids but also realize that there are additional training aids they can use to supplement any provided material.

Some projected training aids are displayed on televisions, but most are viewed with front-screen projection devices, which project the image onto the face of a screen. Other types of projection devices include rear-screen projectors. These are designed for use with special translucent screens that may be mounted over an opening in a wall, with the projection device in a dark room behind the opening. Rear-screen projection systems are permanent because they are incorporated into the design of the classroom. They are also more expensive than front-screen projection devices.

Moulage Kit — Makeup kit containing appliqué wounds and stage makeup; used during casualty simulations to simulate wounds on a manikin or actor.

Computer-Generated Slide Presentations — Computer presentations that are sequenced and displayed like traditional slideshows that use a slide projector with a carousel. Popular software for creating and viewing these presentations include Microsoft PowerPoint® and Apple Keynote®.

Using Projected Aids

- Dim the front lights, if at all possible. This way the projected image is clearly visible, but there is still enough light for students to take notes and for instructors to see the students.

- Have backup materials on hand in case projection equipment fails. For example, keep overhead transparencies as a backup for computer-generated presentations, and be prepared to demonstrate material *personally*.

- Keep a supply of spare projector bulbs, batteries for remote controls, extension cords, and anything else that may be needed in the event of equipment problems.

Video and Multimedia Projectors/Large-Screen Images

A projection system is a device for showing video, television, or computer images on a large screen. Projectors that are bright enough to display a quality video or computer-generated image in a classroom are affordable, portable, and versatile.

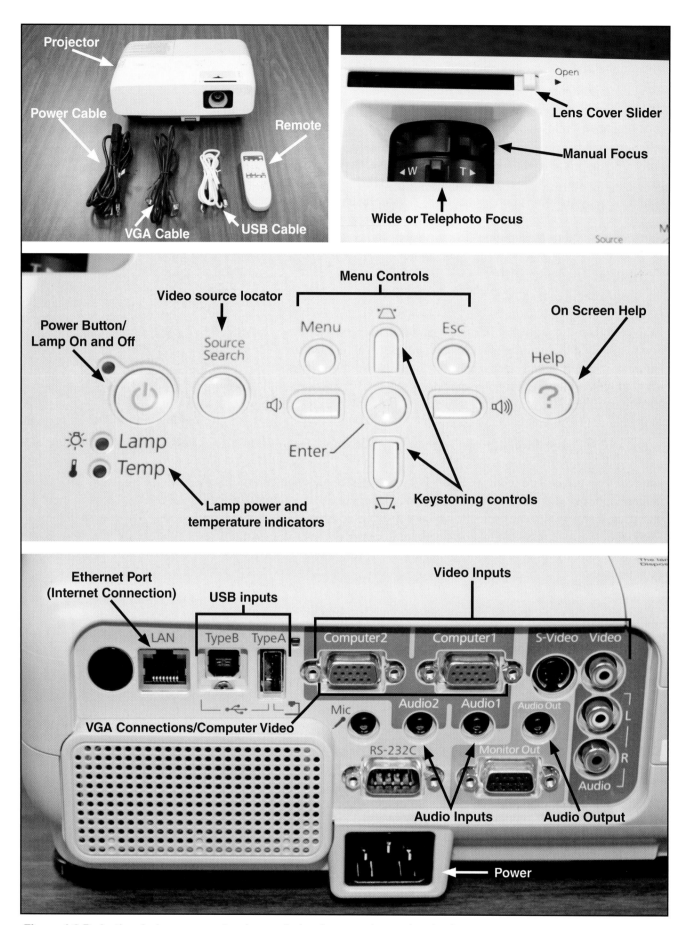

Figure 4.8 Projection devices are used so frequently for classroom instruction that instructors need to be familiar with their components and use.

They can be attached to a variety of media devices, such as DVD players, Blu-Ray players, laptops, desktop computers, and personal media devices **(Figure 4.8)**. Projectors require a screen or wall to display an image.

NOTE: Some departments may still use video cassette recorders (VCRs) to view training materials. This is becoming less and less common as new materials are produced solely on DVD and Blu-Ray at the time of this publication.

Multimedia projectors are even more effective when used in conjunction with laptop or desktop computers. This combination allows instructors to display documents for editing or group discussion, show videos from the internet or the computer's hard drive, or show simulation software to an entire class. Learning to use this instructional medium effectively is essential for instructors.

Keystoning

Keystoning is an effect caused by a projector that is not perpendicular to the screen **(Figure 4.9)**, resulting in a distorted image that is wider at the top than at the bottom. This distortion can be very distracting, because the edges of the image are not parallel and the top and bottom of the image will be out of focus while the center is sharp.

Some portable projection screens may be equipped with a keystone eliminator that allows the instructor to adjust the angle of the screen at the top. Some newer model data projectors include an electronic keystone eliminator, which allows the instructor to correct the keystone image on either a portable- or fixed-projection screen.

Interactive Whiteboards

An interactive whiteboard (also known as an interactive Smartboard®) is a display system that can both show images projected from a computer and allow instructors to interact with those images **(Figure 4.10, p.92)**. A computer projects an image through a projector onto the whiteboard, which is also connected to the computer. The whiteboard becomes a giant touch-screen that permits users to interact with the display, visit Internet sites, and access the computer's applications and files. Using the specific tools that come with the whiteboard, the instructor can "draw" lines on the screen to emphasize portions of a photo. The instructor can use a pen or hand to capture screen images of what an instructor has written during a lecture. The whiteboard can also be used with computer-generated slides.

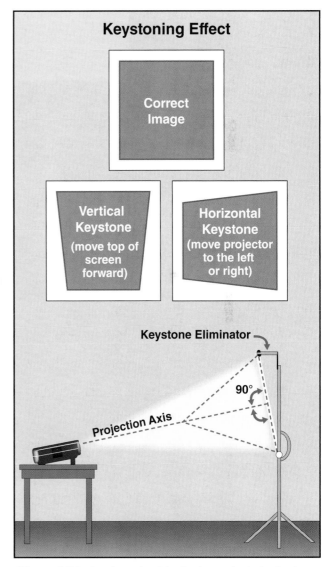

Figure 4.9 Instructors should adjust a projector's display to eliminate keystoning.

Figure 4.10 An interactive whiteboard allows instructors to display images from a computer, write on those images, and save the notes they have written.

Visual Presenters/Displays

Another training device that an instructor can use in many of the same ways as an overhead projector is the visual presenter. This device consists of a small video camera mounted vertically over a tabletop platform **(Figure 4.11)**. Adjustable light units are mounted on either side of the platform. The platform also contains a light source to provide back lighting for transparencies.

The presenter displays images of objects, documents, or transparencies that have been placed on the platform, either on a television monitor or through a multimedia projector. Some models also allow for external audio that can be used as a public announcement (PA) system in a small classroom.

Some examples of how an instructor could use this system in the classroom include the following:

- Display a tool, material sample, or other item on the platform so that all students can view it at the same time.

- Display paper copies of documents without the need to make transparencies first.

- Display original photographs or illustrations without the degeneration that commonly occurs in duplication.

- Display images or text from books or magazines.

- Display transparencies like an overhead projector.

Slide Projectors/Slides and Overhead Projectors

Some departments may still have carousels of slide photographs and transparencies for use on overhead projectors, even though new materials are not being produced using this technology. Both slide machines and overhead projectors are relatively easy to use. Instructors who are still required to use these devices should read the instructions for their use and follow them accordingly.

Television/Programs and Video Presentations

Televisions can be used to present images from videos, visual presenters, or live presentations captured with video cameras. High-definition television (HDTV) provides images that are brighter and have greater clarity and quality than regular television. Large screen sizes also mean better viewing by large groups.

Television has tremendous potential as a training aid device. Distance learning programs broadcast on community-access channels by cable, satellite, or closed circuit can reach large student audiences over vast distances. State or provincial authorities, postsecondary institutions, or any organization wishing to reach a diverse group of students can make effective use of televised lessons. In addition, video recordings are commercially available on a tremendous variety of fire and emergency services subjects.

Some training organizations may also wish to record their own video for use in the classroom. The quality of affordable video recording and editing equipment has improved dramatically in recent years. It is possible for many organizations to produce very high-quality videos in-house. However, organizations must take into account that the time required to properly script, film, and edit a video may be as much as one hundred times the length of the finished product.

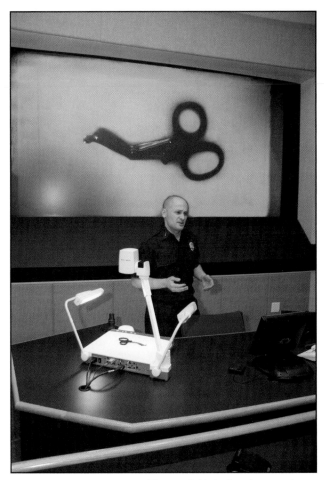

Figure 4.11 A visual presenter can be used to display tools or other objects placed beneath the camera.

Most modern camcorders store video using one of the following methods:

- **MiniDV/HDV** — Small cassettes; HDV has the higher quality.

- **DVD** — Video burned directly to a DVD as video is recorded.

- **Flash Card** —Removable, solid state memory; available in a variety of sizes, capacities, and compatibilities.

- **Internal solid state drive (SSD)** — Similar to a flash card but cannot be removed from the device; offers larger memory capacity than most flash cards but is small enough to support camcorders that are compact and easy to use.

- **Internal hard disk** — Small, usually 2.5" drive similar to a hard disk in a laptop; video is recorded directly onto the drive in digital format.

NOTE: Some departments may still be recording using older camcorder equipment that records film to videotape. While these formats are considered obsolete in the electronics industry, instructors should be aware of the following formats they may encounter: video home system (VHS), super VHS (S-VHS), 8 mm, and Sony Hi-8.

When using a video presentation in class, instructors should observe the following guidelines:

- Always preview the video privately before showing it publicly.

- Emphasize key learning points/objectives before showing a video.

- Start the video before turning on the television, and turn the television off before stopping the video. Some television sets automatically mute the sound and display a blue screen when not receiving a signal. Others display snow and a loud static noise that can be distracting and uncomfortable.

- Cue the video to the desired location in advance when showing only a portion of a recording.

- Pause the video while it is playing when illustrating a teaching point. If the video must continue in order to illustrate the point, mute the sound. Do not attempt to talk over the soundtrack of a video.

- Remain in the room while the class views the video. Instructors who leave during the showing of a video are not aware of any technical problems, classroom disruptions, or other issues that may occur in their absence.

- Do not use a video that takes more than half of the class session.

- Review key learning points/objectives after viewing a video.

Simulators

Simulators are training devices that represent systems, processes, or environments in which actual training would be unsafe, impractical, or prohibitively expensive. Simulators allow some level of recreating these environments for students without the safety hazards. The greater the degree of reality in the simulation, the more effective the learning. The following types of simulators are available for fire and emergency services training:

- Electronic simulators

- Display boards

- Smoke simulators

- Computer simulations

- Virtual reality simulations

- Anatomical/physiological manikins

Electronic Simulators

Electronic simulators are generally tabletop simulations, ranging from animated tabletop models to individual equipment panels like those found on apparatus. For example, electronic simulations of a pump panel may include working gauges, realistic recorded sounds, and warning or trouble messages. Simulations that can be integrated into a tabletop tactical simulator include the following:

- Elements of communication systems

- Alarm/detection systems

- Ventilation fans

- Theatrical smoke machines

- Electric lights

- Miniature models **(Figure 4.12)**

- Video cameras

- Projection and recording training aids

Figure 4.12 Small-scale layouts can be used to practice emergency response techniques.

Display Boards

The component parts of systems can be mounted on display boards and used to simulate the operation of various systems. In this way, an instructor or student can manipulate a system without crawling under an apparatus chassis or into a machine. For example, a display board mounted with the actual working parts of a vehicle air brake system would allow students to practice maintenance inspections quickly and safely. Display boards can be constructed from parts removed from scrapped or salvaged vehicles.

Smoke Simulators

The movement of smoke through a building or area is critically important to fire and emergency services personnel. Smoke movement can be simulated or illustrated by using small-scale mechanical models of high-rise stairwells. Developments in computer modeling allow realistic simulations of smoke movement through complex structures such as shopping malls, tunnels, and high-rise buildings.

Computer Simulations

Computerized simulations of burning buildings, casualty incidents, hostage scenarios, and other fire and emergency services applications are widely available. Computer simulations may be 3D-rendered animations or interactive video. Minimum computer operating requirements with regard to processor speed, hard drive space, amount of RAM, video/graphics requirements will vary. Instructors should ensure that they have access to a computer that meets the minimum specifications before purchasing or installing a computer simulation. When in doubt, the instructor should contact the simulation manufacturer or computer technical support to make sure their equipment meets requirements.

Most computer simulations are purchased on CD-ROM or DVD-ROM and must be installed on a computer's hard drive, although some may run off the CD or DVD without installation. Some software may allow only a limited number of installations, and instructors must work within the electronic user license agreements (EULA) that come with the software.

Virtual Reality Simulations

Virtual reality simulations display fields of view as though students are part of the simulated environments. Environments can be manipulated in response to inputs from students. The simulations change in real time to react to the student's actions. Virtual reality simulations are continually improving in realism, and can be tremendously effective tools for reinforcing procedure-based or protocol-based skill sets, such as incident management or EMS skills.

Most of these simulations are expensive and require an investment in equipment and software. This investment must be weighed against the instructional value of the increased realism of the product. Many simulations have built-in study materials and self-tests. In some cases these may be installed directly into an organization's computer network, allowing the instructor to keep centralized training records and statistics.

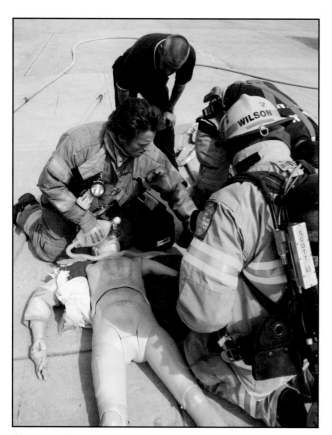

Figure 4.13 Manikins can be used at all levels of EMS training.

Anatomical/Physiological Manikins

The degree of simulation offered by manikins ranges from a simple representation of the human form to audible, visible, or palpable facsimiles of pulse, heart rhythm, reaction to defibrillation, or the ability to intubate or ventilate. Manikins are available to match any level of EMS training provided by an organization **(Figure 4.13)**. Students develop a high level of skill when their training closely simulates the services their jobs require.

Training Props

Training props may be permanent structures or portable devices that are used to simulate specific types of situations and teach subjects such as the following:

- Technical rescue

- Vehicle extrication

- Flammable/combustible liquids spill and fire control

- Transportation incident response and control

Training props are located outside, often far from classroom facilities. They may consist of trenches or collapsed structures, motor vehicles, railcars, ships, aircraft, and/or flammable liquids processing and storage facilities. They

Figure 4.14 Structural collapse props can be manipulated to simulate a number of rescue scenarios.

may be used for a variety of training scenarios, including rescue, property conservation, and fire suppression. Types of training props include the following:

- **Trench rescue** — Trench props typically consist of an earthen berm with a trench cut into it. They are used for shoring and cribbing training.

- **Structural collapse** — Slabs of concrete and construction debris that simulate a collapsed structure, with voids that allow for search and rescue activities **(Figure 4.14)**.

- **Confined space** — Used to represent any type of confined-space situation, including trench or structural collapse. Some props are simply grain silos mounted in steel support frames or storage tanks with limited access. They may be incorporated into a drill tower, smoke building, or live-fire burn building.

- **High-angle rescue** — An open or enclosed drill tower that can be used to simulate high-angle rescue situations. Students can ascend or descend the exterior of the structure, hoist equipment or lower victims, and practice rope skills **(Figure 4.15)**.

- **Vehicle and machinery extrications** — Typically involves a portable prop, such as a vehicle, that can be relocated to different facilities and disposed of after

Figure 4.15 A drill tower can be used for practicing high-angle rescue.

Figure 4.19 Instructors can create mazes out of equipment in the fire station for SCBA training.

Figure 4.20 Gas-fed props may be adjusted to simulate a variety of fire situations.

Figure 4.21 Commercially constructed burn pans provide a controlled scenario for fire extinguisher training.

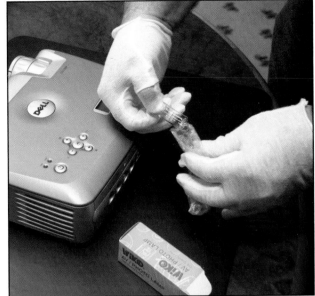

Figure 4.22 Clean, thin gloves can be worn to prevent skin oils from collecting on projector bulbs.

- Do not use solvents.
- Clean chalk and whiteboards completely after using them.
- Clean video and audio heads with an appropriate cleaning device at recommended intervals.

Suggested care guidelines for training aids and devices include the following:

- Follow manufacturer's recommendations for use and storage.
- Place dust covers over equipment when not in use.
- Store manikins properly in carrying cases or closed cabinets.
- Wrap power cords around carts, or remove and store them separately.
- Use lens caps on all optical lenses (cameras and projectors).
- Store handouts in file folders.
- Allow projectors sufficient cool-down time after the bulb has been turned off. Many projectors have both soft and hard power buttons. Follow the manufacturer's guidelines carefully to prevent the fan from disengaging prematurely, which greatly reduces the life span of the bulb.
- Do not leave electronic equipment in vehicles in direct sunlight, or when temperature extremes are expected.

Only qualified repair personnel should perform specialized maintenance of training aid devices. Instructors who are familiar with the equipment may perform routine maintenance, such as the following:

- **Inspecting training props** — Follow jurisdiction SOPs for inspecting props for damage and deterioration, both before and after they are used in training evolutions.
- **Periodically cleaning air filters in multimedia projectors** — Prevent clogged air filters that cause cooling fans to work harder and decrease the life of the unit. This can also be the cause for a unit not working. An instructor should always clean the filter before replacing the projector bulb.
- **Replacing projector bulbs** — Prevent skin oil from covering the bulb surface: Handle the bulb by the porcelain base only **(Figure 4.22)**.
- **Tightening any loose screws or nuts** — Do not overtighten screws or nuts.

Training Aid Benefits

When included as part of an active learning instructional delivery, training aids perform the following functions:

- **Enhancing student understanding** — Because a great deal of what students learn is received visually, training aids increase the ability of students to understand the information in a lesson.

- **Increasing student acceptance** — Seeing an illustration or touching an item will help students accept the reality of the item more easily than simply hearing a description of it.

- **Adding interest to a lecture** —The additional visual or tactile stimulation provided by training aids adds variety to a lecture.

- **Clarifying, proving, or emphasizing a key point** — Students see the key point at the same time that they hear the description, thereby making the point clearer or more emphatic (important). A key point can be proven or validated by using illustrations or examples of actual events.

- **Enhancing memory** — Training aids reinforce the information that is provided verbally in the lecture, making it easier to remember and retain. Research indicates that people have better retention of information that they see and hear at the same time.

- **Helping students organize ideas** —When dealing with complex ideas or processes, students benefit from seeing a list of components on a chart or board. They can follow a lesson better if they can associate an illustration or outline with the words of the lecture.

- **Gaining and maintaining students' attention** — Dramatic images can help get students' attention, then keep it throughout the lecture.

- **Illustrating a sequence of events or steps in a process** — Training aids can establish a sequence of steps, the components of an assembly, or the steps of a theoretical process. They are especially helpful when the sequence is not one that can be demonstrated, such as the circulation of blood in the body.

- **Saving lecture time** — Because students can process more information when visual aids supplement a lecture, instructors can spend less time lecturing, making training more efficient.

Chapter Summary

Fire and emergency services instructors rely on a variety of materials and equipment to deliver instruction, but the most important training materials are effective lesson plans. Instructors should be familiar with all the parts of a lesson plan and understand how they are built on the four-step model of instruction.

A wide variety of training aids are used to supplement lesson plans. Instructors should know how to operate common aids such as televisions, DVD players, audiovisual projection equipment, computers, and basic office suite software. When the desired equipment is unavailable for a particular lesson, instructors should be able to select and operate backup equipment. They should also know how to clean and maintain any equipment they use.

Review Questions

1. What components go into a lesson plan?

2. How do students benefit when instructors use outside resource materials?

3. Why were copyright laws established for training materials?

4. What training aids are used by an instructor in the classroom or training environments?

5. How are training aids beneficial in the classroom?

Learning Environment

Chapter Contents

TRAINING IN PROGRESS
chapter 5

Key Terms

Job Performance Requirements

NFPA® 1041 References

4.3.2

4.3.3

4.4.2

Learning Objectives

1. Describe the classroom settings and arrangements commonly used for fire and emergency services training. [NFPA® 1041, 4.3.3, 4.4.2]

2. Discuss what environmental factors need to be addressed when training at a remote site. [NFPA® 1041, 4.4.2]

3. Summarize the planning considerations necessary before training at a permanent training facility. [NFPA® 1041, 4.3.2]

Chapter 5
Learning Environment

Case History

During a fire academy recruit class, wildland training was conducted at a local military base where several of the base firefighters also needed the training. The culminating event of this multi-day training session was the construction of fire line across an empty field in a remote part of the base. Following construction of the line, a controlled burn was scheduled to demonstrate proper burn-out procedures. Students constructed line across the field in the general direction of a sign that faced away from the field and towards an adjoining road. As the fire line reached the edge of the road, students paused to pose with the sign that read, "DANGER. EXPLOSIVE DISPOSAL RANGE. KEEP OUT." While the students had a nice laugh at the idea of the fire moving toward an explosives area, their instructors had already prepared a site safety plan and consulted with appropriate base personnel to ensure that the area was, in fact, safe and an appropriate area for training. Personnel at the base had simply forgotten to remove the sign.

Fire and emergency services training can occur in a wide variety of locations, although training typically occurs in a training facility, such as a fire station, or at a remote site, such as an acquired structure **(Figure 5.1)**. But wherever training occurs, instructors must be able to control the learning environment to ensure that students are able to concentrate on the lesson and remain safe from potential hazards. Before conducting training, it is essential that instructors evaluate their environment in order to identify and remove potential distractions and hazards.

Figure 5.1 Fire training may occur in a wide variety of locations such as this permanent training facility.

Classroom Environment

The advantage of working in a permanent classroom is that the environment rarely changes, making control of the environment relatively straightforward. Dedicated classrooms were designed for teaching and therefore have

Figure 5.2 Rooms such as this apparatus bay can be repurposed as classrooms if traditional educational facilities are not available.

built-in controls for noise, lighting, and temperature. However, rooms in fire stations or other non-educational facilities may not have the same controls. Instructors must be prepared to adapt to the location in order to create the best possible learning environment **(Figure 5.2)**. In any situation, the instructor should have control over the following elements:

- Seating arrangements
- Lighting
- Temperature
- Noise level
- Audiovisual equipment
- Other classroom considerations, such as power outlets, internet access, and comfort facilities

Seating Arrangements

Seating arrangements can have a considerable effect on the learning environment, and different arrangements are more suitable to different types of lessons. If chairs are not permanently fixed to the floor, an instructor should know how to change the seating in order to make it most effective for the lesson, even though some training facilities require that instructors return the room to its original arrangement after class. Instructors and students must respect the wishes and rules of the organization to return the room to its original arrangement when the lesson is finished.

Seating arrangement types that are commonly used in academic and training situations include **(Figure 5.3)**:

- **Fan** — Permits students to easily see and hear an instructor and also works effectively in small groups.

- **Traditional** — Permits students to see, hear, and interact with an instructor. Student interaction is limited and difficult, but the arrangement is applicable to any size of audience.

- **Auditorium or theater** — Fixed seating for a medium-to-large sized audience that faces a stage or lectern, allowing interaction only between the instructor and the students. May require a sound system so that the audience can hear the instructor; typically lacks any writing surface on which students can take notes.

- **Conference** — Allows for total group discussion where limited or no small-group activities are required. It is most effective for small classes where students are seated around one table.

- **Chevron** — Similar to the traditional arrangement in that students can easily see, hear, and interact with the instructor, but student interaction is limited.

- **Horseshoe or U shape** — Provides a clear view of the instructor, who may be at the open or closed end of the U shape. Permits both instructor presentation and total group discussion, but not small-group interaction. Used for small-to-medium-sized audiences.

Classroom Seating Arrangements

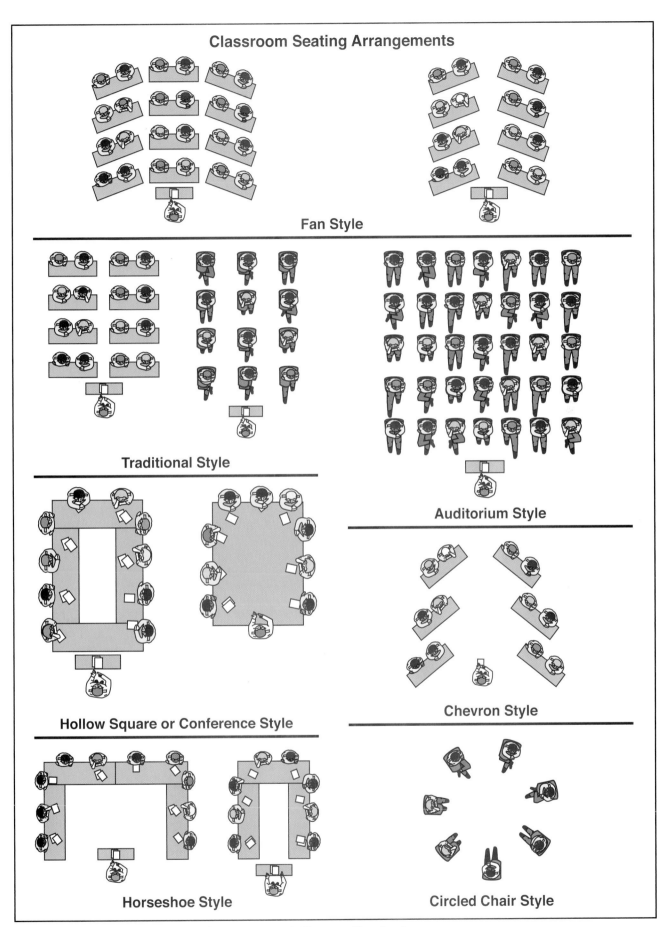

Fan Style

Traditional Style

Auditorium Style

Hollow Square or Conference Style

Chevron Style

Horseshoe Style

Circled Chair Style

Figure 5.3 Each commonly used seating arrangement offers specific advantages.

- **Hollow square** — Arranges tables into a square, with seating along the outside. It is effective for small-to-medium-sized groups and permits both instructor presentation and total discussion.

- **Circled chairs** — Arranges chairs in a circle facing into the center; an open form designed to encourage group participation and discussion. The instructor (or facilitator) sits in the circle with the students. It is most effective for small-to-medium-sized groups where discussion is the primary method of teaching. It is not useful when students are expected to take notes.

Instructors must determine how important it is that students can see and hear the instructor or audiovisual presentation, and how important it is that students can interact with each other. Based on this determination, they should select the seating for the class. For example, if a lesson will rely heavily upon an audiovisual presentation, circled chairs is probably not the ideal seating arrangement.

Another important consideration when seating students at tables is the location of the table legs. Table legs can be both a physical obstruction and a learning distraction. When more seating is required, additional tables should be added rather than attempting to add more seats where table legs are located.

Another issue related to types of seating is the type of work surface, desktop, or table provided. For example, a lesson that requires students to look at blue prints to complete preincident surveys will be difficult to complete if students are seated at individual desks that have a limited work surface. Work surfaces vary and include the following:

- School desktops fixed to an individual chair

- Work surfaces that unfold over the student's lap from between auditorium-type seats

- Tables with varying depths that may accommodate a number of students on one or both sides or are arranged in a U or square shape

- Long conference tables

- Round tables

Instructors may not have the opportunity to choose the type of table or desktop surface for the classroom, and some training organizations may provide only desks or tables with small writing surfaces that do not accommodate an open notebook. Instructors should inspect the physical setting before beginning the class, arrange the seating (if possible) to accommodate the topic, and ask students to store any unneeded items on the floor or in a storage area to prevent cluttering the work surfaces **(Figure 5.4)**.

Seating Comfort

Comfort is as important to learning as how well students can see and interact with the instructor and each other. Frequent rest breaks, usually after every 45 to 50 minutes of instruction, allow students to stand, move around, stretch, and attend to other comfort needs. Delaying a break in order to finish a segment of instruction may be counterproductive, because students lose interest in learning when they are distracted by comfort needs.

Lighting

Permanent classrooms have lighting that is designed for the learning experience. Typically this is a mix of incandescent and fluorescent light, with the primary light source being fluorescent, because it causes less eyestrain and does not glare on reflective surfaces.

Incandescent lighting is often controlled with a dimmer switch that can gradually dim the lights. The dimmer lighting allows students to see images on projector screens or computer monitors but still have enough light to take notes or read handouts. If a classroom does not have dimmer switches, instructors can also lower the lights by unscrewing incandescent bulbs that are directly above screens or computers.

When training must be conducted in a non-classroom setting, instructors should inspect the room or area before class. If the setting does not permit the use of audiovisuals, instructors may have to use a different format of instruction.

Figure 5.4 Instructors should inspect the classroom setting before students arrive to make any necessary adjustments and decisions about work spaces.

Temperature and Ventilation

The temperature of the classroom can create a distraction for students and instructors. Learning environments that are either too hot or too cold tend to preoccupy students as they attempt to make themselves comfortable. Generally, classroom climate is a compromise between hot and cold. This compromise can be difficult to achieve because many heating, ventilating, and air conditioning (HVAC) systems may not be easily adjustable. Instructors should familiarize themselves with the HVAC systems at classroom facilities as follows:

● Check climate controls before teaching in the facility.

● Determine whether controls can be adjusted and how to adjust them.

● Make any climate adjustments within adequate time for the temperature to change prior to instruction.

● Advise students on how to dress for comfort when the systems cannot be adjusted.

● Contact facility personnel if the instructor does not have access to the building's environmental controls.

Ventilation in rooms and spaces located in old buildings that do not have central HVAC systems is another aspect that instructors need to consider. Windows may need to be opened and portable fans used to circulate room air. When temperature becomes a distraction, instructors may need to provide more frequent rest breaks for students. When training in apparatus bays, the bay may need to be ventilated to allow any exhaust to disperse before instruction.

NOTE: In colder climates, training organizations may have indoor facilities large enough to conduct apparatus training indoors. These facilities must have adequate ventilation systems to ensure that apparatus exhaust does not present a hazard **(Figure 5.5, p.112)**.

Figure 5.5 Some training agencies have indoor facilities large enough to conduct apparatus operations. Such facilities should be well ventilated and have adequate lighting. *Courtesy of Spokane Valley Fire Department.*

Noise Level

When inspecting a facility, instructors should attempt to locate and eliminate potential sources of noise. They may need to lower the volume of loudspeakers, radios, and pagers, or simply turn them off. They might also close the classroom door to eliminate hallway noise.

Students who are in-service or on call may have to respond to radios or cell phones during class. Instructors should consult with these students before class sessions to determine how they will be contacted if called to duty. Instructors can then prepare the rest of the class to expect this potential interruption, so that in-service students can leave the class with as little distraction to others as possible.

Audiovisual Equipment

Instructors can also take steps to eliminate distractions before using audiovisual equipment. Both instructors and students will benefit when instructors take time to ensure that the equipment is arranged properly to allow all students to view presentations. Instructors should also take the following steps to avoid distractions when using audiovisual equipment:

- Do not stand between the audience and the projected image.

- Locate the projector so that it does not obstruct students' view.

- Ensure that the projected image fills the screen area without extending over the edges.

- Ensure that the projected image is not distorted.

- Locate the projector so that motor noise is at a minimum.

- Use graphics that are clear, large, and visible from the most remote part of the viewing area **(Figure 5.6)**.

- Elevate small props and demonstration items so that all students may view them clearly.

Whenever possible, instructors should preview any audiovisual aids in the classroom in which they will teach. Doing so allows them to check the compatibility of other material with the equipment that will be used and allows them to view the material from the students' point-of-view.

When using a computer and projector system, instructors should turn on the system, cue the computer-generated slide show, and test the presentation before class. The initial image may be used to welcome students or the system may be turned off until it is needed.

When using audiovisual equipment with which the instructor may not be familiar, it is important to have the facility staff provide instruction in the use of the equipment. Instructors should become familiar with the operation of the specific unit being used. Interaction and cooperation with support staff is essential when an instructor is providing a course on closed-circuit television, interactive television, or computers (computer-based training). A test of all the equipment and remote receiving sites must be performed in advance. Broadcast airtime is valuable, and instructors cannot waste it trying to resolve problems with the system.

Figure 5.6 Make sure that graphics can be seen by everyone in the classroom.

Other Classroom Considerations

Instructors should also prepare for other classroom considerations such as the following:

- Power outlet access
- Internet, phone, and cable television access
- Visual distractions
- Comfort facilities and emergency exits
- Safety hazards

Power Outlet Access

Before beginning a presentation in a remote location, instructors should locate any necessary electrical outlets, determine the need for extension power cords or power strips, and know where extension power cords are located. When extension cords are used, they should be within the length determined by the local fire code, usually 6 feet (approximately 2 m). Instructors should never plug too many pieces of equipment into a single outlet or power strip, as this can overload the circuit. It is a good habit for instructors to unplug all electrical equipment from outlets at the end of the class each day.

Instructors must also eliminate any potential hazards that may result in accidents or injuries by planning and preparing ahead of time for using appropriate electrical outlets, extension power cords, and adapters. Critical safety concerns are protecting electrical cords and eliminating tripping hazards. For example, extension power cords should be taped to the floor or encased in a cover strip to prevent a tripping hazard. Instructors should also have the following information:

- Location of adapters for grounded plugs or power strips
- Condition of power cords (whether cords are frayed or worn or plugs are damaged)
- Location of the main breaker panel and identification of the circuit breaker that controls classroom receptacles
- Locations of timer-controlled automatic power switches that may turn off lights in the classroom during a presentation

Internet, Phone, and Cable Television Access

Internet access is becoming more widely available in classroom facilities, either through wireless networks (Wi-Fi) or wired Ethernet ports. If wired Ethernet ports (wired, broadband internet connections) are available, the instructor should locate these ports and arrange the classroom accordingly. If Wi-Fi is available, the instructor should make sure that all equipment can connect to the network before class begins. It may be necessary to contact the information technology representative at the facility some time before instruction to obtain security passwords for logging into the Wi-Fi network or for assistance with connection issues. When using distance technology, the instructor must ensure that all participants have the proper equipment, login information, and the appropriate level of access to the technology.

If needed, the instructor should also locate telephone and cable television outlets in the presentation room. When they are not conveniently located, it may be necessary to rearrange the seating, move the television or lectern, or arrange for an extension cable.

Visual Distractions

Students can be visually distracted by posters, photographs, maps, and other wall decorations, as well as whatever may be visible outside the classroom window. Before class begins, an instructor should remove these decorations and close the window blinds. If training is conducted in apparatus bays or other work areas, seating should face away from the apparatus, other equipment, or working personnel. The only thing that should ever be visible behind the instructor is a blank wall or projection screen.

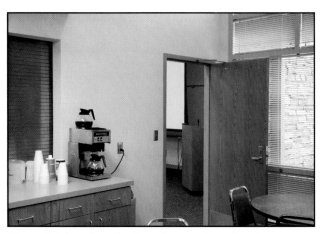

Figure 5.7 Locate refreshments away from the classroom so students do not get distracted by them.

Comfort Facilities and Emergency Exits

During the introduction to a session, instructors should inform students of the location of restrooms, water fountains, smoking areas, storm shelters, and exits. Information about disaster events should be provided when necessary. When refreshments are provided for the session, they should be located away from the students to reduce the temptation for students to move around the room **(Figure 5.7)**. Instructors must also be sure to adhere to local rules for bringing refreshments into the training facility.

Training Ground Environment

The training ground environment (sometimes referred to as the *outdoor learning environment*) can be a challeng-

ing place to teach. The locations used for practical training evolutions can be as varied as the types of evolutions. The training ground environment includes the following facilities:

- Props
- Permanent facilities
- Mobile facilities
- Remote sites
- Acquired structures and facilities

Regardless of the location, the lead instructor is responsible for providing a safe training environment for all instructors and students. The requirements for providing this level of safety are found in national laws, state/provincial laws, local ordinances, government rules and regulations, international consensus standards, organizational policies and procedures, and even case law. The instructor must ensure that safety requirements are met before, during and after training **(Figure 5.8, p.116)**. The sections that follow describe in more detail remote sites and permanent training facilities.

Remote Sites

Remote training sites may include a wide variety of locations. When developing a list of possible remote training sites, instructors then compile a list of available remote sites, including location, name of owner/representative, availability (access and time), water supply source, and possible types of training evolutions that the site could support.

NOTE: For any type of remote site, the instructor must develop a site safety plan and make sure that the site is suitable for whatever training will be done there.

Examples of remote training sites and their potential training uses include:

- **Parking lots** — Used for driver/operator training, supply and attack hose deployment, vehicle extrication, and EMT training.
- **Subdivisions under construction** — Used for driver/operator training and building construction training.
- **Acquired structures** — Used for live-fire evolutions, ventilation training, and forcible entry training. Buildings that have been in a fire may be used for fire pattern analysis and origin and cause determination training. Buildings under demolition may be used for collapse and confined-space rescue training. If live-fire training is conducted in these structures, it must be in compliance with NFPA® 1403, *Standard on Live Fire Training Evolutions*; see Chapter 7, Skills-Based Training beyond the Classroom for more information. For any other uses, safety assessments must be completed before training according to the appropriate standards and regulations.
- **Military or government-owned reservations** — Used for wildland fire suppression, training, off-road driver/operator training, and joint military fire department training.
- **Airports** — Used for aircraft crash/fire/rescue training, driver/operator training, and foam fire-suppression training. When training at an airport, the instructor should contact the tower to obtain clearance for the training.
- **Grain elevators/silos** — Used for technical and rope rescue training.

INCIDENT ACTION PLAN SAFETY ANALYSIS	1. Reach throw bag deployment Location: Worlds of Fun								2. Date April 26, 27, May 4th	3. Time 0900-1630
Division or Group	**Potential Hazards**								**Mitigations** (e.g. PPE, buddy system, escape routes)	
	Type of Hazard: Rope entanglement	Type of Hazard: Missed eddy recovery	Type of Hazard: Trip and fall	Type of Hazard: Impact forces	Type of Hazard: Slip and fall wet surfaces	Type of Hazard: Submersion	Type of Hazard: Impact	Type of Hazard Pulled in water		
Throw bag deployment	x								Tech **shall not** secure rope to person	
Throw bag deployment						x		x	Tech will use self rescue techniques	
Throw bag deployment	x		x	x	x			x	Keep work area clear of trip hazards and caution at edge work	
Throw bag deployment		x					x		Down stream safety with throw bag deployment capabilities	
Throw bag deployment						x			Tech will wear swift water PPE	
Throw bag deployment							x		Tech will direct projectile up stream of rescuer	
Prepared by (Name and Position) Kent Saturday - Instructor Brian Redelsheimer - Instructor										

Figure 5.8 An incident action safety plan is important for ensuring safety when training at a remote site. *Courtesy of Overland Park Fire Department.*

- **Industrial sites** — Used for technical and rope rescue training, hazardous materials spill control, fire-suppression training, and joint-training evolutions with local industrial fire brigades (**Figure 5.9**).

- **Open wildlands** — Used for wildland fire-suppression and off-road driver/operator training (may involve joint department training with controlled burns).

- **Vehicle salvage yards** — Used for vehicle extrication training.

- **Parking garages** — Used for standpipe operations and high-angle rescue training.

- **Warehouses and aircraft hangars** — Used for large area search training, rapid intervention, hoseline deployment, and tactical simulations.

Some remote sites can be used repeatedly, but others may only be available for a single training course or session. Training organizations must always get permission from the property owners or their agents before training at a remote site. Instructors should also thoroughly inspect potential sites in advance, to ensure that it is appropriate for the desired training. It may be helpful at this stage to take photographs, record video, or make a site map. Potential considerations to address during the inspection and planning processes at remote sites are as follows:

- **Weather conditions** — Instructors cannot control these factors, but they should try to lessen their effects on students. Examples:

  - Provide rehabilitation for students who are exposed to temperature extremes and high humidity.

  - Provide shielded observation and waiting areas to protect against strong winds and rain.

  - Provide cleats to add to the soles of shoes or boots when ground surfaces are covered with ice. Sand, salt, and/or ice melt can also be spread to help melt the ice and provide foot traction.

  - Prohibit some operations such as the use of aerial devices or ground ladders during high wind or thunderstorms.

  - Follow regulations and local policies that dictate under what conditions (temperature, humidity, wind, etc.) students may train.

- **Terrain** — The initial inspection should determine how the terrain will affect ladder and apparatus use, site access, and water runoff. If the terrain creates potential safety hazards, instructors should mark these locations on the site map and inform students of areas that are either off-limits or potentially hazardous.

- **Vehicle traffic** — Vehicle traffic may affect training operations conducted on public streets or in parking lots. Take the following actions when training near vehicle traffic:

  - Limit or prohibit public access to the training area whenever possible.

  - Follow policies that regulate the use of safety cones and vests during training to ensure that students use them at emergency incidents **(Figure 5.10)**.

Figure 5.9 Rope training should be practiced in environments that simulate where technical rope rescue might be needed.

Figure 5.10 Use safety vests during practice so that students learn to develop good safety habits.

Figure 5.11 Remember that training exercises can be just as noisy as actual incidents and take proper hearing precautions.

— Involve either the department of public works, the department of transportation, or law enforcement personnel in the training scenario to close roadways or control traffic. This involvement is also a good opportunity for these agencies to become familiar with emergency scene operations.

- **Training ground noise** — Fire and emergency services personnel often work in environments with high noise levels caused by vehicle engines, pumps, sirens, radio transmissions, and shouting. Realistic training scenarios are just as noisy as actual emergency incidents. Take the following precautions to protect students from training ground noise:

  — Follow appropriate guidelines for hearing protection. Use earmuffs or earplugs in environments with high noise levels **(Figure 5.11)**.

  — Turn off vehicle and machinery motors when instructors are giving instructions or explaining procedures.

  — Bring extension cords long enough to allow placement of noisy generators and compressors out of the immediate training area.

  — If noise cannot be controlled, use a microphone and speaker system so that students can properly hear the instructor.

- **Light levels** — Exterior light can affect both teaching and safety. If the light is too bright, students may not be able to see details because of reflected glare. If the light is too low, shadows may conceal important details. Select a location and time of day that reduces the distractions caused by high or low light. Instruction during night training operations is particularly challenging but can be accomplished safely with proper planning. Suggestions:

  — Provide initial instruction in a well-lit area, either indoors or under artificial light.

  — Light not just the immediate training area but also staging areas where tools and other items are kept during training.

  — Make sure the ground is well lit, so that students do not trip or fall.

- **Site space** — Make sure the site is large enough for the planned training. If it is not, training will be less effective and less safe.

- **Exposures** — Before live-fire training, identify potentially exposed structures and personnel. Consider the terrain, water runoff, wind direction, and wind speed.

- **Environmental laws and codes** — Training must always comply with national, state/provincial, and local environmental laws, in addition to building and fire codes and zoning ordinances.

- **Access** — The site map should indicate access points, traffic flow, and the relationship between staging and incident areas. This is especially important if students are in-service during training. Other considerations:

  — Additional personnel may be required to control access to the site.

  — Whenever possible, provide at least two means of access.

- **Water supply** — Instructors should always make sure that a site's water supply is adequate for the training.

Training Ground Safety Regulations and Standards

Instructors must adhere to the following requirements when planning evolutions or selecting training locations:

- NFPA® 1403, *Standard on Live Fire Training Evolutions*
- Occupational Safety and Health Administration (OSHA), federal, state/provincial, and local laws and ordinances that pertain to environmental protection
- All jurisdictional training policies and procedures

Permanent Training Facilities

Many fire and emergency services organizations have access to permanent facilities within their state/province. Permanent training facilities usually contain permanent and portable props required for a variety of training, such as the following:

- **Drill towers**
- **Burn buildings and smokehouses**
- **Flammable/combustible liquid pits**
- **Vehicle driving courses (Figures 5.12 a-d, p.120)**

Before training is conducted at a training facility, instructors should inspect the area to determine the condition of the facility and training props; identify and mitigate any safety concerns; and locate simulated incidents, student parking lots, apparatus staging areas, and observation seating (usually fixed position bleachers). An instructor must be familiar with the training area in order to ensure that training is conducted safely.

At the beginning of any outdoor training session, instructors should give students an overview of the training scenario which includes safety issues, expected outcomes, and unit, company, or individual assignments. Instructors should

Drill Tower — A tall training structure, typically more than three stories high, used to create realistic training situations, especially ladder and rope evolutions.

Burn Building — Structure designed to contain live fires for the purpose of fire suppression training.

Smokehouse — Specially designed fire training building that is filled with smoke to simulate working under live fire conditions; used for SCBA and search and rescue training. Also known as Smoke Building.

Flammable/Combustible Liquid Pit — Training prop designed to provide controlled burns of flammable or combustible liquids; used in training for the extinguishment of flammable/combustible liquid fires.

Vehicle Driving Course — Permanent or temporary training course used for training in apparatus and vehicle driving and operation.

Figure 5.12a A drill tower provides students with a prop to practice ladder and rope evolutions.

Figure 5.12b Burn buildings and smokehouses are specifically engineered to safely withstand fire and suppression conditions.

Figure 5.12c Flammable liquids props allow students to practice suppression techniques in a safer environment.

Figure 5.12d A vehicle driving course allows students to learn how to maneuver and operate apparatus in a safe environment.

then conduct a walk-through of the area or structure that emphasizes exit routes, control zones, and accountability practices. If there are skills that the instructor must demonstrate, this should be done near the beginning of the session.

Instructors should develop a list of potential facilities, including those owned by the jurisdiction, local colleges and vocational/technical schools, and regional and state/provincial training agencies. After compiling a comprehensive list of facilities, the types of training props available, and the names of facility representatives, instructors can plan the types of evolutions that can be performed at each location. Next, instructors can arrange with individual representatives to schedule and coordinate the use of each facility.

Live-Fire Training

NFPA® 1041 requires that a Level II Instructor be present to supervise any high hazard training, such as, **live-fire exercises, controlled burning**, and any fires set for training at in acquired structures. Whenever possible, live fire training should be conducted with props and burn buildings at established, permanent training facilities. Typically this ensures that a Level II Instructor from the facility will be available to oversee the evolution.

But in practice, it is often impossible for a Level II Instructor to be present, especially if training is conducted at a remote site. A Level I Instructor will sometimes have to oversee a live-fire evolution at these remote sites. Before doing so, the instructor should consult with local, county, or state/provincial environmental officials, and must review the requirements in NFPA® 1500, *Standard on Fire Department Occupational Safety and Health Program*, and NFPA® 1403, *Standard on Live Fire Training Evolutions*. This is the most effective way to ensure that the instructor is fully aware of all the issues related to this high hazard training, and is able to take necessary safety measures. Failing to take these steps may put students and the instructor in danger.

For more information on planning training evolutions at the Instructor I level, refer to Chapter 7, Skills-Based Training beyond the Classroom later in this book. In addition, more information on planning, leading, and monitoring training evolutions can be found in the Instructor II section of this book, Chapter 11, Training Evolutions.

Live-Fire Exercises — Training exercises that involve the use of an unconfined open flame or fire in a structure or other combustibles to provide a controlled burning environment. Also known as Live Burn Exercises.

Controlled Burning — Any burn that is safely set and controlled for the purposes of fire and emergency services training.

Chapter Summary

It is the responsibility of the instructor to provide a safe, distraction-free environment that creates optimal learning conditions. Instructors should consider the arrangement of seating, ambient temperature, locations of audiovisual equipment, and other facility considerations.

On the training ground, a Level I Instructor should become familiar with any training facilities that he or she may have access to. In the absence of permanent training facilities, instructors should know how to locate potential remote sites. Some training may occur in the station itself.

When called upon to provide live-fire training, Level I Instructors should attempt to use facilities designed for such training where a Level II Instructor can be present. If training is to be conducted at a remote site, the Level I Instructor can attempt to locate a Level II Instructor to attend the training. If this is not possible, the Level I Instructor must gather the information he or she needs to safely plan, conduct, and monitor live-fire training.

Review Questions

1. What classroom settings and arrangements are commonly used for fire and emergency services training?

2. How can the classroom be best organized for effective learning?

3. What environmental factors need to be addressed when training at a remote site?

4. What should be considered when planning training at a permanent training facility?

Classroom Instruction

Chapter Contents

chapter 6

Key Terms

Job Performance Requirements

NFPA® 1041 References

4.2.3	4.4.5	4.5.2
4.3.2	4.4.6	4.5.4
4.4.2	4.4.7	4.5.5
4.4.3		

Classroom Instruction

Learning Objectives

1. Discuss interpersonal communications. [NFPA® 1041, 4.2.3, 4.4.3; 4.5.4; 4.5.5]

2. Discuss the practice of good listening skills in the classroom. [NFPA® 1041, 4.4.3]

3. Explain presentation techniques that most effectively communicate information to students. [NFPA® 1041, 4.3.2; 4.4.3; 4.4.2; 4.4.7]

4. Discuss the characteristics of the mastery approach to teaching as it relates to the fire and emergency services. [NFPA® 1041, 4.3.2; 4.4.3; 4.4.2]

5. Describe the four-step method of instruction. [NFPA® 1041, 4.3.2; 4.4.3; 4.4.2]

6. Explain instructor-led training approaches to teaching in the fire and emergency services. [NFPA® 1041, 4.3.2; 4.4.3; 4.4.2; 4.4.5; 4.5.2]

7. Discuss distance learning and student-led instruction for the fire and emergency services. [NFPA® 1041, 4.3.2; 4.4.3; 4.4.2]

8. Explain the use of training aids to encourage active learning. [NFPA® 1041, 4.4.6; 4.4.7]

9. Explain the contribution of structured exercises in the classroom. [NFPA® 1041, 4.3.2; 4.4.3; 4.4.2]

10. Describe the factors that affect learning. [NFPA® 1041, 4.4.5]

11. Discuss individual student needs an instructor may face in the classroom. [NFPA® 1041, 4.4.5]

12. Describe reasonable accommodations that instructors can take to address a student's learning disability. [NFPA® 1041, 4.4.5]

13. Discuss a student's substantive rights. [NFPA® 1041, 4.4.5]

14. Describe techniques instructors use to manage student behavior in the classroom. [NFPA® 1041, 4.4.5; 4.5.4; 4.5.5]

Chapter 6
Classroom Instruction

Case History

During a fire chemistry class at a fire station, an instructor found it unusually difficult to get students to participate in discussions. Even when he asked directed questions, he got vague answers and little discussion. He received none of the usual enthusiasm or feedback from the students. After repeated prompting and encouragement failed, he called for a break and took the training officer aside to seek a solution to this problem. Unknown to the instructor, two hours before class, the firefighters had responded to a serious motor vehicle accident in which they extricated an entire family from a vehicle. Two family members were deceased, one was air-lifted to a hospital and not expected to survive, and the youngest, uninjured but in shock, was found wandering aimlessly among the bystanders. It suddenly became clear to the instructor that his students were justifiably not prepared to learn that day after dealing with such a tragic and traumatic incident. The instructor rescheduled the class for a later date.

Classroom instruction is a complicated and multifaceted skill. This chapter provides information on all of the facets of classroom teaching, beginning with the basics of interpersonal communications and concluding with student behavior management. Classroom instruction requires practice for an instructor to become confident with public speaking and giving lectures. After building this confidence, instructors can also focus more of their energies on turning public speaking into effective lecturing and engaging students in active learning. Eventually instructors will also incorporate the ability to manage both time and student behavior. Effective instructors also extend their influence outside the classroom in counseling and coaching sessions. The purpose of this chapter is to introduce the various aspects of classroom instruction.

Interpersonal Communication

Interpersonal communication takes place between individuals every day in casual conversation and has the following characteristics:

- Casual language
- Casual nonverbal clues

- Frequent changes of the speaker and listener roles
- Spontaneity

The tone of the conversation can change based on the perceptions of the two parties. Therefore, it is important that all individuals understand and master the skills involved in interpersonal communication. **Figure 6.1** provides a model of communication specifically oriented toward what an instructor may face in the classroom when attempting to relay a message to students. The instructor must also understand the importance of the message and feedback from students. Interpersonal communication in the classroom consists of the following five basic elements:

- **Sender (instructor)** — The person who initiates the message using both verbal and nonverbal communication.

- **Message (the lesson)** — The content that the sender is trying to communicate. The message may consist of information intended for multiple human senses (sight, hearing, taste, smell, touch).

- **Receiver (student)** — Individual or individuals to whom the sender is attempting to communicate.

- **Feedback to the sender** — Reaction of the receiver to the message and its tone. If this feedback is verbal, the receiver becomes the sender and relates a new message to the original sender, who becomes the receiver. Receiving feedback allows the original sender to confirm reception of the message and to assess the receiver's level of understanding.

- **Interference** — Anything that may prevent the receiver from completely understanding the message.

In a classroom model of instruction, it is the instructor's responsibility to interpret and encode the information in a lesson plan so that students will understand it. All communication takes place within a larger frame of reference. A sender encodes his or her message based on his or her education level, position of authority, personal or ethnic background, and other characteristics. The receiver will then decode the message based upon similar characteristics of his or her own. When the sender takes these characteristics into account, the receiver is more likely to understand the message clearly. Instructors should realize that the way they encode information is based on their own understanding and experience, which is likely to be greater than that of the students. Instructors must learn to encode information at the students' level **(Figure 6.2, p.128)**.

Students, as the receivers of information, will attempt to decode their instructor's message. If the instructor has not taken into account their level of experience, decoding will be much more difficult. After decoding the message, students will relate it to what they already know and determine what its meaning is for them. If instruction is well planned, this meaning will more closely match what the instructor intended.

Students respond to an instructor through feedback. Feedback may be verbal, such as a student asking a question, or nonverbal, as when students appear bored and unmotivated. When instructors pay attention to student feedback, they can modify the lesson to better serve students.

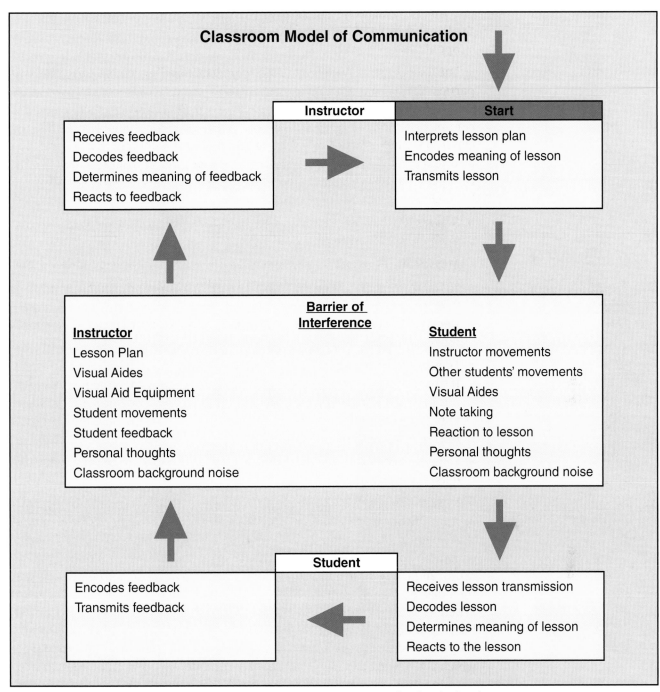

Classroom Model of Communication

Instructor	Start
Receives feedback Decodes feedback Determines meaning of feedback Reacts to feedback	Interprets lesson plan Encodes meaning of lesson Transmits lesson

Barrier of Interference

Instructor	**Student**
Lesson Plan	Instructor movements
Visual Aides	Other students' movements
Visual Aid Equipment	Visual Aides
Student movements	Note taking
Student feedback	Reaction to lesson
Personal thoughts	Personal thoughts
Classroom background noise	Classroom background noise

Student	
Encodes feedback Transmits feedback	Receives lesson transmission Decodes lesson Determines meaning of lesson Reacts to the lesson

Figure 6.1 Students and instructors may face a number of communication barriers in the classroom.

Interference consists of anything that prevents students from fully understanding the instructor's message. For example, if an instructor does not actively monitor student feedback, this can be a major cause of interference. It is just as important for instructors to pay attention to their students as it is for students to pay attention to their instructors. Instructors who are not paying attention to students' nonverbal cues, or who are not listening carefully to their questions may continue to present information even after students have lost interest, become distracted, or become confused by material that requires clarification.

Figure 6.2 A student's silence or lack of feedback may indicate that the student doesn't understand. Improving encoding may increase a student's comprehension.

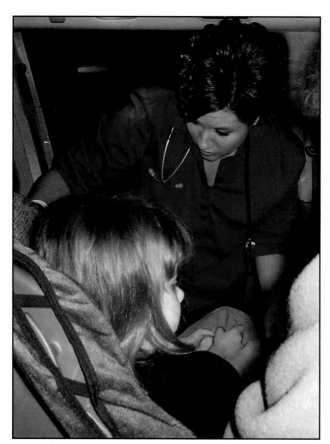

Figure 6.3 Good interpersonal communication is especially important in helping others through hardships.

For communication to be effective, both the sender and receiver must agree on its purpose. Agreement is usually created by a shared situation, such as a classroom environment in which the instructor and student agree that the purpose of their relationship is for the student to learn. In some cases, the purpose must be explicitly stated to ensure that both parties understand it fully. A situation that involves influencing the actions of a subordinate would require that the subordinate understands that the purpose of the conversation involves a change in their attitude or behavior.

There are five general purposes for interpersonal communication: to learn, to relate, to influence, to play, and to help. Brief descriptions of these purposes are as follows:

- **Learning** — Acquire knowledge or skills.
- **Relating** — Establish a new relationship or maintain an existing one.
- **Influencing** — Control, direct, or manipulate behavior.
- **Playing** — Create a diversion and gain pleasure or gratification, as with positive humor.
- **Helping** — Attend to another person's needs or console someone in a time of tragedy or loss **(Figure 6.3)**.

The sections that follow focus more specifically on the verbal and nonverbal components of communication. Both of these components have strengths and weaknesses and inherent interference that instructors must overcome.

Verbal Component

According to research by communication professionals, the words in a message account for only 7 percent of the communication; however, the words in a message – what is being said – carries most of the abstract meaning in communication. Instructors must understand both the power and weakness of words as part of a message. To be effective communicators, instructors must select and use words that accurately symbolize the image that they are trying to convey. This word selection is particularly important when speaking to people who do not have a shared experience with the speaker. Explaining how a smoke detector works to someone who does not have a background in fire science requires fewer technical terms than explaining the concept to another emergency responder.

Instructors should always be aware of their audience or listener. The terms that are common to the fire and emergency services may have another meaning or no meaning at all to the general public. Avoid technical language and fire service jargon when speaking with the public, elected officials, media, and others from outside the profession. Also avoid language that might be considered offensive, gender biased, racist, or otherwise stereotyped.

Cultural Concept of Words

The meaning or symbolism that people place on words depends on their cultural backgrounds. Generally, the meanings of words used in North American English are based on a Eurocentric culture (European-based worldview). Therefore, words have been used to compare other people with this traditionally dominant group. The result has been the common use of terms that place these others at subordinate positions in society by stereotyping or generalizing certain characteristics or traits of a group of people. For example, the obsolete terms in **Table 6.1** are gender biased.

Gender, ethnicity, age, religion, political association, education, and regional background are several ways that people are stereotyped by language. Avoid words that draw attention to these classifications in a negative context in all types of communication. To demean, put down, or degrade people based on the words they use only builds barriers to real communication. It is more productive to attempt to understand other people and show respect for their cultural backgrounds.

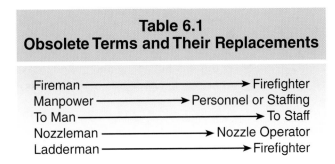

Table 6.1
Obsolete Terms and Their Replacements

Fireman	→ Firefighter
Manpower	→ Personnel or Staffing
To Man	→ To Staff
Nozzleman	→ Nozzle Operator
Ladderman	→ Firefighter

Strong verbal communication is an important skill to cultivate as an instructor. Practicing the following guidelines will help an instructor to hone his or her verbal communication skills:

- **Engage in dual perspective** — Be aware of the receiver's frame of reference. Recognize the listener as having a different culture and attempt to relate to it rather than diminish it or make fun of it.

- **Take responsibility for personal feelings and thoughts** — Use language that is *I-based* such as *I believe . . .* or *I think . . . .* Avoid phrases such as *You hurt me* or *You disappoint me.* Focus instead on language that owns one's feelings and concentrates on the cause of those feelings such as *I am disappointed by your actions.*

- **Show respect for the feelings and thoughts of the other person** — Avoid trying to apply personal feelings to another person such as saying, "I know how you feel." Instead, understand and respect others' positions and build upon those concepts to create strong relationships. A better way of responding in this type of situation is to say, "I'm sorry you have to go through this."

- **Try to gain accuracy and clarity in speaking** — Avoid the abstract language that can cause misunderstandings. Avoid generalizations that result in stereotypes such as "All lawyers are crooks." Generalizations are, in themselves, false. Be clear and accurate in all types of communication.

- **Be aware of any special needs of the receiver** — Be sure to speak slowly and clearly while facing a person when the person is deaf or hard of hearing, for example. This procedure makes it easier for the person to read lips. Do not exaggerate lip or mouth movements because this action is not helpful and may even make the words more difficult to understand.

- **Avoid speaking or addressing a problem while angry or emotional** — Pause and place the conversation on hold until emotions are under control.

Nonverbal Component

Speech communication research indicates that nonverbal communication transmits 93 percent of any message: 55 percent is body language while 38 percent is vocal tone and inflection. Only 7 percent of the transmitted message is actually verbal communication **(Figure 6.4)**.

Nonverbal communication consists of the following elements:

- Body language

- Vocal tone and volume

- Personal appearance

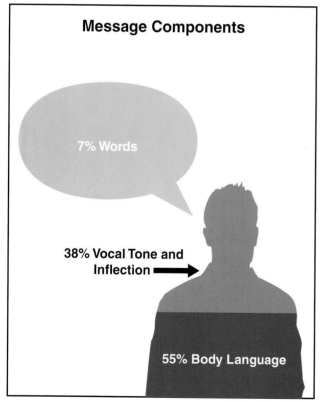

Message Components

7% Words

38% Vocal Tone and Inflection

55% Body Language

Figure 6.4 Instructors should recognize that their words only account for seven percent of interpersonal communication.

An understanding of the importance of each of the elements of nonverbal communication assists the instructor in recognizing and interpreting those signals, thereby improving nonverbal communication. Nonverbal communication can project a person's self-perception, emotional state, approachability, or cultural background. Brief descriptions and recommendations are as follows:

- **Eye contact** — Learn to maintain eye contact while speaking and to modify the amount or duration of eye contact when appropriate. In Eurocentric cultures, good eye contact can convey self-confidence, honesty, trust, and credibility. Averting one's gaze can indicate deceit, dishonesty, insecurity, or anxiety. However, eye contact is also a function of cultural background, so it must be appropriate to the situation, the relationship, and the culture. Examples:

  — Many Native American and Asian societies believe that it is disrespectful to make direct eye contact with a person who is not of the same status.

  — In the wrong context, too much eye contact can be as damaging as too little. Staring into the eyes of a member of the opposite sex can be considered too personal or intimidating.

- **Facial expression** — Learn to match the facial expression to the message. The face can show the six basic emotions: happiness, sadness, surprise, fear, anger, and disgust. To effectively communicate the correct message in a relationship, the facial expression must match the verbal message.

- **Gestures** — Identify and control gestures that are annoying or distracting to others. Learn to use gestures to emphasize and illustrate the message **(Figure 6.5)**. In situations where noise prevents verbal communication, gestures are effective for sending messages such as *come here* and *stop*.

- **Posture** — Maintain good posture when standing or sitting in front of a classroom or assembly. Sitting or standing erect can create the impression of a person with self-confidence and authority. Slouching or standing with stooped shoulders makes a person appear insecure, disinterested, or intimidated.

- **Poise** — Present an image of self-confidence and authority through nonverbal elements, such as good posture and a sense of calm. Instructors develop poise gradually as they become more confident and less nervous when speaking publicly.

Figure 6.5 Nonverbal gestures help to emphasize the message.

- **Vocal characteristics** — Learn to use vocal characteristics that are appropriate for the message and the situation. Practice speaking slowly, using variation in pitch to provide emphasis; use volume appropriate to the situation and proper diction to ensure that words are clearly understood.

- **Vocal interferences** — Eliminate filler words such as *um, er,* or *like,* and empty phrases such as *you know* or *and things like that.* Instructors with a regional or cultural accent may also need to closely monitor their speech to make sure their audience can understand them.

- **Personal appearance** — Maintain a professional appearance at all times. Set an example for subordinates, and require the same level of professionalism from other members of the organization.

- **Touch** — Become conscious of the effect that touch can have on others, both positive and negative.

- **Proximity** — Be aware that different cultures have different interpretations of how close people should be when they interact. Apply this knowledge appropriately.

NOTE: What has been presented in this section is a brief description of nonverbal communication. Instructors are encouraged to seek out other sources of information on this complex topic.

Listening Skills

According to speech communication professionals, listening constitutes from 45 to 53 percent of a person's average day. In the classroom, it is estimated that students spend 50 to 75 percent of class time listening to the instructor, other

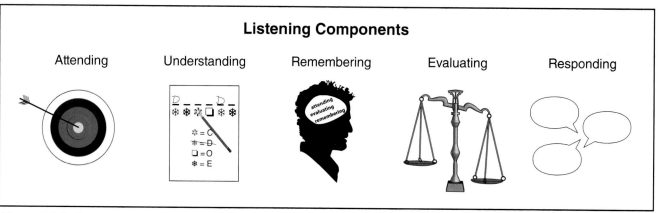

Figure 6.6 An instructor can serve as a role model by practicing the five components of active listening.

students, or audiovisual presentations. Therefore, improving listening skills is essential to effective communication. As role models for their students, instructors must practice good listening skills.

Listening, unlike simply hearing, is an active process that includes attending to, understanding, remembering, evaluating, and responding to the speaker. Instructors can become better listeners by paying close attention to these aspects of the listening process. Descriptions of listening components are as follows **(Figure 6.6)**:

- **Attending** — Focusing on the speaker while ignoring any other distractions; more difficult to achieve outside of a controlled environment. Instructors should ensure that the environment provides as few distractions to the students' ability to attend as possible. Some suggestions for improving the attending step are as follows:

  — Look at the speaker when possible. Think about the speaker and what is being said.

  — Visualize the situation or event that the speaker is talking about.

  — Wait until the speaker has finished delivering the message before responding.

  — Listen to both the verbal and nonverbal messages.

- **Understanding** — Decoding the message and assigning meaning to it involves the following actions:

  — Organizing the message into a logical pattern

  — Interpreting nonverbal clues

  — Asking questions to clarify meaning

- **Remembering** — Retaining information in short term and then long term memory; taking notes, repeating information back to an instructor, using mnemonic devices, and asking questions about unclear information are all ways to aid remembering.

- **Evaluating** — Critically analyzing information to determine how accurate it is, or to separate fact from opinion. To effectively evaluate a message, listeners must draw on their own personal experience, assess the credibility of the speaker, and interpret nonverbal cues.

- **Responding** — Indicating to the sender that the message or information has been understood or requires more explanation; responses may be verbal, such as asking questions or requesting more information, or nonverbal, such as sleeping in class.

Practice is the best way to develop good listening skills. Instructors should listen to speeches or stories on audiotape, and try to repeat the key elements. To improve listening and note-taking skills, an instructor should practice taking notes at meetings or in classes presented by other instructors. These exercises help overcome the barrier created by information overload and pinpoint the essential elements of the message. When instructors have the opportunity to listen to speakers, they should attend the speeches or presentations. While listening, instructors should assess the speaker's strengths and try to emulate those qualities. Instructors should also note any internal and external distractions that arise during the speech and try to minimize such distractions for their own students.

Before classes, small group meetings, or individual counseling sessions, remove barriers to listening in the rooms where the meetings will take place. These barriers may include noise-producing equipment or visual distractions, such as posters on the walls. Wall decorations in classrooms should supplement the course material and not distract from it. During training exercises, try to identify barriers to communication, both over the radio and at the command post.

Presentation Techniques

Presentation is the art of clearly and concisely explaining information in ways that an anticipated audience can understand. It requires both an understanding of interpersonal communication and the ability to apply that understanding to public speaking. For instructors, public speaking usually occurs in a classroom setting with an audience of students. Presentation techniques can also apply to presentations given to superiors, administrative bodies, or the general public.

The sections that follow will describe the characteristics of effective speakers, explain how to organize and sequence a presentation, and describe how to effectively use transitions. The instructor needs to expand on this knowledge and practice each of these methods in order to become proficient in them.

Characteristics of Effective Speakers

The first step toward becoming an effective public speaker is to identify the characteristics displayed by effective speakers. Characteristics that apply to the instructor in the classroom include the following:

- **Audience-centered** — The speaker knows the audience and adapts his or her topic, speech organization, presentation style, and personal appearance to this audience. In the classroom, this involves matching the instructor's presentation style to the students' learning styles.

- **Good development of ideas** — Effective speakers create interesting, appealing, and memorable ways of presenting their information. In a classroom setting, this may include the following:

  — Using relevant examples

  — Telling stories to which the audience can relate

  — Using effective metaphors

- **Good organization of ideas** — Effective speakers organize their material so that their audience is never lost during the presentation. Persuasive speeches include an attention grabber, necessary background information, an illustration of the problem or situation, and finally solutions for the situation. An informative speech may be organized either topically or from the least to most complex portions or subjects.

- **Best choice of words** — It is important not to speak above the intellectual level of the audience by using words they might not understand. It is just as important not to talk below the level of the audience members, insulting their intelligence by being too basic.

- **Good delivery skills** — Effective speakers use the following communication techniques to enhance the words that they have chosen:

  — Keep appropriate eye contact with the audience members.

  — Speak to the entire audience, not just one section or one side of the room.

  — Use appropriate gestures to illustrate mental pictures or emphasize key points.

  — Pause periodically so students can think about what they have heard and ask questions. A good instructor should never feel pressured by silence.

  — Refrain from adding too many "war stories" to presentations.

- **Good vocal characteristics** — Major elements are as follows:

  — Pronunciation: pronouncing each word correctly, stressing the right words or syllables, and pausing where appropriate.

  — Good grammar: correct tense, possession, pronoun agreement, etc.

  — Inflection: varying the tone (pitch) of words, syllables, or phrases to emphasize important points.

  — Variety: changes in loudness, tone, and rate of speech.

  — Enunciation: clearly emphasizing each syllable, accent, and pause. The opposite of enunciating is slurring.

  — Projection: speaking loudly and clearly enough to be heard in the back of the room or auditorium.

  — Rate of speech: speed at which words are spoken. Effective instructors will speak more slowly when presenting new information or emphasizing important points, or when students need to take notes. As students become more familiar with the material, instructors can speak more quickly.

- **Conversational tone** — A relaxed tone makes listeners feel at ease and ready to receive information.

- **Positive attitude** — Effective speakers display a positive attitude about the subject matter they are presenting.

- **Appropriate use of humor** — Appropriate humor can create a relaxed atmosphere and get the attention of the audience. However, instructors should avoid inappropriate humor that may offend members of the audience.

- **Personal style** — Effective speakers use a personal style, capitalizing on their own unique experiences and abilities.

Ethical Conduct

Public speaking has an ethical component, especially in the fire and emergency services. Effective speakers must ensure that their words match their actions. Speakers should reinforce teaching ethics in their presentations whenever possible and never speak against their organizations' ethical codes during presentations or lectures.

Presentation Planning

The following are ways instructors can plan for presentations so that they are prepared and at their most effective:

- Practice the delivery of a presentation. Attempt to put into practice the characteristics of effective public speakers described in the previous section of this chapter.

- Make a video recording of the presentation and review it for distracting actions and speech patterns. Making a recording also enables instructors to experiment with different ways to present materials, which can increase instructional effectiveness.

- Check the presentation materials to ensure that they are complete, in order, and correct for the topic.

- Analyze the presentation to ensure that it is logical in its sequence.

- Get plenty of rest the night before a presentation.

- Relax before a training session.

- Select comfortable clothing in which to deliver a presentation, and always dress appropriately.

- Anticipate potential problems and prepare to resolve them should they occur.

Distracting Behaviors to Avoid

- Pacing around the floor
- Playing with or tapping pens, pencils, and other items
- Jingling keys or change
- Chewing gum, fingernails, matchsticks, or toothpicks
- Overusing pet words or fad phrases such as 24/7

Organization Format

Oral presentations generally consist of three parts: opening or introduction, body, and summary or conclusion. This format follows the basic concept of telling the listener or student the topic of the presentation, detailing the topic, and then restating the main points.

All presentations should follow this general format. Within this format, the information can be presented in a variety of logical sequences (see Methods of Sequencing section). Descriptions of the three parts are as follows:

- **Introduction** — Use the opening of the presentation to get the attention of students. Introduce students to the topic and purpose of the presentation, and tell them how it relates to them or their jobs. Also present a brief summary or outline of the main points to help students remain focused.

- **Body** — Present the information by using a logical sequencing approach along with supporting facts and information. Separate the body of a long presentation into smaller, easily understood segments. Ensure that each segment conveys a single point or idea and has its own opening, body, and summary. Link segments by using transition phrases in their summaries.

- **Summary, closure, or conclusion** — Review the objective of the presentation and how it is relevant to the overall goal of the course. Emphasize the main points and introduce the next lesson or the demonstration that is associated with the presentation.

Presentation vs. Instruction

A lecture is instructional while a presentation is simply a speech. Instruction begins with basic presentation characteristics, and then expands into an interactive experience for the students, and the principles of learning are applied to its construction.

Methods of Sequencing

Experts in the fields of teaching methodology and speech communication have established ways of effectively sequencing information in a presentation. The sequence depends on the topic and the organization of the lesson plan. Generally accepted sequences for instructional delivery include the following:

- **Known-to-unknown** — Begin with information that students are familiar with or already know before leading them into unfamiliar or unknown material. This method is effective because it gives students an opportunity to base their learning experience on something they already recognize.

- **Simple-to-complex** — Begin by teaching the basic knowledge or skill, then introduce more difficult or complex knowledge as the lesson progresses. Basic knowledge and skills are necessary foundations for mastering more complex knowledge and skills. For example, before teaching rigging and hauling techniques, the instructor would teach basic rope skills.

- **Whole-part-whole** — Begin this sequence with an overview of the entire topic or a demonstration of the complete skill in real time. Next, divide the topic or skill into subsections or steps, and describe or demonstrate each of them. Close by providing a summary of the entire topic or a demonstration of the complete skill.

- **Step-by-step** — Teach each individual step in the correct order and then have students practice them in the same order. A variation on this sequence is called *progressive-part*, in which steps 1 and 2 are learned before progressing to step 3. After mastering 1, 2, and 3, the student learns step 4, and so on. Finally, the student must perform all steps sequentially in a single skill.

Instructors commonly use all of these sequences to present new material because they provide a solid foundation for learning. These sequences also help instructors outline the points that are essential to understanding the topic and mastering a skill.

Educational professionals recommend that instructors use several techniques when preparing a lesson to enable them to check for understanding during the lesson. A short list of these techniques include the following:

- Show physical examples of unfamiliar objects or demonstrate unfamiliar processes.

- Diagram a complex, structured set of ideas on a chalkboard or handout, or through other visual aids **(Figure 6.7)**.

- Use demonstrations and modeling where possible, particularly cognitive modeling in which the instructor thinks out loud while performing the physical activities of demonstrating.

- Reinforce aspects that interest students. Build motivation by pointing out the interest value or application possibilities of the new material.

In all lessons, instructors must ensure that they introduce students to the key points, stress these points in the related parts of the lesson, and review and summarize them at the end of the lesson. Even though an instructor may present a lesson segment, he or she should still ensure that the new order of the lesson flows logically using one of the sequential methods.

Figure 6.7 Diagramming ideas will help students understand concepts.

Transitions

For continuity and consistency, instructors use transitions to move students from one portion of the lesson to the next without losing their attention. Transitions preview what will happen next or relate an upcoming concept or skill to a previous one. Effective transitions can create interest, keep attention, and make logical connections between portions of the lesson. The lesson plan should contain the location of the necessary transitions for the benefit of both experienced and inexperienced instructors. The benefits of transitions are as follows:

- **Maintain interest** — Keep the audience interested in the story.

- **Maintain continuity** — Keep the information flowing in a steady, uninterrupted stream.

- **Maintain consistency** — Help ensure that topics and lessons throughout a course are taught in a similar manner with recognizable transitions.

- **Establish relationships** — Show how parts of the topic are related to each other.

- **Provide previews** — Give the audience an idea of what to expect in the next portion of the material.

- **Provide summaries** — Conclude the previous idea or topic.

Knowing when to use transitions is a question of timing. Transitions can be used effectively at the following times:

- Ending one topic and beginning another
- Ending a complete lesson within a series or course
- Starting a new lesson within a series or course
- Moving from one teaching method into another
- Providing rest breaks for students and instructors

The length of time a transition requires will vary according to its use. Announcing a rest break for the class takes only a few seconds, while summarizing a complex topic may take several minutes. Including transitions in a lesson plan helps establish the time required and prevents the lesson from continuing too long.

Speech communication professionals teach two types of transitions for use in oral communication: *verbal* and *nonverbal*. These types may be used separately or together. With practice, the instructor can learn how to use them effectively and with variety.

Verbal Transitions

Verbal transitions provide a summary and/or preview within a single sentence or two. Types/examples of verbal transitions include the following:

- **Summary statement and preview** — Example: *Now that you understand how to operate the components of the SCBA, our next step is to learn how to assemble them into a working system.*

- **Review of the lesson or course agenda** — Example: *Today we saw a demonstration and received some practical training over how to use Class A foam to extinguish a flammable liquid fire.*

- **Change of media** — Example: *In order to illustrate what we have been discussing in the slide presentation, we will now view a video clip that shows how rapidly a fire can develop in a controlled environment.*

Words or phrases that may be useful as transitions include *in addition to, in other words, as well, therefore, in summary,* and *not only.* Use of the words *finally* and *in conclusion* should be avoided in oral presentations, as they give students permission to stop listening. Other ways of using specific words or phrases to express transitions include the following:

- **Repeat key words or their synonyms** — Repetition emphasizes the importance of the word or phrase.

- **Sequence the parts to ensure continuity** — Use words such as first, second, or third to establish the relationship between parts of an idea or process.

- **Include rhetorical questions** — Rhetorical questions (ones that do not require an answer from the audience) help to establish a relationship between the information that has been provided and the information that follows. The instructor's answering the question provides the transition to new subject matter.

Nonverbal Transitions

Nonverbal transitions help an instructor to emphasize a point within a topic. They may consist of a change of facial expression, a pause, a change in vocal pitch or rate of speaking, a gesture, or physically moving from one point to another.

Nonverbal transitions may also be used to move from one teaching method into another. This kind of transition may create some disturbance to student concentration because it involves an obvious change. Altering the light level, turning on audiovisual equipment, or assembling a model takes time and cannot be accomplished effectively while the instructor is lecturing. To make these transitions less noticeable, the instructor may plan on having an aide assemble equipment while the instructor lectures or call for a break when new equipment needs to be set up for the next portion of the lesson.

Media Transitions and Animations

Computer-generated presentations can be constructed with a variety of audio and video transitions between the slides in the presentation. While the Instructor I will not likely have to create large series of slides for classroom use, he or she may adjust a prepared series of slides to tailor the lesson to his or her classrooms. Instructors are encouraged to use the same transitions provided with the remainder of the prepared slides. Adding too many or repetitive animations can be very distracting. Be careful that the animations don't become the items that the student watches and not the content. All visual aids should enhance the presentation – not become the presentation.

Mastery Approach to Teaching in the Fire and Emergency Services

In the fire and emergency services, information and skills must be mastered by students before they progress to new material. The mastery approach to teaching, sometimes referred to as **competency-based learning (CBL)**, requires that the student successfully master the learning objectives or outcomes of the lesson or course. When testing for mastery, instructors base student performance on specific criteria (standards) stated in the learning objectives. Characteristics of the mastery approach are as follows:

- **Competency-based** — Primary focus is on the successful and accurate completion of skills; also known as *performance-based*.

- **Individual-based** — Training is individualized to meet the learning style of the student.

- **Immediate, specific feedback** — Instructors provide feedback to the individual student when the student performs the skill.

- **Modules and multimedia** — Courses and lessons are divided into similar blocks that are supported by a variety of audiovisual training aids.

- **Instructor-supported** — Instructors must help students learn the skill and become proficient at it.

- **Specific objectives** — The ultimate goal of every course is for students to master a set of specific learning objectives.

- **Criterion-referenced testing** — Success is based solely on the mastery of specific criteria at a predesignated level, usually 70 to 100 percent.

Competency-Based Learning (CBL) — Training that emphasizes knowledge and skills that are required on the job. Course objectives involve specific, criteria-based competence in performing tasks or understanding concepts that learners will use in their daily work.

The mastery approach uses criterion-referenced teaching, learning, and assessments, and focuses attention on learning objectives. Students who have problems meeting the desired criteria on their initial efforts get additional instruction, time, and opportunities to perform to the acceptable level. The learning objectives are written to establish the criteria for mastery as follows:

- Identify and clearly describe the learning outcome (behavior). Example: *The student will don an SCBA.*

- Define the important conditions under which the students will perform (conditions). Example: *The student will don an SCBA while wearing full personal protective equipment.*

- Define the criterion of acceptable performance (degree). Example: *The student will don an SCBA while wearing full personal protective equipment within 45 seconds.*

When the material is difficult or complex, instructors must work more diligently to lift students to the mastery standard and may need to spread the learning over a longer time period so that students can assimilate complex concepts. Finally, no student should proceed to new material until he or she has mastered the basic requisite material.

The mastery approach has advantages and disadvantages, although with proper planning instructors can overcome the disadvantages. Some of the advantages of the mastery approach to teaching include the following:

- Students are prepared to advance to more complex knowledge or skills.

- Knowledge that the student possessed before the course is used as a building block for new skills which can make gaining mastery easier for the student.

- Students are made aware of the learning objectives before beginning so that criteria for passing are never in question.

- Time is given to tailor learning to the student's individual learning style to assist the student in gaining mastery.

The mastery approach also has some associated disadvantages, although an instructor can overcome these. Disadvantages include the following:

- Instructors must plan for and provide extra time to ensure that all students master the subject. This may interfere with lesson planning or make it difficult for an instructor to stick to a schedule.

- More effort is required on the instructor's part to teach at the pace of the students in the class.

- Faster students may feel that the slower members of the class are holding them back.

- A wide variety of training materials must be available to meet the learning needs of all students.

Four-Step Method of Instruction

Four-Step Method of Instruction — Teaching method based upon four steps: preparation, presentation, application, and evaluation. May be preceded by a pretest.

The **four-step method of instruction** consists of the following four parts: preparation, presentation, application, and evaluation **(Figure 6.8)**. Taken as a whole, the four-step method is a widely accepted structure for teaching a lesson. The sections that follow describe each step in the four-step method in greater detail.

Four-Step Method of Instruction

STEP 1 PREPARATION

Purpose	How to Accomplish
To prepare the students to learn	Tested methods for preparing students to learn
1. Prepare the mind of students by creating: • Attention • Curiosity • Interest • Desire 2. Create a foundation for learning: Begin associating students' experiences with the lesson's contents.	1. Generate curiosity by asking rhetorical questions or questions that cause students to relate personal experiences to the topic. 2. Create attention by including a personal experience, analogy, or topic-related story. 3. Generate desire by citing the personal benefits associated with mastering the knowledge and skills. 4. Create interest by presenting new concepts, procedures, or equipment. 5. Create continuity by reviewing previous lessons. 6. Determine student knowledge by conducting diagnostic quizzes or pretests.

STEP 2 PRESENTATION

Purpose	How to Accomplish
To communicate content developed to change the behavior of students	Tested methods of presenting knowledge and skills
1. Present knowledge, new skills, concepts, or procedures to students. 2. Instruct, motivate, and educate students.	1. Select the appropriate presentation style for the audience, subject, and desired outcome. 2. Present lectures, demonstrations, and activities. 3. Use appropriate visual aids and props. 4. Explain procedures. 5. Emphasize key points. 6. Explain concepts, philosophies, principles, and implications. 7. Proceed from known to unknown and simple to complex. 8. Use textbooks and other reference materials. 9. Apply active learning principles. 10. Summarize key points and concepts at the end of the presentation. 11. Require students to take notes.

STEP 3 APPLICATION

Purpose	How to Accomplish
To provide the opportunity for students to apply theory, critical thinking, critical decision-making, or psychomotor skills to practical situations	Creative, organized, and tested methods for presenting and practicing practical skills
1. Demonstrate skills-based knowledge through appropriate means. 2. Provide students with the opportunity to perform under supervision. 3. Involve students actively in the learning process. 4. Provide the opportunity to practice and master critical skills in a nonemergency learning environment.	1. Have students perform the task or activity under supervision. 2. Observe performances closely. 3. Check and correct errors. 4. Instill correct habits in students. 5. Check key points and safety points. 6. Develop discussions based on theory, decision-making, or skills application. 7. Conduct periodic skills tests. 8. Assign projects and activities. 9. Assign problems for students to resolve.

STEP 4 EVALUATION

Purpose	How to Accomplish
To evaluate the learning process	Tested methods for evaluating the learning process
1. Evaluate student understanding. 2. Evaluate teaching effectiveness.	1. Have students perform tasks unassisted. 2. Conduct performance tests. 3. Ask prepared questions. 4. Have students demonstrate and explain tasks. 5. Have students observe and critique other student performances. 6. Conduct final examinations. 7. Evaluate notebooks, projects, assignments, and activities. 8. Have students complete course and instructor evaluation forms. 9. Have instructors complete course evaluation forms.

Figure 6.8 The four-step method of instruction covers the important components of instructional delivery.

Preparation

Preparation refers to preparing students to learn and involves an instructor establishing how the lesson is relevant to the students' needs. The instructor can accomplish this by performing the following actions:

- Introduce the topic.
- Gain the students' attention.
- State the learning objectives.
- Explain how the information or skill in the lesson is directly relevant to the students' jobs.
- State the lessons' key points so that students are prepared to listen for them.

Each of these actions will help create a foundation from which the instructor can make the presentation. By relating the topic to previously learned information or past student experiences, instructors can show why the topic is important and how it will benefit students.

Figure 6.9 In the Presentation step, the instructor explains the objectives and structure of the lesson.

Presentation

In this step, the instructor presents the lesson content in an orderly, sequential outline **(Figure 6.9)**. The following items are listed with each key point on the outline:

- Teaching methods
- Learning activities
- Demonstrations and practices
- Listing of instructional support materials needed for the lesson such as audiovisuals, worksheets, and handouts to present the information to students
- Summary sections given at logical stopping points throughout the lesson plan and at the end of the outline

Application

In this step the instructor provides opportunities for students to learn through activities, exercises, discussions, work groups, skill practices, practical training evolutions, and similar learning activities **(Figure 6.10)**. Most learning takes place during the application step, making this step critically important.

Application can be combined with presentation so that students apply the lesson content during activities that require them to think, manipulate tools, or demonstrate skills. Typically, application is related to performing the operations or steps of a task. Students may also demonstrate skills during an exercise that are not directly related to the steps involved to complete a given task, such as how to do any of the following:

- Give a presentation
- Lead a group discussion or brainstorming session
- Apply research methods
- Demonstrate outlining and writing techniques

Figure 6.10 During the Application step, students can practice skills.

Evaluation

In the fourth and final step, students demonstrate how much they have learned through a written, oral, or practical examination; written tests are typically used to evaluate whether students have learned cognitive information, while practical tests are used to evaluate skill ability **(Figure 6.11, p.145)**. The purpose of evaluation is to determine whether students achieved the lesson objectives or course outcomes.

Instructor-Led Training (ILT)

Instructor-led training (ILT) is the most prevalent approach to teaching in the fire and emergency services. ILT has the advantage of being flexible, economical, and familiar to both students and instructors. Aspects of ILT include the following:

- Generating and maintaining student interest
- Giving an illustrated lecture
- Leading discussion
- Providing demonstration
- Motivating and encouraging students
- Reinforcing learning
- Asking effective questions

Multiple Instructors

The purpose of using multiple instructors is to combine their knowledge and experience so that students are better able to meet the course learning outcomes. It can be an effective educational technique and a unifying force between organizations. One variation is known as team teaching, in which multiple instructors teach the same topics simultaneously with different groups of students, providing a more effective use of class time and smaller student-to-instructor ratios **(Figure 6.12, p.146)**.

Usually the instructor with the most knowledge or experience in a particular topic teaches the cognitive and demonstration portions of the lesson to all classes, then joins with other instructors in supervising the practical training evolution. Multiple-instructor or team-teaching sessions have the following advantages:

- Provide an effective use of resources from multiple areas and specialties.
- Allow an instructional delivery method that works well when the topic is broad.
- Provide students with an exposure to a wide variety of teaching methods and skills training.
- Keep the attention of the group by utilizing each instructor's different voice, pace, and personality.

To prepare for multiple-instructor presentations, consider the following suggestions:

- Make an extensive course plan that outlines each instructor's role and time commitment.
- Maintain communication between all instructors to ensure course continuity and consistency.
- Choose instructors whose teaching styles contrast, yet balance one another.
- Decide in advance who will teach which topics.
- Review all lesson outlines together so that each instructor knows what the others are doing.
- Agree on and use the same format for all audiovisual materials.
- Designate one lead instructor per topic.
- Determine time commitments and require each instructor to adhere to them.
- Agree that all instructors will be present for the entire course, not just when it is their turn to teach.
- Meet with other instructors to review session results.

Generating and Maintaining Student Interest

Generating student interest is about more than just encouraging students to pay attention — it is about making them desire more information about the topic and making them want to participate in the learning process. Interested students are open and responsive and want to concentrate on what they are learning. As a result, they will also be more willing to actively participate in the learning process.

Generating interest is only the first step. Instructors must help students maintain interest throughout the lesson and the course. To help maintain interest, instructors need to show students a personal connection with the lesson. The following are strategies for helping students maintain interest:

Figure 6.11 Practical tests allow instructors to evaluate students' skills.

- **Relate learning to student interests** — Material relevant to student experiences illustrates the overall usefulness of the information presented.

- **Offer material that pertains to students' professional goals, duties, and tasks** — Students are more likely to be curious about information that has particular importance to their professional futures.

- **Use humor appropriately** — Use humor spontaneously, and be sure to laugh with people but not at them.

- **Stimulate emotions** — The experiences that students bring to training sessions evoke a range of emotions. Instructors can use these experiences to stimulate student interest.

- **Explain and illustrate with examples, stories, analogies, and metaphors** — These techniques make abstract concepts more relatable to students.

- **Use questions to stimulate interest** — With practice and experience, instructors can learn to pose appropriate, well-timed, thought-provoking questions that encourage participation and promote understanding.

- **Use unpredictability and uncertainty** — Anticipating the unexpected is exciting, and students who do not know what will happen next are more likely to pay close attention. As long as students feel safe and know that no one will be hurt, this technique can be an effective way to keep students interested.

Figure 6.12 In team teaching, several instructors can work with groups of students simultaneously. Doing so helps to maintain a low student-to-instructor ratio.

Words to Teach By

Your students have entrusted you with their most valuable possession, time. Don't you dare give them anything less than your best.

Be Prepared: Know your material, prepare your classroom, master your audiovisuals (including the machines), and have a backup plan.

Preview your video presentations. Use only those portions that are important to your lesson.

Be excited about what you teach; it's contagious!

Courtesy of Rod Smith, Assistant Chief, Lane County Fire District No. 1, Veneta, Oregon.

Illustrated Lecture — Instructional technique in which audiovisual training aids accompany a lecture, in order to clarify information and facilitate interaction with the students.

Giving an Illustrated Lecture

In the **illustrated lecture** format, the instructor explains a topic through spoken words and the use of audiovisual aids, such as:

- Computer-generated slide presentations, such as PowerPoint® or Keynote®
- Illustrations on dry-erase boards or chalkboards
- Drawings and photographs
- Recorded video on DVD or computer

The illustrated lecture format is an effective method for providing facts, rules and regulations, clarifications, examples, and definitions. It allows one speaker to reach an audience of any size, from a single student to a full auditorium. Many students can be taught at the same time while the instructor only prepares one presentation. Another advantage is that students are familiar with this format, so they are aware of what to expect and what is expected of them.

Computer-generated slide presentations are the most widely accepted visual aid that instructors use to accompany their lectures. Although these presentations can be a valuable asset, it is important to remember that they are merely tools to help illustrate key points or generate discussion. They should never constitute an entire lesson or be the foundation on which the lesson is built.

When giving an illustrated lecture, consider the following recommendations:

- Incorporate time for asking questions into your lesson plans. Pose questions to students throughout the lecture, and allow them to ask questions either during the lecture or at the end of the session.

- Be prepared to ask questions extemporaneously when it becomes clear that the students may be losing interest. Direct questions to students who are paying less attention than others.

- Use affective listening skills to pay attention to student feedback.

- Avoid presenting too much information at once; students need time to process new material, especially if they are also taking notes.

- Provide supplemental information using handouts and reference lists.

- Break lectures into smaller segments of about 12-18 minutes. Intersperse these lecture segments with discussion groups or skill practice time.

- Provide a note-taking guide to allow students to take notes on the verbal portion of the lecture without having to also write information from the slides.

- At the end of each segment, have students work in pairs or small groups to compare notes, ask each other questions, and discuss the lecture material.

- Give students 3 minutes at the end of the class to write down everything they remember from the lesson.

- Provide a clear preview of the information that will be contained in the lecture.

- Include only essential and relevant information in the lecture.

- Review frequently, after each lecture segment and at the end of the lesson.

Leading Class Discussions

In contrast to the illustrated lecture method of delivering instruction, the discussion method allows more interaction between instructors and students. The instructor talks with the group rather than to the group. Group members talk to the instructor and to each other, either in small groups or as one large group **(Figures 6.13 a and b, p.148)**.

Lesson plans may include instructions for structured discussion sessions in either large or small groups. These instructions usually provide topics for discussion. As instructors become more experienced, discussions may result spontaneously as a response to student questions. Instructors should remember that discussions are less predictable than lectures in terms of the amount of class time they require.

During a discussion, instructors and students can interact in the following ways:

- Exchange views and ideas
- Ask questions and receive answers
- Provide examples based on experiences
- Arrive at conclusions
- Form a consensus

For this method to be effective, students must have a basic knowledge of the subject before the discussion begins. The discussion method is not a good format for introducing new material to inexperienced students.

Figures 6.13 a and b Large and small group discussions allow instructors and students to interact in ways that lectures do not.

Discussion as Active Learning

Group discussions are an example of active learning, a form of instruction in which students participate in classroom activities and are forced to think about what they are doing. Research at every level of education has demonstrated the benefits of active learning. The benefits of classroom discussion include the following:

- **Fosters improved student understanding** — Group discussions give students an opportunity to reflect on the lecture material.

- **Improves student communication skills** — Small group interaction forces students to learn to listen effectively, develop their positions on topics, and logically discuss information.

- **Improves cooperation within a group** — Helps to create a sense of teamwork and cooperation between students.

- **Places the responsibility for learning in the hands of the student** — Increases the student's sense of ownership of the learning process.

Whole Group Discussions

In whole group discussion, the lesson plan contains the basic information for the discussion. If the instructor selects the topic, then he or she should determine whether or not the topic can generate enough interest for a whole group discussion. A whole group discussion can help students to accomplish the following learning objectives:

- Share information and knowledge.
- Apply theories and critical thinking skills.
- Express personal views and ideas.
- Collaborate and work as a team.
- Clarify attitudes, values, and beliefs.

An instructor should establish the time required for the discussion and ensure that it is available in the class period. The instructor should also develop an opener for the discussion, which may consist of a short narrative, case study, hypothetical situation, or problem. These openers and topics may be provided in prepared lesson plans. Because discussions can be time-consuming, the instructor must ensure that the time is used efficiently and the topic is specific enough to help students stay focused.

When planning for whole-group discussions, instructors should select the type best suited for the topic and time frame. The two most common categories of the whole group discussion format are as follows:

1. **Guided** — The instructor presents a topic to a group, and the members of the group discuss ideas in an orderly exchange controlled or guided by the instructor. The intent of this type of discussion is for students to gain knowledge from other group members, modify their own ideas, or develop new ones. As facilitator, the instructor's role is to guide the discussion and meet the lesson objectives in the following ways:

   — Keep the discussion on the topic.

   — Add pertinent details.

   — Ask thought-provoking questions.

2. **Conference** — A conference discussion is less controlled than a guided discussion. In this method, instructors are facilitators not teachers. They do not tell the group how or what to think nor steer the results of the group's thinking in a personally preferred direction. The intent is for the students to understand how they view a topic rather than being steered to a destination by their instructor. The instructor's responsibilities in this format include the following:

   — Providing background information on the topic.

   — Stating or restating problems, asking questions, or clarifying students' comments. Other than this, the instructor should allow the students to control the discussion, and should not actively participate.

   — Controlling or eliminating bickering and irrelevant discussion, reconciling differences of opinion, and uniting students

NOTE: The term conference is used for both a discussion format and a type of meeting that has the same purpose only on a larger scale.

It is also important for the instructor to develop a means of closing the discussion. The closer may include a summary of the problem and a list of the solutions developed in the discussion. Students may also be asked to write their own summaries of the discussion — an exercise that causes them to rephrase and restate the major points generated in the discussion.

Small Group Discussions

In small group discussions, instructors do not actively participate. Instead, they select a student to facilitate or lead the discussion in each group. The main advantage of this format is that students express their ideas and opinions more openly with their peers than they do when an instructor is present. Small group discussions are most effective when:

- The task is structured.
- Students are experienced in working with others.
- The learning outcome is clearly defined.
- Students have time to prepare for the discussion.

The instructor's role in this format is to define group goals, establish a time frame for discussion, and monitor the groups to make sure students stay on task. When the discussion is finished, instructors may want to have students write summaries of their discussions, or present their findings to the rest of the class. Prepared lesson plans will generally indicate when small group discussions are desirable in the lesson plan, how much time should be provided for the discussions, and what prompts or topics should be provided to the various small groups.

Leading Discussions

Both large and small group discussions require that instructors demonstrate leadership, and make sure that discussions lead students toward achieving course goals. Instructors should monitor how involved students are in the discussion, who is and is not participating, and whether the discussion is on track. Leading a discussion requires that an instructor or facilitator assume the following roles:

- **Director** — Move the discussion along and do not allow it to bog down in trivia or sidetrack to another issue.
- **Gatekeeper** — Ensure that all students have an opportunity to speak and no one dominates the discussion.
- **Timekeeper** — Remind students of the time remaining for discussion or summary.

In taking on these general roles, instructors will have to perform the following specific tasks:

- Open the discussion by stating the topic or problem to be solved.
- Paraphrase students' contributions to ensure that they understand the material.
- Ask questions to make sure that students understand their own positions, and those of their classmates.
- Act as a resource for additional information and statistics.
- Summarize the results of the discussion.

NOTE: Instructors who regularly plan small group discussions should take the time to develop these discussion leadership skills in students who will facilitate the groups.

Discussion Techniques

A variety of techniques may be used to direct the outcome of a discussion. These techniques apply to both large and small group discussions and include the following:

- **Brainstorming** — Students try to generate as many ideas as they possibly can, operating under the principle that there are no bad ideas. The group then evaluates the ideas and decides which ones have the most merit. Brainstorming requires students to use creative thinking to propose a solution to a problem based on their knowledge and experience.

- **Nominal group process** — In this format, the discussion closely imitates an organizational decision-making process that students will encounter in their jobs. This technique is more structured than brainstorming and requires that ideas be more realistic. Steps:

  1. Begin the session by having students write a list of the pros and cons of the topic.

  2. Have students present their lists to the group, each speaking in order until all have commented.

  3. Correlate, examine, discuss, and rewrite comments presented.

  4. Have the group select the top five considerations.

  5. The instructor summarizes the findings.

- **Agenda-based process** — The instructor provides an agenda of topics or key points, which students then research and prepare reports to give to the group. In the discussion, students may ask questions or express opinions on the reports.

> **Nominal Group Process** — Classroom discussion format that requires students to follow a decision-making process similar to the processes that they will encounter in their professional duties.

> **Agenda-Based Process** — Classroom discussion format in which an agenda of topics or key points is provided to students for them to research, report on, and discuss as a group.

Providing Demonstration

Demonstrations are an effective way to teach manipulative skills, physical principles, and mechanical functions. In the cognitive domain, demonstrations are used to illustrate theoretical or scientific concepts that students are not expected to perform. In the psychomotor domain, they are used to model a task or skill that students must learn to perform; this is the most common use of demonstrations for training in the fire and emergency services. **Table 6.2, p.152** provides some general guidelines for demonstrating skills.

Emphasize Safety

Because of the hazardous nature of work in the fire and emergency services, instructors must emphasize the importance of safety while demonstrating every step of a skill or task. Many students want to be able to perform a skill quickly when they first learn it, but skill and speed come only with practice. Trying to perform a skill without having carefully learned the steps or developed coordination can be a safety hazard. Instructors should always stress the importance of safety when demonstrating a procedure, during practice time, and in final student evaluations.

Table 6.2
Skills Demonstration

Preparing for a Demonstration
Know clearly what task is to be demonstrated and its learning objective.
Be proficient in every step of the demonstration by practicing in advance with all instructors who will be involved.
Acquire all equipment and accessories, ensure that they work, and arrange them for use.
Arrange the room or demonstration area so that all students can see and hear the demonstration.

Demonstrating the Skill
Begin the demonstration by linking new information with the students' current knowledge.
Explain what the demonstration will show the group how to do.
Explain why the skill is important.
Demonstrate the skill once at normal speed.
Repeat the demonstration step by step while explaining each step slowly.
Repeat the demonstration again while a class member or the group explains each step.
Consider using a video camera and large-screen monitor when the group is large in order to allow students to see the process up close or observe small details.
Allow students the opportunity to ask questions and clarify any misunderstandings.
Ask for a student volunteer to demonstrate the skill while explaining the steps. Give reassurance by coaching and guiding the student through the process. Offer suggestions or corrections during the demonstration.
Provide the opportunity for students to practice, and allow them to supervise and correct each other as they become skilled. Again, closely monitor student activities when students practice potentially dangerous skills for the first time.
Reassemble the group and demonstrate the skill one more time at normal speed and/or one more time slowly as the group explains the steps as a summary. Relate the skill to the learning objective and performance on the job.

The instructor demonstrates a task while explaining how and why it is performed **(Figure 6.14)**. The students absorb this information through sight and hearing. One preferred method for demonstrating a psychomotor skill is as follows:

Step 1: Perform the skill at normal speed so students can see an overview of the skill.

Step 2: Perform the skill at a slower speed, emphasizing each part individually, so that students can see the details of the skill.

Step 3: Perform the skill a third time, at normal speed, with explanation during performance.

When students practice the skill, they use psychomotor skills and add the sense of touch to their learning experiences. The following positive advantages can easily outweigh any disadvantages when using demonstrations in both the cognitive and psychomotor domains:

- Students can receive immediate feedback.

- Instructors can readily observe behavioral changes.

- Students have a high level of interest when participating.

- Instructors can easily determine whether students have achieved the learning objectives.

- Learning skills correctly, in a safe environment and under careful supervision, gives students the confidence to perform the same skills on the job.

Potential drawbacks of the demonstration method include the following:

- Instructors must plan for extensive preparation and cleanup times, especially when using such items as power tools, hose, breathing apparatus, and cardio-pulmonary resuscitation (CPR) manikins.

- Careful lesson planning is important because assembly and practice can use much of the class time.

- Large groups of students require extra equipment for practice as well as additional instructors for supervising, coaching, and enforcing safety regulations. It is imperative that instructors closely monitor students who are practicing potentially dangerous skills for the first time.

- Skills that must be performed or practiced outside depend on the weather. Instructors must have a contingency plan available in the event of inclement weather conditions.

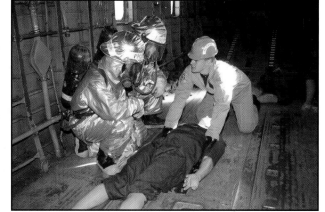

Figure 6.14 Demonstrating a task is an effective training method.

Motivating and Encouraging Students

Students often have to be motivated and encouraged to succeed. Most students want to succeed and usually arrive at a training session with the desire to complete the course or curriculum successfully. This self-motivation may arise from their desire to do any of the following:

- Keep a job

- Get a promotion or raise

- Gain recognition

- Feel important

- Join a group (organization or club)

Fear of failure is a major psychological barrier that prevents people from taking risks. This same fear may hold students back or cause them to believe that they can't accomplish a task. If students believe that an instructor genuinely wants them to succeed and will give them the tools to do so, they are more likely to be motivated and overcome the fear of failure. Instructors can motivate students and encourage their successes by offering the following instructional enhancements:

- **Provide quality instruction that helps students who try to learn** — Make the first experience with a new subject or topic safe, successful, and interesting. First impressions are important and have a lasting effect on future learning.

- **Provide evidence that student efforts make a difference** — Stress the importance of the amount and quality of effort needed for success in learning tasks before students begin. While students are ultimately responsible for the effort they put forth; emphasizing the importance of effort, without threatening, accomplishes the following objectives:
  — Establishes student responsibility
  — Reduces feelings of helplessness
  — Increases perseverance
  — Generates feelings of pride and accomplishment

- **Establish clear expectations** — Make the learning goals and evaluation criteria clear. When students know what to expect and how they are progressing, they are more likely to succeed. They need to know exactly what they are to learn and how well they are performing in preparation for testing.

- **Provide continuous feedback about student progress** — Instructors who provide learning and testing criteria, continuous and constructive feedback, and appropriate coaching and encouragement will have confident and successful students. A verbal pat on the back can aid a student's self-esteem tremendously.

Reinforcing Learning

Instructors reinforce learning by applying two different methods: repetition and behavioral reinforcement. The first approach involves repeating, re-emphasizing, and reviewing key points with the students. The second approach involves encouraging students' attempts to learn, acknowledging their successes, or correcting their mistakes.

Repetition

Building in repetition is an important part of organizing a presentation. In a lecture, it includes clearly stating the topic and learning objectives in the introduction and summary, and detailing the topic in the body of the presentation. In the skills demonstration, repetition occurs when the instructor demonstrates the entire skill and then repeats it in small segments. When presenting any material, emphasizing and repeating key points helps to ensure that students recognize their importance.

When the material or skill is important enough to be emphasized repeatedly, students take this as a cue to practice and learn. Instructors may emphasize the importance by telling students that they will see certain material or similar problems again on a test. Instructors can reinforce the material by providing opportunities to practice and apply similar skills and knowledge.

Behavioral Reinforcement

Behavioral reinforcement is based on a psychological theory that connects changes in behavior with the consequences of that change. The change in education may include properly learning new information, learning a new skill, or altering a behavior.

Behavioral reinforcement is about establishing rewards for students' successes or good behavior (positive reinforcement) and negative consequences for their failures or bad behavior. In the fire and emergency services, rewards for success typically include promotion or commendations. In the classroom, it may be as simple as a compliment or encouragement after a student performs a skill properly or masters a theoretical concept. Educational research has demonstrated that students learn faster and make permanent behavioral changes when their successes are met with positive reinforcement.

Establishing negative consequences for poor behavior is another type of behavioral reinforcement. Failing to pass an exam or skills test are examples of negative consequences in the classroom. When a student behaves unsafely on the training ground or at a scene, a reprimand from an instructor or officer could be considered negative consequences.

Negative Reinforcement

The opposite of positive reinforcement is negative reinforcement. While positive reinforcement praises good performance, negative reinforcement punishes poor performance. Negative reinforcement is intended to make students so afraid of failure that they stop performing poorly. Educational research suggests that negative reinforcement should be avoided as it is not as effective as positive reinforcement. It is better to allow the negative consequences of poor performance (failing a class or missing a promotional opportunity) to motivate students rather than punishing their failures.

Asking Effective Questions

Instructors use questions for a variety of reasons, both to receive feedback on how instruction is progressing and also to stimulate student interest and critical thinking. Questions are used to achieve the following objectives:

- Promote discussion and critical thinking.
- Stimulate interest and arouse curiosity.
- Motivate students to acquire knowledge on their own.
- Assess students' level of understanding.
- Control the behavior of disruptive or nonparticipating students.
- Provide an opportunity for students to openly express their ideas and opinions.
- Provoke interest that generates related questions.
- Review and summarize information.
- Assess whether students have achieved the lesson's learning objectives.

Students' responses to questions can also help instructors recognize the need to alter a lesson plan or adjust their teaching style. For example, instructors may realize that they need to incorporate techniques more appropriate to their students' learning styles.

Some curriculum developers include prepared questions in their lesson plans, but instructors should also know how to create effective questions of their own. Being able to create a good question also allows the instructor to evaluate prepared questions so that the questions can be improved if needed. Guidelines for developing and asking questions include the following:

- **Plan and/or review main questions in advance** — Questions should help students achieve desired course outcomes or learning objectives, and be appropriate for their location within the lesson plan.

- **Write and arrange questions in a logical order** — Start with questions that request basic information before moving on to questions that require critical thinking.

- **Phrase questions clearly** — Whenever possible, use clear, simple language so that students focus their attention on the answer, not the question. When a question is complex enough that it will require explanation, develop the explanation in advance.

- **Ask only one question at a time** — Avoid asking a series of questions in succession without waiting for a response to each question.

- **Be sure that the wording of the question doesn't make the answer obvious** — Students will recognize the intended answer and perceive that the question is a waste of time.

- **Allow a wait time** — When questions are directed to the entire class, wait until there is a response. It may take time before a student raises his or her hand to answer.

- **After waiting, call on a student directly** — Following the wait time, address a student directly by name. Permit the student time to respond, and do not hurry, especially when the student is shy.

- **Never use questions to intimidate, embarrass, or humiliate students** — Intentionally intimidating, embarrassing, or humiliating a student is inappropriate and unprofessional.

- **Distribute questions evenly** —Make sure to call on as many students as possible.

- **Ask questions at a variety of levels and of a variety of types** — Instructors should use all types of questions that are appropriate to the topic and the students' learning styles.

- **Adapt questions to students' ability level** — Matching the questions to individual student abilities ensures that most students will be able to answer at least some of the questions.

- **Ask appropriately challenging questions** — Questions should *never* be so easy that no thought is required.

- **Avoid asking questions too soon** — For questions to be effective, students must have the knowledge to answer them. Some questions that are intended to determine a student's current level of knowledge or opinion, however, can be asked early in the session.

- **Follow up on student answers** — Instructors can elicit further response by using techniques such as inviting elaboration, encouraging other class members to respond, or remaining silent. Examples:

— In the first instance, once a student has answered the question, the instructor may ask, "Could you expand on your answer?" as a way of encouraging the student to go into greater depth or detail.

— The instructor may also want to involve other students by asking them to provide an additional idea, fact, or experience to the first answer.

— While instructors may be uncomfortable with silence during a class, being deliberately silent can be an effective tool when asking questions. The instructor's silence can cause a student to elaborate on the initial answer.

New instructors should practice developing questions and including them in their lesson plans or outlines. When there is extra time in a session, the questions can be used to help students focus on the presentation's key points. Questions can also be used to start group discussions as time allows.

More Details on Wait Times

Inexperienced instructors often are uncomfortable with the silence that follows their questions, as students try to formulate their answers. This discomfort causes instructors to quickly answer their own questions, even though this was never their intended reason for including the questions in their lesson plans. Instructors should wait for students to respond, even if the wait time seems lengthy. Another tactic is to encourage students to answer with leading phrases such as *I know you're all listening; somebody knows* or *Give it a shot*. If instructors had originally directed a question at single student, they can redirect the question to another student if the first one takes too long to answer.

Question Types

Different types of questions produce different kinds of answers. When considering which kind of question to ask, instructors should consider what they want to accomplish at that particular point in the lesson. Instructors can use the following types of questions to start discussions, stimulate thinking, provide feedback on how training is being received, and enable students to assess their learning and manage their own learning gaps **(Figure 6.15)**:

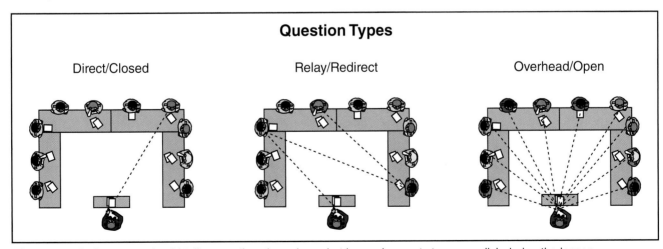

Figure 6.15 An instructor should tailor questions based on what he or she wants to accomplish during the lesson.

- **Rhetorical** — Rhetorical questions are used to stimulate thinking. They do not necessarily have one correct answer, and often do not call for a spoken response. For example, an instructor might open a safety lesson by saying: *What are the most important pieces of equipment you will use on an emergency scene to protect yourself from injury or exposure? By the end of this lesson, you will know how to answer this question.*

- **Closed** — This type of question has a limited number of possible answers. The instructor is able to anticipate and judge the accuracy of student responses. Example: *What is the definition of flashover?*

- **Open** — This type of question has many acceptable answers. The instructor has general criteria for judging the accuracy of an answer, although students' answers may be unexpected. Example: *What information can you gain during size-up?*

- **Direct** — The instructor directs this kind of question to a single student, who must then respond. This type of question is not frequently used with adult learners because it can make students uncomfortable. However, asking direct questions can be an effective way to control an unruly student.

- **Overhead** — The instructor asks a question of the entire class, not just one student. Any member of the class is free to respond, either by calling out the answer or by raising a hand and waiting to be recognized. This technique is helpful in starting discussions or offering ideas or opinions. If no one answers, the instructor can then direct the question to an individual student. Instructors may also allow students to consult with each other in groups to produce the answer.

- **Relay** — Instead of answering a student question, the instructor asks the rest of the class to answer. Relay questions are a good way to open a discussion or stimulate interest, but instructors should avoid this technique when they do not know the answer to a question. In these circumstances, it is better to say, "I don't know."

- **Redirected** — This type of question is useful when a student asks a question that the instructor believes the individual should know. The instructor can ask the student to provide small amounts of information that, taken together, will answer the original question.

Responding to Students' Answers

Instructors should prepare for student responses to questions they pose and understand the proper way of responding to those answers or new questions. Some basic guidelines for instructors are as follows:

- Use positive reinforcement. If a student answers a question correctly, the instructor might say, "That is absolutely right" or "You seem to have a good understanding of this topic."

- When a student answer is only partially correct, positively reinforce the correct portion, then redirect the question back to the student or ask another student to complete the answer.

- Always provide correct answers if the students do not. Providing correct answers benefits the entire class. Correcting incorrect responses should not be confused with correcting incorrect behavior. Getting a question wrong is not an indication of a deficiency on the part of the student and should not be portrayed as such. An appropriate response could be "That is close. Maybe I didn't ask the question clearly. What I am asking is . . . ."

Instructors often give the standard reply of OK to all responses, even if they are off-track or clearly wrong. Instructors are sometime reluctant to discourage responses, so they accept all answers while tactfully trying to steer the group to the right conclusion. But taking a wrong answer and asking either why it is wrong or where it may fit appropriately in the lesson is a technique that allows students the following opportunities:

- Think and analyze problems.

- Compare facts and ideas, and apply them to different situations.

- Critique their responses and find correct solutions.

- Explore and discover new methods of application.

Answering Students' Questions

Answering students' questions is one of the most difficult things for instructors to do. Some students may pose questions that on the surface appear to be logical but are really complex, illogical, or off the topic. An instructor can respond to these types of questions in the following ways:

- Provide the answer to a question when you know the answer or are the best person to have the answer. When neither of these is the case, defer the question to a more knowledgeable source such as a senior instructor or administrator. Be aware that the question could be controversial or distract the class.

- Direct a question to another participant when there is a high probability that another participant will respond correctly. This approach can be used to generate group discussion.

- Defer questions that are beyond the scope of the course, or tell students that they will learn the answer later in the course.

- Defer questions that require time to research the correct answer. Never bluff students by providing false or misleading information. Doing so can destroy an instructor's credibility.

Distance Learning and Student-Led Instruction

Instructor-led training, as described in the previous section, is the most common teaching method found in the fire and emergency services. Distance learning and student-led instruction are alternatives to ILT that are becoming more common as new technology is introduced. The following are instructional delivery methods that are alternatives to ILT:

- Computer-based training (CBT)

- Self-directed learning

- Individualized instruction

Instructors must select the most appropriate method based on factors such as the audience and topic. Distance learning and student-led instruction are not independent of one another, and effective instructors can incorporate more than one method into a presentation.

NOTE: Many of the techniques and methods described in the Instructor-Led Training section also apply to distance learning as well. For example, questions may be asked via e-mail or in chat windows rather than in a classroom, but the way they are handled – through positive reinforcement, redirection, and appropriate feedback – is still the same.

Questions about Distance Learning

There are certain questions to ask before beginning a distance learning program in your department, such as the following:

- Do you have sufficient hardware and network speed to support distance learning?
- Do you have enough computers for the students in your station?
- Is the material able to be taught in a large group or does it require individual study? If individual, how are the logistics handled in the station?
- Can the amount of distance learning being requested be handled efficiently by existing personnel? If not, is overtime available for individuals who monitor distance learning on their off-days?

Computer-Based Training (CBT)

Many training programs have begun using **computer-based training (CBT)** modules and programs that allow students to work at their own pace **(Figure 6.16, p.162)**. CBT may also be used in a more structured format to provide **distance learning**. CBT programs minimize the interaction between a student and an instructor. In some cases, the instructor may present an illustrated lecture remotely over the Internet or closed-circuit television. In other cases, the instructor may only be involved in answering questions that arise as students read information on their own and complete assignments.

The variety of different methods for presenting CBT make it difficult to include a comprehensive list in this manual. The AHJ should inform the instructor as to the products and computer technology he or she will be using to deliver instruction. Instructors should use whatever resources are necessary to familiarize themselves with the instructional system. In any such system, psychomotor skills demonstrations and practical training evolutions will still take place in person on the training ground.

> **Computer-Based Training (CBT)** — A variety of self-study in which the student completes work on a computer with minimal communication with an instructor. *Also known as* E-learning, Blended E-learning, or Online Instruction.

> **Distance Learning** — Generic term for instruction that occurs when the student is remote from the instructor, and a medium such as the Internet, Interactive Television, or mail service is used to maintain communication between the two and submit assignments.

What This Means to You

Computer-based training is a broad term that incorporates many specific types of electronic learning environments. You may hear CBT referred to as any of the following:

- E-learning
- Blended e-learning
- Blackboard ™ and Web CT ™
- Moodle ™
- D2L (Desire 2 Learn) ™
- Online instruction or online training
- Distance learning

Different CBT platforms require different kinds of software to function effectively. Instructors must make sure that students' computers have software that is compatible with the course, including the following:

- Internet browsers
- Computer operating systems (for example, Windows™ or Macintosh™)
- Word processing programs
- Document readers, such as Adobe Acrobat Reader®
- Unique software needed for the course

When facilitating CBT, instructors sometimes take on the role of computer support specialist. If they cannot help students who have technical problems, instructors should know whom to contact and do so in a timely fashion whenever technical difficulties arise. No student should be penalized because a piece of equipment, software application, or computer did not work properly.

Questions about Distance Learning

A major issue of concern with all CBT types is security. Security begins when students enroll or are assigned to a course or program. Each student is assigned a unique password that provides the necessary level of access to the course website or database. This access should not include the test bank of questions and answers, other students' grades, or archival material such as assignments or tests from previous classes. Instructors should follow the security protocols established by the AHJ when delivering computer-based training.

The instructor must take precautions when corresponding with students through e-mail. First, instructors should follow all e-mail policies and procedures in their organization. In the absence of these policies, instructors should use good judgment in e-mail correspondence. An instructor should always be careful when writing an e-mail message because of the possibility that the message may reach the wrong party or be shared with others without the instructor's knowledge. Instructor and student e-mail lists must be strictly controlled to ensure that they are not distributed to unauthorized persons or groups. E-mail communications may be misdirected, forwarded, altered, or distributed to unauthorized persons or sites. Confidential information such as student test results must never be transmitted via e-mail.

CAUTION

After an e-mail has been deleted, traces of the message still remain on the user's computer system.

Instructors should familiarize themselves with all the software used in the CBT system. Many of these tools are useful for any distance learning scenario, and instructors may wish to augment a distance learning program by using these tools. Software used in CBT programs could include the following:

Wiki — Website that allows users to update, edit, or comment on the original content using their own Internet browser; allows for the rapid creation and deployment of websites and collaborative work on documents.

Blog — Abbreviation for *web log*; refers to a list of journal entries or articles posted by a single author or group of authors. Includes comment sections where readers can engage in conversation about entries.

File Sharing — Practice of making files or documents on one computer or server available to the general public, or to a selected group of individuals who are given access to the files. Allows users at remote locations to have access to the same materials without the need to put those materials on CD-ROM, memory drives, or other media.

Social Networking — Websites that allow users to be part of a virtual community. Users can communicate through private messages or real-time chat, and share photos, video, and audio.

Teleconferencing — Telephone service that allows multiple individuals at remote locations to have an audio-only meeting.

Web Conferencing — Meeting service that combines teleconferencing with an Internet-based sharing service, enabling users to communicate in real time while viewing and interacting with a computer-based presentation.

Figure 6.16 Computer-based training permits more opportunities for independent study and remote instruction.

- **Wikis, blogs,** and **file sharing** services
- **Social networking** systems
- Live streaming audio and video
- Chat sessions
- **Teleconferencing** and **web conferencing**
- Course management system (CMS)
- Learning management system (LMS)

CBT instructors should be aware of the ways that this format may interfere with their ability to effectively deliver a message. Feedback from students is minimal, and the technology presents an additional barrier between the instructor and the students. To overcome this interference, instructors may need to make the following adjustments to their instructional delivery:

- Wait longer for students to answer questions. Whether the CBT uses a text/chat-based platform or streaming audio/video, there is a time lag when asking questions over the Internet.
- Limit your movements. Live streaming video will be broadcast more clearly if there is not a great deal of motion being captured. Stay within the filming area of the camera and be able to reach any computer controls easily without disrupting the presentation.

- Direct any questions to individual locations participating in the lesson rather than asking overhead questions to the entire group. This ensures that each location is present and participating.

- Give clear instructions for media transitions. Students may have to switch cameras for views, visit specific websites, or access particular files during a presentation and must be told to do so at the proper time.

- Allow time to deal with technical issues that may occur during the lesson. If a computer support specialist is not available in person, locate a contact number that you can call to get support if needed. This contact could be a member of your department or organization, or a representative of the software publisher or hardware manufacturer.

Interactive Television (ITV)

ITV is used to link multiple classroom sites together and permits one instructor to reach more students **(Figure 6.17)**. It is a popular approach to distance education. Each site is able to see, hear, and talk to the other sites.

Self-Directed Learning

In **self-directed** or **independent learning**, individual students work at their own pace to accomplish course objectives in any way they choose. Students are solely responsible for achieving these objectives, which may be determined by the instructor or chosen by the student. An instructor is not involved in the delivery of the training, although one may act as a facilitator in some cases. As a result, the effectiveness of this method is heavily dependent on the student's level of

Self-Directed Learning — Method of instruction in which individual students work at their own pace to accomplish course objectives in any way they choose. Course objectives may be determined by the instructor or chosen by the student, but course content is always determined by the instructor. *Also known as* Independent Learning.

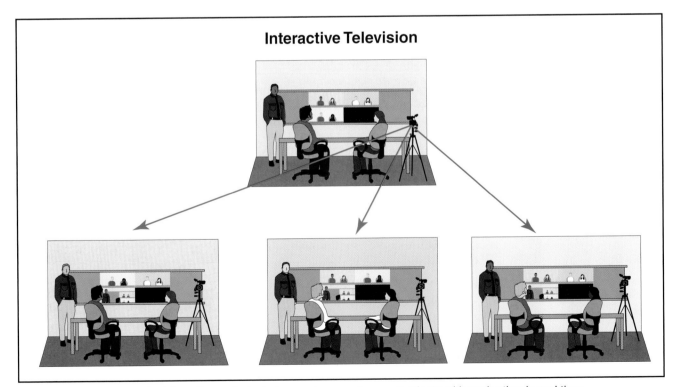

Figure 6.17 Interactive television allows students in remote areas to communicate with each other in real time.

motivation. However, this aspect of self-directed learning does not relieve the instructor of the responsibility of ensuring that the student accomplishes the intended tasks and skills in appropriate formats.

In self-directed learning, the instructor and the individual schedule several meetings to examine the progress of the independent study. Instructors are available to answer questions, evaluate learning achievements, and guide the student, but the learning process is completely the student's responsibility.

Quite often, this format of instruction motivates students to discover things above and beyond lesson requirements. Instructors should be aware that not all types of training programs, particularly basic-level skill programs, are suited to this type of instruction.

Individualized Instruction

Individualized Instruction — Adapting teaching methods to suit individual students' specific learning styles, so that students will be better able to achieve learning objectives.

Because students possess a variety of learning styles, some of those styles may not enable a student to progress with a group. An alternative teaching method is **individualized instruction**, in which instructors adapt their teaching methods to suit individual students' specific learning styles, so that they will be better able to achieve learning objectives. This approach may enable students who would not succeed in a typical learning environment to successfully achieve learning objectives.

Individualized instruction is a tool for an instructor to use in combination with other traditional methods, but it is not a substitute for the instructor. Individualized instruction does not imply solitary learning, the primary component of self-directed learning. Individuals need to work with others to meet certain requirements and share experiences. They also work under the supervision of an instructor or mentor who ensures that they meet lesson or chosen individual objectives.

Individualized instruction is based on the following three premises:

- **Student's needs and preferred learning style** — The method of instructional delivery for individualized instruction is directed at an individual student rather than a group or class.

- **Learning objectives or competencies required by the occupation** — Unlike self-directed learning where the learning objectives may change or be determined by the student, individualized instruction usually occurs within the context of a course where the learning objectives are competency-based and will be evaluated.

- **Instructional strategies and media that fit the needs of the student** — Because individualized instruction is individually paced, it is flexible in terms of the time taken to learn the objectives and the student's goals.

Regardless of the methods used, frequent student-instructor contact is necessary. This contact enables the instructor to facilitate learning by evaluating progress, prescribing new learning objectives or different learning methods, and encouraging students. With individualized instruction, the instructor's role is different from the traditional role. The instructor manages learning resources, guides students, and interacts with them but is not the sole or primary resource for learning as in the traditional classroom.

Many organizations use individualized instruction techniques in their training programs. Some of these instructional techniques are as follows:

- **Learning activity packets** — Uses packets with sequenced activities and reading assignments. This method is the most familiar of the many types.

- **Tutorial instruction** — The student gets one-on-one instructional help from a peer, another class member, or the instructor.

- **Programmed learning** — A systematic process of introducing information in small, sequential steps followed by questions that reinforce learning. This method either uses a workbook or is technology-based and requires computer access.

Using Training Aids

Regardless of the type of instruction, training aids are integral to engaging student interest and encouraging active learning. Training aids vary depending upon the training need. See Chapter 4, Instructional Materials and Equipment, for more information on the various types of training aids.

Audiovisual aids are the most common training aids instructors use to supplement lectures. These materials may be provided alongside a curriculum from an instructor's department or agency. Generally, these aids consist of a computer-generated slide presentation (PowerPoint® or Keynote®) and perhaps still images and illustrations. Instructors should seek out additional aids in both audio and video formats to supplement their lecturers.

Instructors must also consider how they actually use teaching aids. The following guidelines are helpful when using visual aids:

- Illustrate a single concept or idea in each visual.

- Introduce audiovisual training aids just before presenting them. Students may be distracted by visual aids that are on display before it is time to actually use them.

- Display steps in sequence individually when illustrating the steps in an operation. Displaying them all at once can be confusing. After introducing all the steps individually, instructors can display them together so that students can see how they are related to each other.

- Avoid using multiple training aids simultaneously, except when their use has been carefully considered and strategically integrated into the lesson plan.

- Apply training aids in ways that emphasize the message, not the equipment.

- Keep eye contact with students when using a visual aid.

- Ensure that there is enough space for all students to see visual training aids.

- Ensure that all students in the presentation room can hear audio training aid devices clearly.

- Display projected or nonprojected visual training aids above the eye level of seated students.

Audiovisual training aids are also important during demonstrations. Models and simulations can first be used by instructors to show how they are used. Students can view video recordings in the training ground area to show step-by-step instructions while an instructor helps individual students. Props and equipment are also forms of audiovisual aids important to demonstrations.

CBT, self-directed learning, and individualized instruction all benefit from audiovisual aids as well. Instructors facilitating these instructional methods should become familiar with presenting audiovisual aids on the Web. Aids may be located on a central website (streaming video), distributed from a database, or sent as attachments through email. Audio of in-class lectures may also be recorded and made available in digital formats. Handouts may be sent as files or made available for download. Also, instructors may have to learn to share computer generated slides on web conferencing software to communicate with remote students.

All of these are examples of using audiovisual aids to improve instruction. Familiarity with these methods is often dependent upon what computer hardware and software is available to the students and to the instructor. Instructors should take additional preparation time to ensure that they understand and can use the audiovisual aids necessary for the type of instruction they will be providing.

What This Means to You

Many people are intimidated by technology and are afraid to even try using equipment or software to find out what it does. Chances are that any technology that your organization provides will not be broken or ruined by testing its capabilities before instruction begins. Learning about your audiovisual aids allows you time to find any potential problems before instruction begins. Many times, instructors fail to use audiovisual aids successfully because they did not take the time to troubleshoot initial problems. The following are guidelines for getting accustomed to audiovisual aids:

- Test the equipment before instruction begins so that using it becomes natural.
- "Play" with any software that you have to use as a facilitator in CBT instruction.
- Use help menus and manuals to clarify issues.
- Seek out experts who have used the equipment to answer questions.
- Contact manufacturers with questions.

Structured Exercises

Structured exercises include a variety of instructional methods that actively involve students in the learning process. Prepared lesson plans may include structured exercises for instructors to lead. The sections that follow provide brief descriptions of the following structured exercises that instructors may encounter:

- Case studies
- Role playing
- Simulations
- Field and laboratory experiences

Case Studies

Case Study — Description of a real or hypothetical problem that an organization or an individual has dealt with and may face in the future.

A **case study**, sometimes referred to as a *scenario*, is a description of a real or hypothetical problem that an organization or an individual has dealt with and may face in the future. Typically, a case study reviews and discusses detailed accounts of past events and then allows students to analyze the situation and synthesize possible answers to the problem. The purpose of studying past incidents is to be prepared for similar circumstances in the future. Case studies are more effective for experienced personnel, because students need to be able to relate the scenario to their own past experiences.

Case studies provide students with the opportunity to discuss ideas and solve problems. These discussions develop their ability to examine facts and analyze situations in order to reach a conclusion or determine a course of action. The instructor provides students with time to review, research, and discuss the situation. Face-to-face or electronic communication between students must also be established to encourage student interaction. Students must be willing and able to communicate and defend their suggestions to other members of the group.

Role Playing

In role playing, students act out the role of a character in a scenario to prepare them for situations they may encounter while fulfilling their duties. Role playing can be used when training personnel for a variety of tasks or situations, such as public information officers who interact with members of the community or public safety telecommunication personnel who must receive and dispatch calls during emotionally intense times.

At the end of the role playing, the instructor debriefs both participants and observers. This debriefing gives students an opportunity to explain the feelings and actions they had during the role playing and further understand the objective of the activity. The instructor should summarize the scenario and reinforce the importance of any positive behavior that was exhibited.

The advantages of role playing include the following:

- Encourages application of knowledge and practice of skills.
- Permits students to practice under life-like conditions without the danger of fatal consequences
- Improves understanding of critical features of interpersonal relations
- Allows students to identify multiple approaches to a problem
- Increases the development of empathy through a simulated experience
- Helps develop critical consciousness
- Provides a quick, economical classroom activity that can be performed in a variety of environments
- Prepares students for emotionally challenging events such as dealing with trauma patients

    Despite these advantages, instructors should also be aware of the following disadvantages of role-playing:

- Preparation can be very involved and time-consuming. Consider using case studies as the basis for role playing scenarios, which reduces the preparation time for both.
- Role playing can take time to perform and may result in students digressing from the topic when they are bored, uninterested, or see no value in the activity. Fully explain all activities and the importance of them as well as how they relate to the students' work-related duties.
- Role playing depends on the ability of students to involve themselves in the characters and scenario, which depends on the internal motivation of each student. Instructors can influence student motivation to some extent. Remind

students that role playing is the closest they will come to real-life encounters in a controlled setting and they should not take anything personally when they are in character for the activity.

Simulations

Training simulations allow students to participate in scenarios that represent real-life situations. They may take many forms, including practical training evolutions and computer-based training (CBT). Simulations permit students to experience a situation and see the results of their decisions without the negative results that can occur at an actual emergency. A simulation may include elements of role playing such as students taking on assigned duties and interacting with one another.

Figure 6.18 Tabletop simulation models are a cost-effective way to conduct certain types of training.

A tabletop emergency management drill is an example of a simulation that is economical and effective **(Figure 6.18)**. Confined-space rescue training that permits actual operations in a simulated hazardous environment is an example of a practical training evolution. CBT permits individual students to operate apparatus pump panels, simulate command of structure fires, and even attack a computer-created structure fire. The key to all simulations is to ensure that they effectively reflect the equipment, procedures, protocols, and situations that students will encounter on duty.

Field and Laboratory Experiences

Field and laboratory experiences involve elements of the demonstration and simulation methods where students have the opportunity to inspect, use, test, and evaluate equipment or processes, either in actual installations or in laboratory settings. In the field, students are typically given a tour of an installation. For example, they may be permitted to observe a fire detection and suppression systems test or see the steps required to replace a component.

In a laboratory, students can see models of equipment, such as cutaways of apparatus engines, pumps, or sprinkler control valves **(Figure 6.19)**. They may perform chemistry experiments to simulate fire behavior or fire spread in an enclosed space. The instructor explains the equipment or process, demonstrates the steps required, and observes students as they repeat the skills. Students may work independently or in groups. Instructors may also choose to give students a challenge, such as providing them with a defective SCBA regulator and asking them to repair it.

Factors That Affect Learning

Students who are struggling to learn new material may be become frustrated, which further distracts them from the learning process. Instructors must realize that there may be an underlying problem with students who are not having success. Once instructors discover the underlying cause, they may be able to help students resolve some of these frustrations. Some students need assistance from the instructor to overcome or resolve their problems. Until then, these students may reach learning plateaus in their learning processes.

Learning Obstacles

Generally, obstacles to learning consist of external pressures and concerns that make the ability to focus on learning difficult and cause frustration. Frustrations that come from fear and worry include the fear of not knowing how to study appropriately, fear of ridicule by the instructor or classmates, or fear of failure if they cannot perform as expected. Many students come to class with personal worries, such as leaving someone at home who is sick or trying to resolve financial problems.

The learning environment can present obstacles for students as well. Learning situations where students must stand or sit too long make it difficult to concentrate and learn. Poor lighting and ventilation also have negative effects on learning. Students are also distracted from learning if they must train in dangerous conditions on a poorly organized training ground. They will be more concerned about their safety than about learning.

Other frustrations stem from anxiety or boredom, which may be the result of poor instruction. A student's personal feelings such as anxiety or boredom are other obstacles to learning. Students will become anxious if they perceive that they are not prepared for the class or do not see the relevance to their jobs. When the individual is not interested in the subject and the instructor does not gain that student's attention through motivational tactics and relevance, there is higher likelihood that the audience will become bored. Lectures that are too long and instruction that provides little, if any, opportunity to practice quickly lose student interest. Lack of training aids and improper teaching methods quickly bore students and reduce learning. **Table 6.3, p.170** lists some areas of student frustrations

Figure 6.19 Cutaway models allow students to study the inner workings of equipment and machinery.

Learning Plateaus

A **learning plateau** can be compared to the landing in a flight of stairs — it is a break in upward progress **(Figure 6.20, p.170)**. Some students stay there briefly, while others become stuck because they are discouraged or become discouraged because they feel stuck. Students sometimes create their own learning plateaus from emotional responses such as fear of failure and boredom. These emotions occupy their minds and interfere with their concentration and progress.

Learning Plateau — A break or leveling of a student's progress in a training course or class.

After students master the procedural steps of a skill, they need to practice until they meet a desired skill level. Once they reach this level, they will be exposed to more information and skills and expected to progress to the next skill level.

Individuals may become discouraged if they have not been able to practice a task enough to feel proficient at a certain level, or they may find it more difficult to reach a particular skill level. At this point, further progress seems impossible, and an individual may feel like quitting. Athletes often experience plateaus in developing skills. Students, like athletes, must be coached and receive positive feedback as they practice.

Table 6.3
Areas of Student Frustration

Fear or Worry	Discomfort	Poor Instruction
• Fitting in, acceptance	• Personal strength and stamina	• Class too advanced
• The class situation	• Eyestrain	• Class too simple
• Failure	• Difficulty hearing	• Instructor unprepared
• Ridicule	• Classroom too hot or too cold	• No opportunity for participation
• Keeping up with requirements	• Uncomfortable seats or poor seating arrangements	• No variety in presentation
• Personal problems		• Class too large
• Family	• Dangerous training conditions	• No direction
• Health		• Relevance not explained
• Money		

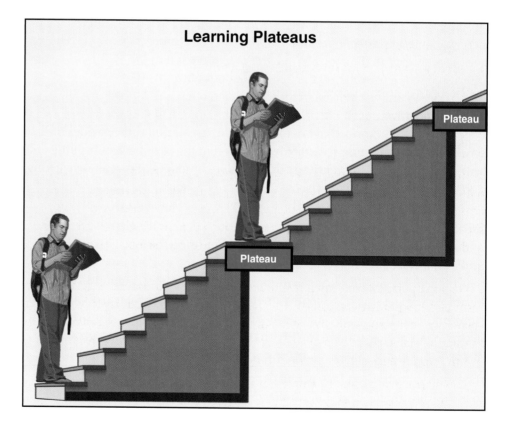

Figure 6.20 Learning plateaus occur commonly and can be frustrating to students but can also be overcome.

Instructors should let students know that these learning plateaus are normal, help them recognize signs of frustration, and work with them to overcome problems. One solution is for students to keep practicing until they thoroughly understand the skill and the procedures become automatic. Another solution is to take a break, direct students to review and think about the task for a while, then return to the task after some time away.

When students cannot get past plateaus, it may be that they have formed improper habits or tried to learn something beyond their abilities. But instructors should also consider that they may have failed to provide proper assistance. Instructors should review their methods of instruction to ensure that they are able to communicate and demonstrate effectively.

Individual Student Needs

Students with different learning abilities and personalities will require varying amounts of the instructor's time. While some students will be quick to grasp a concept or learn a skill, others may need individual instruction or tutoring to remain with the class. Instructors must be able to adjust the pace of the course to the students' rate of understanding, otherwise students will become discouraged. Sometimes students' behaviors and personality types require special attention from the instructor to make sure that they are engaged with the material or not disturbing other students. Instructors must therefore be able to recognize the traits of time-consuming individuals and learn how to manage them.

Students can be classified into the following seven categories, based on their learning ability and personality type:

- Students with low literacy levels
- Students with learning disabilities
- Gifted students
- Slow learners or slow students
- Nondisruptive, nonparticipating students
- Disruptive, nonparticipating students
- Nondisruptive, successful students

Students with Low Literacy Levels

The traditional definition of a *literate person* was any person 15 years old or older who is able to read and write. Because societies are becoming more complex and based on information and technology, the U.S. *Workforce Investment Act of 1998* redefined literacy as the ability to read, write, speak in English, and compute and solve problems proficiently enough to function on the job, with one's family, and in society.

Generally, fire and emergency services training divisions will not provide any form of remedial instruction in reading or writing. However, instructors must recognize that some students need additional assistance to overcome their low literacy levels. Assistance may take the form of referrals to adult education programs, employee assistance programs (EAPs), or personal tutors.

Low literacy level students may have difficulty taking notes and keeping up with the material as it is presented. As a result, it is even more important that instructors follow the guidelines earlier in this chapter for effective lectures. To additionally aid low literacy students, the instructor should make sure that textbooks, tests, and handouts have the following features:

- Short sentences and paragraphs
- Double-spaced lines
- Directional headings and wide margins

- Type that is large enough to be read easily
- Vocabulary should be simple, and all terms should be easily found in a glossary

When writing on an easel pad or marker board, the instructor should use large, plain letters, and print rather than use script or cursive **(Figure 6.21)**. When giving exams, the instructor should always make sure that directions are simple. They may want to provide pictures, tables, graphs, or charts to help illustrate and divide up large quantities of text.

Figure 6.21 Print in large letters so writing is legible to the whole class.

Students with Learning Disabilities

Learning disabilities consist of a wide variety of disorders. It is estimated that 3 to 13 percent of the general population of the U.S. has some type of learning disability. Most are neurological in origin and affect an individual's ability to perform the following actions:

- Understand or think
- Use the spoken or written word
- Perform mathematical functions
- Perform fine psychomotor skills

Officially, the U.S. *Americans with Disabilities Act (ADA)* divides learning disabilities into three major categories:

- **Speech and language disorders** — Difficulty producing speech sounds, using spoken language, or understanding what other people say
- **Academic skills disorders** — Difficulty reading (dyslexia), writing (dysgraphia), and calculating (dyscalculia)
- **Miscellaneous learning disabilities** — Difficulty performing fine motor skills (dyspraxia), learning nonverbal skills, and other difficulties

Students with learning disabilities may have average to high intelligence but perform poorly on tests due to their particular disability. Students with any kind of learning disability are at a disadvantage.

Instructors should indicate at the beginning of a course or lesson that anyone who has learning disability should contact them privately. This private meeting will allow the instructor to identify appropriate accommodations for the student. Instructors may also have a question on their class registration sheets that asks if the individual has any type of learning disability.

In a legal liability context, students are required by U.S. Federal law to have documentation proving that they have a learning disability. If students do not have documentation, they will need to be diagnosed and/or provide documentation before the instructor can make appropriate accommodations. The organization's human resources department may be able to provide testing and referral assistance for students. Government agencies and large private organizations that provide training may also offer evaluation and assistance for employees with learning disabilities or refer them to appropriate agencies.

NOTE: In Canada, instructors are required to make some accommodation for students with learning disabilities. Unlike the United States, the level of documentation required to prove a disability varies between provinces and is governed by provincial rather than federal law.

Instructors can make a limited number of reasonable accommodations in most cases of learning disability without having documentation. If a student requires more than these basic instructional changes, the instructor requires documentation that describes specifically which accommodations the student needs. Basic accommodations for students with learning disabilities include the following:

- Tutoring
- Developing individualized instruction
- Providing additional feedback on progress
- Allowing more time on tests
- Moving students with disabilities closer to the front of the classroom
- Providing a reader for or audio recording of assigned reading
- Assigning one student to take notes for another

NOTE: In the U.S., persons who have learning disabilities are protected from discrimination by three laws: Individuals with Disabilities Education Act (IDEA), Rehabilitation Act, and ADA.

Gifted Students

Children who were gifted students in elementary and secondary school continue to be fast learners when they become adults. Gifted adult learners will be present in instructor classrooms and must have their individualized needs met just like average and low performing students. Gifted adult students will usually accomplish more than is expected of average students, and they may study and learn very well without much supervision.

The U.S. Department of Education has defined a gifted student as one who demonstrates achievement or potential ability in one or more of the following five areas:

- General intellectual ability
- Specific academic aptitude
- Creative or productive thinking
- Leadership ability
- Visual and performing arts

Figure 6.22 Some students may achieve greater understanding by getting help from another student instead of the instructor.

The difficulties that gifted students have to overcome is boredom or disinterest. Because they understand and retain new material more quickly and accurately than their peers, they may lose motivation and become disengaged from the learning process, or even become disruptive to other students. They may leave the course with a low opinion of the instructor, the curriculum, or the training department as a whole.

Instructors can turn the presence of gifted students into an asset. Because gifted students are often ahead of other class members, they can be given more creative assignments and then asked to present their findings to the class. Another approach for instructors is to use a gifted student as a tutor for a slow student, learning disabled student, or low literacy level student **(Figure 6.22)**. While assisting other individuals, gifted adult students improve their own retention. At the same time, the student receiving the help may feel more comfortable learning from a peer rather than an instructor. At the very least, above-average students need to be motivated by challenging assignments that meet their ability level, even if these assignments are beyond the scope of what the rest of the class is doing.

Slow Learners or Slow Students

The term slow learner or slow student includes those with borderline intelligence, which is defined as the minimum intelligence required for a person to function normally and independently in the world. Instructors will usually be able to identify slow students soon after beginning a class. Although indications that a student is slow may be familiar and strong, instructors should be careful when categorizing a student as slow. A student may appear to be slow to comprehend because an instructor does not give clear instructions. Students may also have difficulty understanding because of the following reasons:

- Physical disabilities
- Learning disabilities
- Low literacy abilities
- Lack of language proficiency

For students who do fall into the category of slow learner, the instructor may need to arrange for the following methods of assistance:

- Private conferences
- Special assignments
- Individual instruction

Instructors may need to reevaluate and revise their subject matter or instructional methods so that slow learners are able to meet the course objectives and requirements. A student may have difficulty grasping information and skills in one lesson or category, yet may excel in other areas. Therefore, instructors should develop assignments and lesson plans with these types of student abilities in mind. Instructors should always provide positive feedback as students accomplish course objectives.

Nondisruptive, Nonparticipating Students

Nondisruptive and nonparticipating students include those who are timid or introverted and appear to be daydreaming, distracted, or uninterested. In courses where students are attending instruction for a long period of time, instructors may use several methods to engage the nondisruptive, nonparticipating student.

Instructors should ask students privately about their level of participation, their attitudes toward the class, or any distractions they may have. By asking simple personal questions during breaks, students may readily provide answers because they appreciate the interest and attention. The instructor should also remind students that, as members of the class, they have a responsibility to learn and participate. Instructors who show an interest in their students often are able to motivate them to participate. These students will normally make every attempt to fulfill the class requirements and please an instructor who shows interest in them.

Shy or Timid

The shy or timid individual may be hesitant or at a loss for words when expected to respond or participate and may actually be afraid to respond aloud or participate during class discussions. Instructors should avoid calling on these students until they have become comfortable with the class and the instructor. To help facilitate this, instructors should encourage shy students to participate in informal or small-group discussions. Success in these activities will encourage them to be more outgoing in formal class discussions or when giving presentation.

The instructor may also talk with these students during breaks to help them become comfortable with the learning process, the instructor's teaching style, and course expectations. Instructors who use these simple methods of making students feel comfortable will help overcome shyness and encourage them to participate in the class.

Bored or Uninterested

Many quiet students may be above average in ability but because of circumstances – such as uninteresting subject matter, unfamiliar terms, boredom, and long and technical lectures – they may drift mentally. Instructors can redirect attention by asking direct questions or beginning activities that require student participation rather than just listening. Instructors should be alert for the following signs of daydreaming and boredom:

- Glazed looks
- Gazing around the room
- Doodling
- Thumbing through materials not related to the subject

Students who are uninterested display little energy and attention. Instructors should note the lack of interest in these students and check with their supervisors or other instructors to determine whether they have exhibited any personal or other problems. Instructors will want to gather as much information as possible in order to plan strategies for working with these types of students. A supervisor or other instructor may indicate that a student previously experienced the following situations:

- Required counseling or tutoring in other courses
- Attempted to take a class beyond the level of readiness
- Coped with health, emotional, family, or learning difficulties that interfered with classroom performance.

Disruptive, Nonparticipating Students

Disruptive, nonparticipating students act in a way that is inappropriate for a classroom or training setting. They may distract the class by being overly talkative or aggressive, showing a lack of respect for the instructor or the course, or trying simply to draw attention to themselves. In addition to stalling class progress, in some cases this may even create a safety hazard.

Instructors should never allow these students to control the class with their inappropriate behavior. One way of managing these students is to call on them regularly, redirecting their disruptive energy into constructive participation. But if tactful attempts to change the students' behavior fail, instructors should take whatever disciplinary action they feel is appropriate, such as asking them to leave the session. Instructors should tell disruptive students that cooperation and constructive participation is expected upon their return. Continually disruptive students can also be reported to their supervisors or commanding officers.

Talkative and Aggressive

Talkative, aggressive, and extroverted individuals can monopolize a discussion and prevent others from participating. The first approach for an instructor is to make a private appeal to the student. *When* this approach does not alter the student's behavior, the instructor may assign a special project to the student. While the disruptive student is occupied, the remainder of the group will have an opportunity to participate.

In almost every class, there is a small group who prefer to talk among themselves rather than participate in the current activity or discussion. In these situations, instructors must recapture the attention of the group. Instructors should tell the disruptive students that they can discuss special problems after class rather than taking time away from the whole class.

Show-offs

Individuals who like to show off may use a group situation to perform and gain attention for themselves. Sometimes their performances help put other students at ease and get others to participate, but show-offs must know when to stop and share the floor. Instructors should call the class to order and review the main points of the lesson to redirect attention away from the show-off. If the show-off tries to respond to all the instructor's questions, the instructor should encourage other students to respond, and remind the show-off that his or her classmates need an opportunity to answer as well.

When this technique fails, a direct and effective solution to this problem is to tell the show-off that the classroom is not the place for this type of behavior and that disruptions of any kind will not be tolerated. The timeliness and manner in which an instructor delivers such an ultimatum determines its effectiveness. When students understand that cooperation is important and expected, instructors will have few if any problems. When problems persist, the instructor should always follow the organization's disciplinary policies and procedures.

Instructors should never tolerate inappropriate behavior that creates an unsafe condition for students **(Figure 6.23)**. Although the instructor should not reprimand the student in front of the class, this type of situation can be an opportunity to discuss safety violations and use the behavior as an example of what can cause an accident, injury, or fatality. This example can provide a strong object lesson not only for the show-off, but for the rest of the class as well.

Figure 6.23 When an instructor sees inappropriate or unsafe behavior such as wearing safety clothing incorrectly, he or she should correct the behavior immediately.

Nondisruptive, Participating, Successful Students

Nondisruptive, participating, successful students are actively engaged in the learning process and are eager to contribute from their knowledge and experiences. This term describes the majority of students in most fire and emergency services courses.

When other students demand too much of the instructor's time and attention, these students may be overlooked, causing them to become frustrated with the instructor, their classmates, or the course. Instructors should take every opportunity to involve these students in class activities. It may also be helpful to enlist their assistance when dealing with some of the other types of students, through peer teaching or mentoring.

Students' Rights

Like all citizens, students should have equal access to fundamental rights and privileges, such as those guaranteed by the Civil Rights Act or the Americans with Disabilities Act. In an educational setting, this includes the following:

- Privacy of records and test scores
- Freedom to hold and express an opinion different from that of the instructor or organization
- Equal access to the learning environment
- Fair and equal treatment in class
- A non-hostile learning environment free of discrimination or harassment
- A safe learning environment

Any departmental or organizational regulations that limit these rights are illegal. Any rules or regulations that may be perceived as infringing on students' substantive rights should be reviewed, validated, and communicated to students at the beginning of the training session or course. These rules and regulations must be consistently applied to all situations and students throughout the program.

Reasonable regulations that are necessary to protect students during training activities can be justified even though they may be perceived as infringing on student rights. For example, requiring hard hats on a construction site and requiring full turnout gear on the drill ground are safety regulations. A student's freedom to choose not to wear them is irrelevant because the regulation to wear them is in the interest of safety.

In some cases, organizations may have regulations that students perceive as unreasonable. For example, although prohibiting eating in the classroom is a safety regulation appropriate for a biology or chemistry lab, it may be inappropriate for adults who come directly from work to an evening classroom lecture session. Students tend to ignore such unreasonable regulations, and instructors are reluctant to enforce them.

Student Behavior Management

Managing student behavior can be difficult to master, but it is one of an instructor's most important skills. Instructors must be able to prevent disruptive individuals from interfering with the class, or they risk losing students' respect and failing to accomplish the learning objectives. When disruptive individuals are beyond the instructor's management skills, formal disciplinary action may be necessary to remove them from the course or use outside influences to control their behavior. In any case, the ultimate goal of student behavior management is the correction of disruptive behavior.

In an adult learning environment, some instructors believe that behavior management is unnecessary because peer pressure will keep unruly students under control. Peer pressure can be effective in some situations, but it is ultimately the instructor's responsibility to deal with disruptive students. Even when peer pressure is partially effective, it may still be beneficial for the instructor to speak to disruptive students in private or take stronger disciplinary measures.

Most organizations have policies for managing issues involving student problems and performance; however, the best action is to prevent problems before they occur by being proactive. The sections that follow provide information on the following techniques for correcting or changing student behavior:

- Reviewing policies
- Counseling
- Coaching
- Providing peer assistance
- Mentoring
- Controlling disruptive behavior

Reviewing Policies

Students may intentionally or through lack of information violate training policies. As a result of this behavior, one of the first priorities for an instructor is to review the rules, regulations, and policies of the training division with students.

Students who are returning to a familiar learning environment may already be aware of the organization's rules and regulations. However, the instructor must consistently promote, support, and enforce these policies so that students respect and adhere to them.

Instructors and students who travel to a variety of learning sites must become familiar with and follow each facility's rules and regulations, which generally address the following concerns:

- Safety
- Attendance and tardiness
- Responding to emergencies from class
- Level of expected class participation
- Methods of evaluation
- Assignment due dates
- Class cancellations due to weather or other causes
- Student parking
- Dress and grooming
- Breaks or rest periods

Facility Information

At the beginning of a course or class, instructors should discuss important information about the training facility with their students including the following:

- Facility layout
- Use and cleanup requirements
- Safety plan
- Emergency reporting procedures
- Evacuation plan
- Off-limit areas
- Smoking regulations (specifically smoking areas)

Counseling

Some students engage in disruptive behavior because they are having difficulty meeting learning objectives or having problems adjusting to training. Such students may benefit from **counseling**.

Counseling is a broad term that refers here to helping a student to adjust, redirecting a student's behavior, or eliminating barriers to learning. It is a way to resolve both learning and behavioral issues, and may include such actions as the following:

- Giving advice
- Having discussions
- Giving tests that help identify problem areas
- Providing vocational assistance

Counseling — Advising learners or program participants on their educational progress, career opportunities, personal anxieties, or sudden crises in their lives.

Counseling sessions between instructors and students should only focus on issues relevant to the students' progress in class. Occasionally this may be because students have social anxieties or personal crises that prevent them from participating in class activities, or completing course requirements. However, instructors should never assume the role of therapist when a student appears to have a psychological or emotional problem. In that situation, the instructor should follow organizational procedures, such as notifying the student's or the instructor's supervisor. Students who need professional counseling can typically get access to these services through their EAPs.

Counseling sessions between students and instructors must be done in private. The student must feel that the instructor is sincerely interested and considers the individual as a potential colleague. It should be obvious to the student that the purpose of a conference is to help resolve seemingly difficult problems that may interfere with the learning process. Instructors must encourage students to explain and express their feelings about any troublesome situation.

Counseling sessions can also be an effective way to handle behavioral problems. Forcing students into more acceptable behavior generally fails, because force causes resistance, and students do not like to be reprimanded. But the sense of partnership created by successful counseling makes students more likely to listen to the instructor's advice. Instructors must learn and practice appropriate counseling and positive reinforcement methods that motivate students to perform properly.

Training organizations usually have a formalized process for documenting behavioral issues, and typically this involves completing some type of counseling form. It is important for new instructors to be aware of the organization's process, and realize that it is far more involved than the simple and immediate measures they can implement in class. Some organizations may be required to maintain records on counseling for accreditation purposes.

Instructors must consult with the organization and follow its policies on counseling students and completing the counseling form. The general guidelines for an instructor are as follows:

- Meet and talk with the student.
- List the exact facts on the form of what behavior the individual is displaying. On the form, describe the student's behavior exactly.
- State objectives that communicate what is expected of the student and record these on the counseling form.
- Discuss the issue with the student and agree upon solutions.
- Explain what actions will be taken if the student does not comply with the objectives and solutions.
- Have the student sign the form to acknowledge that counseling was conducted.
- Give a copy of the counseling form to the student and retain the original.
- Forward a copy of the form to the training institution.
- Forward a copy of the form, via the chain of command, to the student's supervisor, chief, or manager.

When counseling fails, instructors must take disciplinary action. This should be done privately, calmly, and in an atmosphere that shows a willingness to help. Instructors must begin these sessions with encouragement and praise for good work, then suggest a constructive course of action, focusing on the mistake instead of the student. In most situations, demonstrating a sincere interest in students is more effective than making them feel inferior or inadequate.

Coaching

Disruptive behavior often results from frustration or confusion, and instructors can help students overcome these behaviors through **coaching** techniques. For instructors, coaching is the process of giving motivational correction, positive reinforcement, and constructive feedback to students in order to maintain and improve their performance.

> **Coaching** — Process in which instructors direct the skills performance of individuals by observing, evaluating, and making suggestions for improvement.

To be effective, the feedback needs to be positive, immediate, direct, and frequent. It can either be as simple as telling the student how well a task has been completed or involve a formal counseling session when a change in negative or inappropriate behavior is required. Private industry generally subscribes to a formal coaching model that contains the following four steps, modified for an instructional setting:

Step 1: Describe the current level of performance — Describe levels in a positive manner. Specify behaviors that could be improved using specific examples. Do not state that a student is doing something wrong; simply say that it can be done better, safer, or more efficiently.

Step 2: Describe the desired level of performance — State exactly what is required to provide clear direction for the student.

Step 3: Obtain a commitment for change — Ensure that the student commits to the desired level of performance. In some cases this commitment is considered a binding contract and becomes part of a student's permanent record.

Step 4: Follow up on the commitment — Observe the student to determine whether his or her performance has improved, or schedule a follow-up meeting to discuss progress. If the student does not perform to the desired level, more coaching may be necessary. If this is unsuccessful, the next step would be formal, professional counseling .

Feedback from instructors must be objective and precise in its description of desirable and undesirable behavior. Instructors must not fall into the trap of just providing critical phrases such as *that's wrong – do it again – but the right way this time*. That type of feedback does not inform the students of their error or explain how to correct it. A better example would be as follows: *That was good, but you've forgotten what the rope needs to have on the running end before you tighten it.*

Asking errant students questions allows them to stop, think, and recall the information they are attempting to apply. Some students will take longer than others to perform this process, but they will all remember better in the future because they were forced to recall it themselves. On occasions when students do not recall the information, the instructor can carefully review it with them.

Providing Peer Assistance

In the learning environment, a peer is someone who is equal in status, either socially or professionally. Peer assistance involves having students help each other in the learning process. Some students are too afraid or intimidated to perform in front of an instructor until they feel confident in their abilities and may be disruptive as a result. These students feel more comfortable practicing with a peer.

Students who have grasped the knowledge or skill and can explain it to others make good peer assistants. It also helps if they have background experiences that enable them to explain how classroom activities can be applied on the job. Peer assistants can work with other students who have difficulty grasping concepts or learning new skills, or who need supervised practice time in a more relaxed atmosphere.

Mentoring

Mentoring places a new student under the guidance of a more experienced professional or another student who acts as tutor, guide, and motivator. Mentoring situations occur outside the classroom, usually in the job environment. Many instructors have acted as mentors, either formally or informally. Instructors often guide the actions of new employees on the job, just as they guide the actions of new students in the learning environment or training evolution. Instructors must make themselves available to students who seek career guidance and counsel.

Typically, a mentor is usually someone other than the instructor who guides student actions in real experiences on the job. Mentors must be chosen carefully and selected for their experience, interest, patience, and communication abilities.

The primary purpose of mentoring is to prepare students for advancement within the organization through the direction of a positive role model. Mentoring programs enhance management skills, improve productivity, and encourage diversity. Mentors assist their students in the following ways:

- Serving as role models
- Providing guidance in career planning
- Assisting in gaining specialized training
- Providing outside resources
- Providing challenging work assignments
- Monitoring students' achievements

Both mentors and students should be volunteers who are enthusiastic and supportive of the program. When mentoring is approached as a mandatory activity, the individuals involved may be resentful or participate only partially. In that case, the mentor may not provide the most positive role model. The accomplishments of both the mentor and the subordinate should be acknowledged throughout the process.

In some business texts it is suggested that the mentor should not be a direct supervisor to the subordinate. However, in the military, the concept of mentoring begins with the supervisor. According to the U.S. Air Force Promotion Fitness Examination Guide, a mentor is a trusted counselor or guide. The immediate supervisor or instructor is designated as the primary mentor (coach, counselor, guide, role model, etc.) for each student in the course. This designation in no way restricts the student's ability to seek additional counseling and professional development advice from other sources or mentors.

Controlling Disruptive Behavior in the Classroom

Disruptive behavior may be the result of instructor- or student-caused circumstances. One student or group of students may repeatedly cause disruptive behavior or it may be an isolated single event. Either way, the behavior distracts from the learning environment, may result in an unsafe practice, or wastes valuable time. Generally, student-originated disruptions may take the following forms:

- Arriving late
- Speaking at inappropriate times
- Talking with others about unrelated topics
- Sleeping in class, accompanied by snoring
- Showing off
- Interrupting others
- Sidetracking discussions
- Acting blatantly insubordinate and disrespectful

When these types of behavior occur, it can be challenging for instructors to maintain their composure and control the atmosphere of the classroom. Adults usually resent any implication that someone else controls their behaviors, but instructors can redirect behaviors to beneficial outcomes when they manage situations appropriately. The sections that follow describe both instructor- and student-caused disruptions, as well as formal disciplinary procedures.

Instructor-Caused Disruptive Behavior

Some disruptive behavior results from the actions of the instructor, whether those actions are intentional or not (see **Table 6.4**). For example, instructors who are intimidating, overly controlling, or unprepared may cause students to react in a way that is disruptive to the class.

Table 6.4 Unfavorable Student Reactions to Instructor Actions	
Instructor Actions	**Student Reactions**
Intimidates	Feels insecure
Shows impatience	Shows fear
Attempts to overcontrol	Rebels
Rambles without a goal	Shows no interest
Gives dull lectures	Feels unstimulated or bored
Runs overtime	Becomes fidgety

Instructors must never attempt to intimidate a student physically, verbally, or emotionally. Intimidation demonstrates lack of respect and will often result in confrontation. Exhibiting impatience with a student does not enforce the image of an instructor who is concerned with the student's learning experience. Impatience does not take into consideration the slow learner who needs additional time to develop an answer, or even the gifted learner who may have many ideas to express. When the instructor is student-oriented, intimidation and impatience should not occur.

When instructors attempt to over-control students and classroom environments, the learning experience may become too stiff and structured for some student learning styles. Instructors should not rely on strict rules that may become barriers to learning. Being flexible and adjusting to the needs of students, the changing environment, and the variety of subject matter are all ways that an instructor can create a controlled yet healthy learning atmosphere.

Instructors who ramble through a lecture are generally unprepared for the class sessions, a fact that students will readily recognize. Students will begin to discount what an unprepared instructor says and become disinterested in the subject matter they are meant to be learning. Lack of preparation also shows a lack of respect for students, the topic, and the learning experience. Preparation and practice are essential to good teaching. They also provide the basis for interesting and exciting lectures rather than dull ones. To prevent boredom, instructors must encourage students to participate in the instruction and enjoy the experience.

Finally, good preparation and practice will also prevent sessions from running overtime. Students understand that a lecture may exceed the posted time limit occasionally due to unforeseen circumstances. However, they will resent instructors who perpetually exceed the time limit for no apparent reason other than attempting to include too much information into the session. As a student's resentment about a course increases the likelihood that the student will behave disruptively will also increase.

Student-Caused Disruptive Behavior

Instructors should try to determine why some students behave in ways that disrupt the class. Students may bring their disruptive behaviors with them. For instance, a student working a second job or overtime the day before class may fall asleep in class. Many adults who attend training classes have true concerns with competing commitments such as juggling family and work while finishing training requirements, worrying about money problems, and dealing with other similar events in their lives. Students appreciate any concern an instructor shows because instructors who show concern also show respect for the individual. Most students return that respect by cooperating with instructors and fulfilling class requirements to the best of their abilities.

Although there is no real excuse for disruptive behavior, a student may believe that the behavior is legitimate. Students may create some disruptive behavior for reasons other than as a response to the instructor. A previous experience may have prepared these students to react inappropriately based on a perception of what the instructor might do. Students may not understand why they must attend the class. There may also be students who enjoy displaying their knowledge at the expense of the instructor. Finally, the instructor may be confronted with a student who wants or needs attention and uses disruptive behavior to gain it. In each of these situations, the instructor may have to rely on tactics that have been developed by the education profession.

The student who does not understand why it is important to be in the class may exhibit boredom. One tactic instructors may use with bored, *Why am I here?* students is to plan the lesson with activities that guide students to discover exactly why they are there — activities that enable them to determine just what is in it for them. This tactic requires matching the students' needs to the topic of the course. The instructor should ask these students to express their internal and external motivations as well as their professional needs. The instructor then helps students to determine the relationship between their needs and the course content for themselves.

When it is necessary to regain the attention of students who are disrupting by talking among themselves on items other than the topic at hand, instructors may try the tactic of calling on one of the individuals. While trying to not embarrass the person, the instructor makes a statement that summarizes the topic and asks a simple opinion question that directs the student's attention back to the lesson. Doing this more than once is not advised.

Some students feel that they already have superior knowledge to instructors and do not need to be in class. These students may attempt to question the instructor into revealing inadequacy or ignorance of their subject matter. Such students may also desire to display their own knowledge to their peers. The following list offers suggestions for dealing with these types of students:

- Show confidence in your role as content expert. Remember that these students would not be in the class if they were the experts.

- Tell the class you will get the information and get back to them if you are unsure of an answer. Then do it! Being responsive is more important than being perfect.

- Respond to the student, but continue to manage class time, and consider the interests of others when engaged in a dialogue with an individual.

- Always smile. A smile is disarming and indicates willingness to listen and discuss.

- Do not embarrass students when they expose their limitations publicly. In doing so, you can lose their respect and that of the rest of the class.

- Avoid getting into a battle of wills with such students. They are also adults and may actually have specialized information. Becoming antagonistic with them robs the class of their information and disrupts lessons.

- Let participants know that their questions have merit.

Chances are that other students have the same questions and are too shy or embarrassed to ask, but they can contribute to finding the merit through an open discussion. Because of the positive reinforcement, everyone gets involved, all benefit from the discussion, and everyone grows comfortable with participating.

A student who is disruptive may be seeking needed attention, but instructors must be careful not to reward this behavior by paying too much attention to that student's actions. Some behaviors will simply stop; some will not. When it does not, the L-E-A-S-T method of progressive disciplinary action is suggested as follows:

Learning Objectives

1. Discuss agencies and organizations where instructors can find the most current information about safety guidelines and regulations. [NFPA® 1041, 4.3.2, 4.3.3]

2. Describe the responsibilities of the instructor as a safety role model. [NFPA® 1041, 4.4.2]

3. Explain the details required to plan for safe training. [NFPA® 1041, 4.3.2, 4.3.3, 4.4.2 , 4.4.3]

4. Discuss the elements of evolution control. [NFPA® 1041, 4.4.2, 4.4.3]

5. Describe the information given during a psychomotor skills demonstration. [NFPA® 1041, 4.4.2, 4.4.3]

6. Explain a simple training evolution. [NFPA® 1041, 4.4.2, 4.4.3]

7. Explain the safety concerns surrounding live-fire training. [NFPA® 1041, 4.3.2, 4.4.2]

8. Identify types of increased hazard exposure training other than live-fire training. [NFPA® 1041, 4.3.2, 4.4.2]

9. Identify topics that an EMS instructor is qualified to teach. [NFPA® 1041, 4.3.2, 4.4.2]

10. Describe legal liability.

chapter 7

Key Terms

Job Performance Requirements

NFPA® 1041 References

4.3.2

4.3.3

4.4.2

4.4.3

Skills-Based Training Beyond the Classroom

Learning Objectives

1. Discuss agencies and organizations where instructors can find the most current information about safety guidelines and regulations. [NFPA® 1041, 4.3.2, 4.3.3]

2. Describe the responsibilities of the instructor as a safety role model. [NFPA® 1041, 4.4.2]

3. Explain the details required to plan for safe training. [NFPA® 1041, 4.3.2, 4.3.3, 4.4.2 , 4.4.3]

4. Discuss the elements of evolution control. [NFPA® 1041, 4.4.2, 4.4.3]

5. Describe the information given during a psychomotor skills demonstration. [NFPA® 1041, 4.4.2, 4.4.3]

6. Explain a simple training evolution. [NFPA® 1041, 4.4.2, 4.4.3]

7. Explain the safety concerns surrounding live-fire training. [NFPA® 1041, 4.3.2, 4.4.2]

8. Identify types of increased hazard exposure training other than live-fire training. [NFPA® 1041, 4.3.2, 4.4.2]

9. Identify topics that an EMS instructor is qualified to teach. [NFPA® 1041, 4.3.2, 4.4.2]

10. Describe legal liability.

Skills-Based Training Beyond the Classroom

Chapter Contents

Chapter Summary

Classroom instruction involves exercising a great many skills simultaneously. An effective instructor must be an effective communicator. Interpersonal communications and effective public speaking are the first skills that an instructor should cultivate. These skills include effective lecturing, using audiovisual aids, and transitioning between parts of a lesson.

Instructors should understand that in the fire and emergency services they are required to emphasize mastery of skills and criterion-referenced testing. They must also learn effective questioning techniques, how to lead a class discussion, and how to facilitate structured exercises during lessons. Instructors should also be familiar with alternate forms of instruction such as computer-based training (CBT).

Finally, effective instructors must make adjustments to classroom instruction for individual students' learning abilities, behavior, and personalities. Addressing individual student needs requires time management in the classroom, counseling skills, and coaching. In addition, instructors must manage disruptive students to ensure that such students do not hinder the learning of others.

Review Questions

1. What are the five basic elements of interpersonal communication in the classroom?

2. What are the strengths and weaknesses of verbal communication?

3. What are the three elements of nonverbal communication?

4. How does an instructor use good listening skills in the classroom?

5. What are the characteristics of effective speakers?

6. What is the mastery approach to teaching?

7. What is the four-step method of instruction?

8. What is distance learning and student-led instruction?

9. How can training aids encourage active learning?

10. How do structured exercises contribute to the learning process?

11. What factors can affect learning?

12. What accommodations might an instructor make for a student with a learning disability?

13. What substantive rights does a student have?

14. Why is it important for instructors to manage student behavior in the classroom?

Documenting Discipline:
Solving Problems in Progressive Steps

The following steps provide progressive actions to take when employee or student discipline is necessary:

Facts: State the problem and focus on specific behavior. Document all behavior and conversations:

1. *Keep an incident diary/calendar or file.* Begin to make notations of incidents when it has become necessary to speak to an individual about undesired actions. Note undesirable behaviors, frequency, discussions about behaviors.

2. *When making notes, state facts (problem or issue).* Write down what the individual did or did not do and when based on expectations; state the conversation with the individual.

3. *Use these facts to write a disciplinary action memo.* Include who, what happened, where, when, and what will be done. Follow organization policy on filing or distributing the memo to appropriate personnel and to the individual.

4. *Include in the memo a specific objective, solution, and action that will be taken.* Show your attempt to help the employee/student succeed (see below).

Objectives: Set objectives that will communicate a specific expectation:

1. *If undesired behavior continues, meet formally with the individual.* Discuss the problem, refer to previous discussions and file notes, and set and state expectations for the individual to meet in order to change behavior. Be specific.

2. *Follow up the meeting with a written memo.* State in writing the problem and the expectations discussed in the meeting. Follow organization policy on filing or distributing the memo to appropriate personnel and to the individual.

Solutions: Determine solutions that will help the individual reach the objective:

1. *In the meeting, offer solutions or plans that will help solve or correct the problem.* Suggestions may include (1) attending a class or training seminar or working with a tutor and (2) getting assistance or coaching from a specific individual in setting priorities, completing assignments, getting information or resources, and checking work or progress.

2. *Give solutions orally to the individual and follow up with a written memo.* In the memo state facts, objectives, solutions, actions, and consequences (such as suspension, pay reduction, transfer, or termination). Follow organization policy on sending copies to the individual's immediate supervisor, personnel file, or other references.

3. *Always follow oral warnings with a written warning.* A written follow-up to a discussion verifies that the discussion occurred and clearly identifies steps for the individual to follow.

Actions: State what actions will be taken if objectives are not met, and follow up with written memo.

Implement actions as necessary and as stated in the memo.

Adapted from: *Documenting Discipline*, American Media, Inc., West Des Moines, Iowa 50265

Figure 6.24 Instructors must perform disciplinary action in a careful, methodical, and professional manner.

student who wants or needs attention and uses disruptive behavior to gain it. In each of these situations, the instructor may have to rely on tactics that have been developed by the education profession.

The student who does not understand why it is important to be in the class may exhibit boredom. One tactic instructors may use with bored, *Why am I here?* students is to plan the lesson with activities that guide students to discover exactly why they are there — activities that enable them to determine just what is in it for them. This tactic requires matching the students' needs to the topic of the course. The instructor should ask these students to express their internal and external motivations as well as their professional needs. The instructor then helps students to determine the relationship between their needs and the course content for themselves.

When it is necessary to regain the attention of students who are disrupting by talking among themselves on items other than the topic at hand, instructors may try the tactic of calling on one of the individuals. While trying to not embarrass the person, the instructor makes a statement that summarizes the topic and asks a simple opinion question that directs the student's attention back to the lesson. Doing this more than once is not advised.

Some students feel that they already have superior knowledge to instructors and do not need to be in class. These students may attempt to question the instructor into revealing inadequacy or ignorance of their subject matter. Such students may also desire to display their own knowledge to their peers. The following list offers suggestions for dealing with these types of students:

- Show confidence in your role as content expert. Remember that these students would not be in the class if they were the experts.

- Tell the class you will get the information and get back to them if you are unsure of an answer. Then do it! Being responsive is more important than being perfect.

- Respond to the student, but continue to manage class time, and consider the interests of others when engaged in a dialogue with an individual.

- Always smile. A smile is disarming and indicates willingness to listen and discuss.

- Do not embarrass students when they expose their limitations publicly. In doing so, you can lose their respect and that of the rest of the class.

- Avoid getting into a battle of wills with such students. They are also adults and may actually have specialized information. Becoming antagonistic with them robs the class of their information and disrupts lessons.

- Let participants know that their questions have merit.

Chances are that other students have the same questions and are too shy or embarrassed to ask, but they can contribute to finding the merit through an open discussion. Because of the positive reinforcement, everyone gets involved, all benefit from the discussion, and everyone grows comfortable with participating.

A student who is disruptive may be seeking needed attention, but instructors must be careful not to reward this behavior by paying too much attention to that student's actions. Some behaviors will simply stop; some will not. When it does not, the L-E-A-S-T method of progressive disciplinary action is suggested as follows:

- **Leave it alone** — Wait to see if the behavior goes away; it might be an isolated occurrence.

- **Eye contact** — Look at the student long enough to make eye contact. Eye contact tells the student *I see what you are doing* and also implies *Now stop it.*

- **Action** — Take action when the behavior continues. The action is usually a comment to the entire class stressing the importance of being attentive in class or a question directed to the problem student. Call on the individual and ask a question about the topic. In this subtle manner, instructors can communicate the knowledge that they are aware of how students are behaving.

- **Stop the class** — Stop the class and discuss the problem with the student if the disruptive behavior becomes too frequent. Taking a break is the most tactful way of stopping a class.

- **Terminate the student** — Expel the student from the class if discussing the problem was not effective. Take appropriate disciplinary measures, and document them.

An advantage of being in a paramilitary organization such as the law enforcement, fire, and emergency services is that the instructor generally has the authority of an officer in the classroom. Hopefully, instructors do not need to use this authority in order to maintain classroom control.

Taking Formal Disciplinary Action

Instructors should make every attempt to help a disruptive student, but if these attempts fail, disciplinary action becomes necessary. Instructors should be familiar with organizational policies and follow them to the letter. The student's behavior should be thoroughly documented in order to justify the disciplinary actions **(Figure 6.24)**. This includes the following steps:

- Record the date and behavior whenever class must be interrupted to manage the student's behavior.

- Keep documentation in a secure location.

- Draft a memo to the student, detailing the disruptive behavior. This memo should state that you are seeking formal disciplinary action based upon the student's classroom behavior. Also, you may make a suggestion for the action you recommend be taken.

- Send a copy of this memo to the chief/manager and training officer.

- Await formal action by the training division.

Training organization regulations may provide instructors with the option of dismissing an individual from a class. If so, a paper trail of notes, memos, and counseling forms is valuable. The documentation must show progressive reprimands or disciplinary actions that may end with or result in an individual being removed from a class.

Legal and ethical issues may require or dictate that instructors have supervisory authority while conducting classes. This level of implied authority becomes critical when facing disruptive behavior and trying to maintain an appropriate classroom atmosphere for other students. Instructors must understand and not act beyond their levels of responsibility and authority as directed by local policy.

Chapter 7
Skills-Based Training Beyond the Classroom

Case History

A station was conducting rapid intervention team (RIT) training using a RIT training trailer. Students were practicing emergency exits (bailouts) from a second story window approximately 15 feet (5 m) above the ground. The students were meant to tie a rope anchored in the trailer around their waists to provide braking as they descended. As a safety measure, each student was also attached to a second life safety rope/belay system with a braking device. Other students were monitoring the safety system on the ground and could provide braking for a student coming out of the window if something went wrong.

After a few successful attempts, one of the students decided that he had devised a better way to perform the bailout maneuver. He traded the standard rope he was supposed to use for a smaller diameter rope. He fashioned a seat harness from a length of runner and wore a sport climbing braking device. With this new rig, the firefighter attached himself to the safety rope and rolled out of the window. He began to fall and realized that he could not grip the smaller rope in his turnout gloves to slow himself.

Fortunately, the students monitoring the life safety rope were able to brake his descent. Although he landed roughly on his SCBA bottle, he was otherwise uninjured.

Had an instructor been monitoring the situation more closely, perhaps the student's attempt to experiment would have been noticed and prevented. Maintaining a safe training environment requires diligence throughout training to ensure that students are performing skills according to instructions.

Classroom instruction is only one portion of an instructor's role in the fire and emergency services. The other role is guiding students through the application step of the four-step method of instruction. This guidance may occur in the classroom. Frequently, other locations such as acquired structures, permanent training facilities, medical facilities, and fire or clinical laboratories will be used to teach skills. Regardless of the location, instructors should understand their responsibilities when teaching skills. The first is to maintain a safe training environment. Injuries and especially fatalities are unacceptable in training scenarios.

The second responsibility is to teach skills with mastery as the ultimate goal. Realistically, students may not reach mastery during one class but will reach a level of competency necessary to satisfy learning objectives. Students will need to continue practicing their skills after classes are completed. Students' future safety and the safety of their classmates depends upon instructors who help them to perfect key skills. This chapter presents instructors with the basic information needed to safely teach skills.

Resources: Safety Guidelines, Regulations, and Information

Instructors should remain current with the ever-changing safety guidelines and regulations that various government agencies and standard making organizations have developed. A wide variety of information is readily available from entities such as the following:

- Federal government agencies
- State/provincial and local governmental occupational safety and health agencies
- Standards-writing organizations
- Professional organizations and associations

Instructors must ensure that they receive information from credible sources, such as these. Awareness of these resources and their contact information are valuable assets for any instructor.

Federal Government Agencies

Numerous federal government agencies in North America are responsible for developing, regulating, and ensuring safe workplace policies. Four that may be of the greatest use to instructors are as follows:

- **National Institute for Occupational Safety and Health (NIOSH)** — U.S. agency responsible for investigating, researching, and evaluating safety and health hazards in the workplace.
- **Occupational Safety and Health Administration (OSHA)** — U.S. agency responsible for setting and enforcing workplace safety and health standards; can issue citations and fines. In federal OSHA states, OSHA enforces regulations that apply only to private and federal firefighters in non-state-plan states.
- **Canadian Centre for Occupational Health and Safety (CCOHS)** — Canadian federal government agency that provides information and policy development regarding work-related injury, illness prevention initiatives, and occupational health and safety information.
- **National Institute of Standards and Technology (NIST)** — U.S. agency that promotes standardization and measurement of various sciences and technologies. NIST often has information on fire science or testing results for fire equipment.

NOTE: Many states have their own occupational safety regulations that state agencies enforce. State plans must meet or exceed federal requirements. See **Appendix E** for a list of state-plan states and non-state-plan states. Instructors are encouraged to have a current copy of their state's plan if one exists. Regulations that apply to fire and emergency services personnel vary from state to state.

Other organizations may have more specialized regulatory information that instructors may need to seek out for specific training situations. The following U.S. federal agencies can provide information on weapons of mass destruction (WMD), PPE for high-threat incidents, and bioterrorism training, among other training topics:

- **Department of Homeland Security (DHS)** — Agency that has the missions of preventing terrorist attacks and minimizing damage from potential terrorist attacks and natural disasters. Other federal agencies that are under DHS include:

  — **Federal Emergency Management Agency (FEMA)** — Agency tasked with responding to, planning for, recovering from, and mitigating disasters.

  — **United States Fire Administration (USFA)** — Provides national leadership to foster a solid foundation for the fire and emergency services; emphasizes information about fire prevention, firefighter preparedness, and emergency response. The National Fire Academy (NFA) is part of the USFA.

  — **Emergency Management Institute (EMI)** — Serves as the national focal point for the development and delivery of emergency management training to emergency services responders at all levels, public and private, to minimize the impact of disasters on the American public.

- **Centers for Disease Control and Prevention (CDC)** — Agency that collects and analyzes data regarding disease and health trends.

- **Environmental Protection Agency (EPA)** — Agency that sets policy and regulations for protection of the environment.

- **U.S. Department of Transportation (DOT)** — Agency that establishes the national curriculum and regulations for EMS personnel and equipment.

- **U.S. Department of Defense (DOD)** — Agency that regulates military, civilian, and federal fire and emergency services personnel stationed on federal property.

  NOTE: Agencies in both Canada and the U.S. share information and materials. Some Canadian safety regulations are based on or modeled after NFPA® standards and OSHA regulations.

State/Provincial and Local Safety and Health Agencies

States/provinces and local governmental occupational safety and health agencies often have review and enforcement functions. In Canada and the U.S., states/provinces or local agencies may have to follow regulations that differ from, expand upon, or exceed national rules. They may also have to follow additional regulations that are not addressed at the federal level, such as those mandated by state/provincial environmental agencies.

Ideally, instructors should know the federal, state/provincial, and local regulations that are likely to impact their training evolutions. When in doubt about regulations, instructors should know how to contact their state/provincial and local governmental occupational safety and health agencies, state/provincial fire training academies, state/provincial fire marshals offices, or state EMS agencies to inquire about which regulations may be applicable for a particular training evolution. Instructors should not limit their inquiries to regulations for fire and emergency services. State/provincial and local agencies may also have safety regulations written for other industries or organizations that apply to fire and emergency services training. For example, regulations for construction workers on a roof may be applicable to firefighters training for vertical ventilation scenarios. Fire and emergency services trench-rescue operations may be governed by regulations for shoring and cribbing that apply to private contractors who lay underground cables and pipelines **(Figure 7.1)**.

Regulatory agencies may have consultants or educators who can review pertinent safety regulations with instructors who are planning a training curriculum or course. State/provincial and local health departments or agencies can also provide statistical data and safety programs, as well as information on diseases and their prevention.

Standards-Writing Organizations

Standards-writing organizations develop and issue operating procedures and design requirements for various industries, including the fire and emergency services professions. Consensus committees composed of industry representatives develop most of these standards. These standards do not become law until a government authority adopts them. The primary standards-writing organizations involved with the fire service are as follows:

Figure 7.1 Instructors should be aware of industry safety regulations that may apply to emergency services training.

- **National Fire Protection Association® (NFPA®)** — Develops minimum safety standards and guidelines that many training organizations adopt. Government and other agencies can adopt NFPA® standards as their guidelines for safety compliance. Instructors must be aware of and familiar with NFPA® standards that relate to safety. These standards guide the performance of live-fire training evolutions and other high-hazard training and are updated on a schedule.

- **American National Standards Institute (ANSI)** — Coordinates the private sector voluntary standardization system through ANSI-accredited member organizations; ANSI does not develop standards but facilitates their development through the consensus process. ANSI-approved standards include the following:

  — Respiratory protection practices

  — Physical qualifications for using respiratory protection equipment

  — Fit-testing methods

- **Underwriters Laboratories Inc. (UL): U.S. and Canada (ULC)** — Tests and certifies fire-extinguishing agents and equipment. Agents and equipment that meet these requirements are said to be UL/ULC listed. Certification tests and UL/ULC acceptance provide consumers with independent documentation on product-performance characteristics.

Sample List of NFPA® Standards

- **NFPA® 1041, *Standard for Fire Service Instructor Professional Qualifications*** — Identifies the professional levels of competence required of fire service instructors.

- **NFPA® 1402, *Guide to Building Fire Service Training Centers*** — Lists guidelines to follow when building training facilities (including burn buildings, smoke buildings, and combination buildings) and when conducting outside drill ground activities.

- **NFPA® 1403, *Standard on Live Fire Training Evolutions*** — Lists guidelines to follow during live-fire training evolutions at acquired structures, facilities designed for live-fire training, and exterior props, including information on student prerequisites, structures and facilities, fuel materials, safety, and instructor qualifications.

- **NFPA® 1410, *Standard on Training for Initial Emergency Scene Operations*** — Contains minimum requirements for evaluating training for initial fire suppression and rescue procedures used by fire department personnel engaged in emergency scene operations.

- **NFPA® 1500, *Standard on Fire Department Occupational Safety and Health Program*** — Contains guidelines for fire departments to follow in order to ensure the health and safety of firefighters.

- **NFPA® 1583, *Standard on Health-Related Fitness Programs for Fire Department Members*** — Outlines a complete health-related fitness program designed for fire departments, including job descriptions, rehabilitation, nutrition, and wellness components.

- **NFPA® 1584, *Standard on the Rehabilitation Process for Members During Emergency Operations and Training Exercises*** — Contains guidelines for developing rehabilitation programs that can be implemented at incident scenes or on training exercises.

Professional and Accrediting Organizations

The following fire and emergency services professional organizations are important sources of safety information and model programs:

- International Association of Fire Chiefs (IAFC)

- Canadian Association of Fire Chiefs (Association canadienne des chef de pompiers) (CAFC/ACCP)

- International Association of Fire Fighters (IAFF)

- National Volunteer Fire Council (NVFC)

- North American Fire Training Directors (NAFTD)

Fire and emergency services instructor associations and safety organizations also provide information on safety and networking opportunities. These organizations often provide information and sources to instructors who are not members, but who need information for their programs. Some of these organizations include the following:

- Fire Department Safety Officer Association (FDSOA)

- International Society of Fire Service Instructors (ISFSI)

- American Society of Safety Engineers (ASSE)

Some national organizations have as their founding purpose the accreditation and certification of fire and emergency organizations and personnel. Accrediting and certifying organizations are as follows:

- National Registry of Emergency Medical Technicians (NREMT)
- International Fire Service Accreditation Congress (IFSAC)
- National Board on Fire Service Professional Qualifications (ProBoard)

Instructor as Safety Role Model

When instructors emphasize safety during training, students are more likely to use safe practices during emergency response operations. The instructor is a primary role model for safety and must take that role seriously. Instructors cannot just mention safety guidelines and expect students to follow them. Instructors must demonstrate and reinforce these guidelines. Because instructors constantly interact with personnel in planning and presenting courses, they set the stage and serve as role models for following safety requirements. Following safety guidelines or plans that the organization develops or adopts has a significant effect on reducing injuries and fatalities in training and at emergency incidents.

Know Safety Policies and Guidelines

Be sure you are aware of your organization's safety policies and guidelines for each emergency services training course that you teach. If you don't have a copy, get one. If you are not sure how to implement these policies and guidelines, talk with other instructors. If a policy is in place and you, as an instructor, do not follow its guidelines, you may be held liable for injuries to students. In addition, fire and emergency services organizations conduct emergency operations using NIMS-ICS. You must become familiar with the locally adopted ICS and accountability model procedures and then integrate them into training exercises.

Safety is an issue that must be continually emphasized. Instructors must devote appropriate time in every session to discussing all aspects of safety. Safety awareness and practice begin during training sessions. Instructors increase awareness and help prevent accidents during training in the following ways:

- Describing applicable safety requirements or procedures to students in the following forms:
  - Providing rules and guidelines in writing.
  - Reading the written rules and guidelines aloud as the students read them silently.
  - Having students sign a statement that they have read and understood all safety rules and regulations. In some departments and organizations, this signature is mandatory **(Figure 7.2)**.
- Creating an Incident Action Plan (IAP) for any high-hazard drill or application, and briefing all instructors and students on the IAP before training begins.
- Describing the proper safeguards and equipment used for preventing accidents.

- Describing possible hazards and explaining the necessary precautions **(Figure 7.3)**.

- Briefing students on relevant techniques, procedures, tools, facility characteristics, and appropriate safety rules before starting the evolution.

- Planning carefully for training scenarios.

- Ensuring that appropriately trained personnel assist in supervising scenarios.

- Reviewing emergency procedures, emergency evacuation plans, and verbal or alarm alerts with students before the evolution.

- Inspecting and repairing tools, equipment, props, and apparatus before starting training sessions.

- Assigning a safety officer to each training scenario based upon a prepared IAP.

- Assigning additional personnel (more than the minimum) for safety positions depending upon the scale of the training evolution and the severity of danger.

- Modeling and reinforcing safety policies and procedures by personally adhering to them.

- Being aware of human factors among students that can contribute to unsafe conditions, such as improper attitude, complacency, lack of knowledge or skill, and physical limitations.

Figures 7.2 Instructors should describe procedures as well as require students to read applicable rules and sign waiver statements.

Figure 7.3 Make sure students are informed about likely hazards before they practice skills.

Figure 7.4 If necessary, designate a qualified individual to serve as Safety Officer.

When planning practical training evolutions, instructors must identify and eliminate potential hazards. Instructors must also plan to address the necessary precautions to prevent injury while training, train students to recognize job hazards, and teach them how to control or eliminate these hazards. These steps help minimize the level of risk and prevent injuries.

The instructor in charge of training may also function as the safety officer. When the instructor cannot function as both lead instructor and safety officer, the instructor should appoint another qualified individual as the safety officer for the training evolution **(Figure 7.4)**. Fire and emergency services programs often train nonemergency services employees. Although these students may not be required to perform all aspects of the curriculum on their jobs, instructors must enforce all safety procedures as these employees participate in the course. It is still important that they follow safety guidelines even though all training procedures may not pertain to or affect them.

NOTE: Establish and use IAPs during all types of emergency incidents and high-hazard training evolutions. See **Appendix F** for copies of ICS Forms 201 through 206, 215, and 215a which are used for developing written IAPs. Also include use of a personnel accountability system.

Planning for Safe Training

After locating the necessary resources to inform safe decisions about training evolutions, it is then up to instructors to plan those evolutions and put the information into practice. Training ground instruction requires thorough planning. Most instructors will already be familiar with the skills they are teaching because of their basic, entry-level training and experience from performing emergency response functions. This experience provides a firm foundation for teaching practical training evolutions. However, before leading instruction on the training ground, even experienced instructors should practice so that they can safely and correctly perform the skills they will demonstrate. The sections that follow discuss important actions regarding planning safe training.

Verifying Instructor Skill Level

Above all, instructors should be honest with themselves about their own ability levels and knowledge. Over time, an instructor's emergency responder skills may decline due to lack of practice. Instructors should recognize their own strengths and weaknesses. They should rely upon their strengths as much as possible and find courses or training materials to help them improve upon their weaknesses.

Instructors should also be honest with supervisors if they do not have the skills to teach particular lessons. If an instructor feels that he or she does not have the proper skills to teach an assigned lesson, the instructor should seek out courses to gain the skills and recommend a better-qualified instructor to teach the course.

If another instructor cannot be found, training cannot continue until the available instructor has completed the necessary skills training needed to be qualified. It is important for the instructor to acquire the necessary skills as soon as possible; delaying training indefinitely harms the credibility of the instructor, the course, and the training division. Good instructors find the resources that they need to offer accurate and safe training demonstrations.

Inspecting and Repairing Facilities and Props

It is important to inspect training facilities, props, tools, and equipment before beginning a course or scenario. Inspections ensure that they are in working condition and that the training environment will be safe. If inspections show that equipment is unsafe or badly damaged, the instructor should report this to the AHJ and either reschedule training, train without the faulty equipment, or conduct the training at a facility with functional equipment.

During entry-level recruit classes, some inspection, maintenance, and repair can be assigned to class members as a training activity. But maintaining some items, such as respiratory breathing equipment, requires certified or authorized personnel. The AHJ should establish an inspection time schedule based on industry practice, manufacturer's recommendations, and local needs. Generally, inspections by emergency response personnel of tools, facilities, apparatus, and equipment should occur on the same schedule as in the stations **(Figure 7.5)**.

Figure 7.5 Training equipment should be inspected on the same schedule as equipment in a fire station.

Keep thorough records of all maintenance, repairs, and replacements **(Figure 7.6, p.202)**. The records provide a basis for developing an accurate operating budget, justifying repairs or replacements, and assessing equipment's overall value. See Chapter 9, Records, Reports, and Scheduling, for additional information. In all cases, maintenance and repairs that are beyond the capabilities of students or instructors should be delegated to certified or authorized repair personnel.

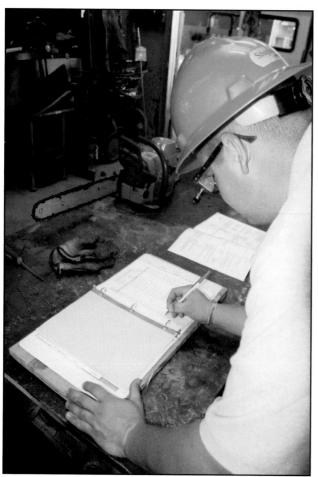
Figure 7.6 Thorough and accurate record-keeping is a must for all equipment.

Identifying Training Hazards

Level I Instructors should be familiar enough with prepared lesson plans, the training facility, any training prop, and the evolution to be conducted to identify the hazards associated with training. Students should be informed during the training briefing of hazards they will face as part of training. If the appropriate hazards are not addressed in a lesson plan, instructors should modify the lesson plans to include appropriate safety instructions. Training hazards can range from activities that may cause injury to those that could cause death. Instructors should identify all types of hazards before beginning training.

Evolution Control

Both simple and complex practical training evolutions must be controlled. Controlling an evolution involves the following elements:

- **Supervising** — Instructors directly supervise students to make sure they practice skills safely and correctly.

- **Monitoring** — Instructors observe the progress of the evolution to make sure students accomplish the learning objectives.

- **Teaching** — When appropriate, instructors present new or related information during the evolution.

- **Managing** — Instructors apply the elements of the NIMS-ICS to control and coordinate the evolution as though it was an actual emergency situation.

It is impossible to effectively control the evolution if there are not enough instructors to supervise all the students. A ratio of 5 students to 1 instructor is typical, but larger or more complex evolutions may require more instructors **(Figure 7.7)**.

Psychomotor Skills Demonstrations

Skills demonstrations begin with giving the following information:

- An explanation of the skill

- Why it is important

- How it relates to other skills

- How many people are required to perform it

- When it should be performed

After this general overview, the instructor should perform the skill at normal speed, then perform it again slowly while explaining each step. Next, the instructor should encourage students to ask questions. The instructor should repeat the slow-speed demonstration until students are able to verbalize the steps of the skill. At this point students are ready to practice the skill themselves. The slow-speed demonstration is the transition between the presentation step and the application step.

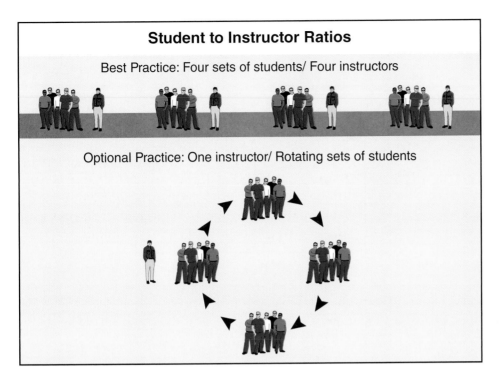

Student to Instructor Ratios

Best Practice: Four sets of students/ Four instructors

Optional Practice: One instructor/ Rotating sets of students

Figure 7.7 Depending upon the number of available instructors, adjustments may need to be made to maintain the proper student-to-instructor ratio.

The instructor should guide and coach the students as they practice, then have the students critique and coach each other as they practice in small groups **(Figure 7.8)**. Once or twice during a practice session, instructors may need to demonstrate the entire skill. Instructors must show the skill steps correctly and in sequence. The end of the session is a particularly good time to do this. Students should be encouraged to practice skills during rest breaks, during free time, and at the beginning of the next training session. When students have perfected the skill, they are ready for evaluation.

Planning, preparation, and practice are essential to a successful skills demonstration. The instructor who does not appear proficient at a skill will lose credibility with students and waste valuable training time by having to repeat or correct skill steps.

Simple Training Evolutions

Simple training evolutions (generally defined here as those that do not involve live fire) share some training techniques in common with psychomotor skills training. The main difference is the number of students involved and the training location. Simple training evolutions involve small numbers of students performing a single skill that requires only a few tasks. Examples include the following **(Figure 7.9 a – d, p.204)**:

- Lifting and setting a ground ladder
- Using a portable fire extinguisher
- Lifting and moving patients
- Forcing entry through a door

Figure 7.8 Students can reinforce valuable skills by observing each others' work in small teams.

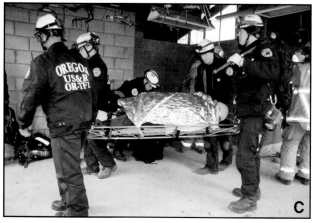

Figures 7.9 a-d Lifting and placing a ground ladder, using a portable fire extinguisher, lifting and moving patients, and unloading a hoseline are all examples of training evolutions that require students to perform only a few tasks.

- Taking and recording patients' vital signs
- Deploying and advancing an attack hoseline
- Driving and parking a fire apparatus or ambulance

These types of training evolutions may involve from one to five active students and require only one or two instructors for supervision. Students repeat the evolution until they are able to perform it without error. When more than one student is involved, they rotate positions so that both have the opportunity to experience and practice each part of the skill.

The instructor begins an evolution by performing the following actions:

- Explaining the learning objectives or outcomes
- Demonstrating the evolution, which may require the use of an experienced group of responders to perform the evolution for students to observe when the evolution involves more than one student
- Relating the evolution to the classroom lecture
- Emphasizing the safety requirements for the evolution

Once the students begin practicing, the instructor monitors their performance. If students perform poorly, make an error, or violate safety protocols, the instructor should stop them immediately and correct their behavior. Immediate correction forces students to recognize the problem and adjust their behavior.

Simple training evolutions should be performed as though students were involved in a real emergency incident, which means that they must wear appropriate PPE during the training evolution **(Figures 7.10 a and b)**. All applicable policies and procedures that would affect personnel at a real incident must be followed, including using the NIMS-ICS.

Practical training evolutions should also be practiced with both the minimum and maximum levels of staffing that the organization requires. For instance, when an engine company is staffed by one person who may arrive at the incident ahead of the rest of the crew, that scenario should be part of the training. When a company is normally staffed by four people but has a minimum level of three, the training scenario should be practiced using both three and four people. By following these suggestions, students will practice and learn the skills they are required to use when they are on duty.

Figures 7.10 a and b Students must train with the same equipment they would use during a real incident. *Photo b courtesy of Bob Esposito.*

Increased Hazard Exposure Training

NFPA® 1041 includes the following examples of increased hazard exposure training scenarios:

- Live-fire exercises
- Hazardous materials
- Above and below grade rescue
- Evolutions that require the use of power tools

Increased hazard exposure training is dangerous even under the very controlled conditions found at permanent training facilities. NFPA® 1041 therefore requires that a Level II Instructor supervise both students and Level I Instructors during this type of training.

Regardless of level of instructor certification, if an instructor must lead increased hazard exposure evolutions, he or she must be prepared and qualified. The instructor should learn the qualifications that his or her state/province and municipality requires for these types of training evolutions and ensure that the qualifications are met before continuing with the training. If the instructor has any doubts about his or her qualifications or experience, any at all, the training should be postponed until the instructor has gained the proper qualifications and become more knowledgeable about the standards and regulations that apply.

Live-Fire Training

Purpose-Built Structure — Building specially designed for live-fire training; fires can be ignited inside the building multiple times without major structural damage.

Wildland Fire — Unplanned, unwanted, and uncontrolled fire in vegetative fuels such as grass, brush, or timberland involving uncultivated lands; requires suppression action and may threaten structures or other improvements.

Live-fire training is an important part of both entry-level and experienced firefighter training. Entry-level personnel learn new skills and experienced personnel develop their existing skills. The decrease in actual fire fighting incidents and the assignment of entry-level personnel to EMS duties has resulted in fewer opportunities for personnel to experience live-fire situations. Therefore, live-fire training evolutions may be the only experience some personnel receive. Live-fire training evolutions can involve the following categories:

- Scenarios at structures acquired with the specific purpose for interior live-fire training

- Scenarios at **purpose-built structures** at training facilities built for interior live-fire training

- Scenarios involving exterior fires, including transportation fires, **wildland fires**, and flammable/combustible liquid fires (**Figures 7.11 a-c**) at a remote site or a training facility

NFPA® 1403, *Standard on Live-Fire Training Evolutions*

To ensure the highest level of safety, all live-fire training evolutions must meet the requirements of the appropriate sections of the most current edition of NFPA® 1403, *Standard on Live Fire Training Evolutions.* While this standard is not legally mandated in all jurisdictions, noncompliance with the standard has resulted in injuries and fatalities for which instructors were held criminally and civilly responsible. In October 2004, the Centers for Disease Control and Prevention (CDC) from the U.S. National Institute for Occupational Safety and Health (NIOSH) issued a Workplace Solutions document titled "Preventing Deaths and Injuries to Fire Fighters during Live-Fire Training in Acquired Structures" that outline the precautions to take when engaging in live-fire training (see **Appendix G**). Any instructor leading live-fire training should make every effort to prepare and instruct based upon this standard.

Acquired Structure Training

Acquired Structure — Structure acquired by the authority having jurisdiction from a property owner for the purpose of conducting live fire training or rescue training evolutions.

Firefighter injuries and fatalities during live-fire training in **acquired structures** have contributed to many of the training-related casualty statistics in recent years, so instructors and training administrators must take great care when designing or leading this type of training. Part of the danger in these situations is that acquired structures are usually in deteriorating condition and have been scheduled for demolition. Sometimes fire and emergency services organizations have been invited to burn the structures because burning may be

Figures 7.11 a-c Training for fighting exterior fires may take place at a permanent training facility (a and c) or at a remote site (b).

the least expensive way for the property owner to eliminate a building that has outlived its usefulness. As a guideline, instructors should use the checklist provided in NFPA® 1403, Annex B (see **Appendix H**). Following that checklist will help ensure that training at an acquired structure is conducted safely and legally.

Acquired structures that are used for live-fire training must meet the safety requirements of NFPA® 1403, and sometimes this can only be accomplished by making improvements to the structure before training. Any building or structure that cannot be made safe may not be used for interior structural fire fighting training. An instructor should also consider the cost of making the acquired structure safe enough for the proposed type of training. However, if the cost of improvements outweighs the potential benefit of the training, instructors should locate another structure in which to train.

Once a site has been selected, the structure has been acquired, inspected, and repaired, and all necessary permits for the live-fire exercise have been obtained, an instructor then considers the type of training best suited for the specific structure. There will always be a tendency to overreach and set goals and learning objectives that cannot be achieved given the limits imposed by the particular structure. The following factors establish the limits of the types of training that can be performed at the structure:

- Total number of students
- Instructor to student ratio
- Students may not possess the necessary prerequisite skills
- Safety considerations
- Equipment availability
- Location and access

Advanced planning is critical to the success of any practical training evolution involving acquired structures. When planning for a live-fire exercise in an acquired structure, instructors must consider a variety of issues or factors that can have an effect on the training evolution. No live-fire training should be attempted until the following issues are considered and plans made to address them:

- Environmental conditions
- Structural condition
- Training possibilities
- Instructor responsibilities
- Fuel usage
- Water supply requirements

Environmental Conditions. While climate conditions affect every training evolution, their effect on acquired structures can be extreme. Wind speed and direction, humidity, temperature, and time of day all affect the training environment. Weather extremes are common in many locations, from below-freezing cold to high temperatures and humidity. Hazards such as lightning, hail, and high winds may also present additional dangers when severe storms approach.

Equipment noise, light levels, and even nearby vegetation are important factors that can affect the outcome of a training exercise. When these factors combine with climate conditions to create environments that are detrimental to learning or are inherently unsafe, instructors may have to cut training sessions short or cancel them outright.

Structural Conditions. Acquired structures must comply with NFPA® 1403, specifically the Structures and Facilities section of its Chapter 4. Before conducting live-fire training, the structure must be inspected to determine whether repairs are necessary to comply with the standard. If the instructor is not qualified to perform this inspection, a trained inspector should be brought in to perform this task.

Asbestos at Acquired Structures

When a certified inspector has detected the presence of asbestos, the building owner is required to use certified personnel to remove and dispose of the materials. Safety officers and instructors should be familiar with federal, state/provincial, and local regulations for asbestos abatement and hazardous waste disposal. By complying with these laws, both instructors and organizations avoid the dangers of liability created by exposure to and removal of asbestos.

Training Possibilities. An instructor must first determine whether it is even possible to use a structure for live-fire training. Environmental laws, for example, may prohibit the burning of a structure because of its location. The structure may also have been designated as a historical landmark. If live-fire training is not possible, perhaps the structure might be suitable for forcible-entry training, ladder evolutions, search and rescue operations, or a class on building construction. In any event, the building must undergo a complete and thorough inspection.

Instructor Responsibilities. The instructor must have written permission from the rightful owner of the property in order to burn a structure. The instructor must also apply for and receive the appropriate permits from the local jurisdiction. Permits may be required from the fire and life safety division, the building inspections office, state/provincial environmental authority, or the local residential code enforcement office. Having these permits on display is an important part of public relations, demonstrating to citizens that the fire and emergency services organization adheres to the same restrictions as the rest of the community.

When using an acquired structure, instructors conducting live-fire or other training evolutions must consider the effect on the surrounding neighborhood. Refer to **Appendix H**, Structural Live-Fire Training Forms, for sample forms that may help instructors prepare letters and public announcements. The appendix also contains the Live Fire Evaluation Sample Checklist for acquired structures that can be found in NFPA® 1403.

In order to meet his or her responsibilities as an instructor, the instructor should perform the following actions:

• Distribute a notice (letter or brochure) to each resident living within a reasonable distance of the structure, informing them of the date and time of the training event, a description of the training activity, and its effect (such as street closures) on the surrounding area.

- Plan the placement of hoselines and apparatus carefully, and consider how they may least restrict access to the neighborhood.

- Notify the water department when hydrants are involved.

- When an acquired structure is located in an area with limited water flow, flush water mains so that rust and sediment do not cause problems for pumping operations or surrounding households.

- Prepare water supply and flow analyses. Instructors must know the required fire flow for the structure, including safety margins.

- Video or photograph surrounding structures, vehicles, and grounds. If neighboring property is damaged by the training evolution, these videotapes and photographs help document the conditions present before the training activity began. Video documentation may be important if legal claims arise later.

- Hold a briefing with all participants to explain the training evolutions. Take all participants on a walk-through inspection to familiarize them with the structure's layout and exits.

Fuel Usage. Misuse of fuels is a contributing factor in many live-fire training incidents. Although all live fires in acquired structures are dangerous, following the NFPA® 1403 requirements regarding fuel will lessen the possibility that students or instructors will be injured. There may also be additional requirements for fuel usage in the state's OSHA regulations for live-fire training that the instructor should adhere to. Safety is always the primary concern during live-fire training exercises. It is generally safe to use propane torches or fireplace lighters to ignite the fuel and then remove the igniting device from the structure once the fire has started. Instructors must adhere to the following requirements:

Figure 7.12 Debris found in or around an acquired structure should be removed before training.

- All fuels must have burning characteristics that are known and controllable.

- Never use unidentified materials, such as debris found around or in a structure. Remove all such materials before training takes place **(Figure 7.12)**.

- Never use pressure-treated materials or any materials containing pesticides or harmful chemicals.

- Use only enough fuel to create a fire of the desired size. Never use more than this amount.

- Control the structure's fuel load to prevent flashover or backdraft conditions.

- Never use flammable or combustible liquids in live-fire training at acquired structures.

- Assess all factors in the fire room that could affect the growth, development, and spread of the fire, in order to predict fire behavior.

- Remove all highly combustible materials from the structure, including carpets, floor coverings, foam mattresses, and furniture.

- Document and check against the materials and construction requirements allowed in a live-fire training evolution per NFPA® 1403:

— Furnishings

— Wall and floor coverings and ceiling materials

— Type of construction of the structure (type of roof and combustible void spaces)

● Document the dimensions of the fire room.

● Ensure that a safety officer supervises while a designated ignition officer ignites the fire.

NIST Study on Fuel Pallet Size in Training Evolutions

NIST recently completed a scientific study of two firefighter training deaths at live-fire incidents. The first was in an acquired structure; the second was in a purpose-built burn building at a training facility. In both cases, the supervising instructors increased the fire loads beyond safe levels, despite having started the scenario with fire pallets that were within acceptable limits.

In the case of the purpose-built burn building the instructor in charge added a polyurethane couch mattress to the fuel load after the original fuel load produced smoke but very little fire. After allowing the mattress to burn in a closed room, firefighters entered to extinguish the fire. But the structure was filled with smoke and they became disoriented. After they had been in the structure for three minutes, the outside vent team broke a window in the burn room. The resulting backdraft killed the firefighters inside.

In the case of the acquired structure, the instructor was killed when his personal protective equipment (PPE) failed. The training fire had been burning all day, with the instructor adding fuel periodically to ensure that the fire was burning adequately for the next training evolution. But the structure had no windows and was built to contain heat, so after five evolutions, the heat trapped inside the structure had risen to dangerous levels. When the instructor entered to add fuel for the sixth evolution, his PPE could not withstand the high temperatures.

NIST is continuing to research these incidents and has been conducting experiments using fuel pallets of varying sizes and with varying materials to better understand what fuel materials and pallet sizes are the safest for use in training scenarios. As their research continues, instructors are cautioned to always follow the proper protocols for fuel loads and pallet sizes.

Further information on this study can be found in the following NIST document:

Fatal Training Fires: Fire Analysis for the Fire Service

By Daniel Madrzykowski

Water Supply Requirements. Water supply requirements for fire fighting in rural and suburban areas are provided in NFPA® 1142. These requirements should be applied to fire attack during live-fire training evolutions. There must be reliable water sources for the duration of any live-fire evolution. In this sense, water supply operations during a live-fire exercise represent the equivalent water supplies needed at actual fires.

Many acquired structures are in locations that are not convenient to hydrants or other water sources. These locations provide an excellent opportunity for training evolutions on water shuttle, portable dump tank, large-diameter hose deployment, drafting, and relay pumping operations. After completing training about how to get water to the location, the live-fire exercise can continue at the acquired structure.

Figure 7.13 Permanent training structures are found on many fire training grounds.

Purpose-Built Structures

Purpose-built structures are usually found at permanent training facilities **(Figure 7.13)**. These structures typically have temperature sensors to monitor the rate of temperature rise within the unit. Fuel sources may be LPG, natural gas, or Class A materials such as untreated lumber or straw.

All interior structural fire training evolutions must meet the requirements of NFPA® 1403. The safety requirements discussed earlier in this chapter from NFPA® 1403 that apply to acquired structures also apply to purpose-built structures with the following exceptions:

- Multiple fires can be lit in purpose-built structures.
- A single water supply may be used.
- Additional requirements for testing and inspection of burn structures.

Exterior Fires

Exterior fire-suppression training may include evolutions that simulate low fire load fires, transportation fires, flammable/combustible liquids fires, and wildland fires. This training can be conducted at a permanent training facility or a remote site, with one or more companies or training agencies. Depending upon the location of the training and the type of fuel used (such as Class B fuels), there may be environmental requirements that should be met. Instructors should check with the AHJ that enforces the federal environmental regulations. In addition, many exterior fires such as those with exterior props or Class B materials may be governed by requirements in NFPA® 1403.

Figure 7.14 Small prop fires are versatile in outdoor training evolutions.

Small Prop Fires. These fires are used to train entry-level students and industrial fire brigade members how to use portable handheld extinguishers to control all classes of fires **(Figure 7.14)**. Training evolutions usually take place outside, in an area where the spread of fire is limited or nonexistent. They involve small quantities of fuel, which typically consists of Class A materials (in the form of shipping pallets) or Class B materials contained in small burn pans. Similar LPG- or natural gas-supplied burn pans are also available.

Instructors demonstrate the appropriate procedure based on the type of fuel and extinguisher, and students then repeat the procedure, practicing it until they are proficient. In all cases, a backup extinguishing system must be present, usually in the form of an experienced crew with a charged attack hoseline.

Medium to Large Prop Fires. These training fires use permanent training props that are contained in burn pits. They are typically fueled by Class B materials such as LPG, natural gas, or other flammable/combustible liquids. Valves located outside the pit and supervised by a fuel-control officer are used to turn off fuel supplies. An ignition officer is designated to start the fire using an approved ignition device, sometimes with an electrically energized source. Medium to large props include the following:

- Vehicle fire props
- Dumpster fire props **(Figure 7.15)**
- Shipboard props
- Aircraft fire simulators **(Figure 7.16, p.214)**
- Railcars
- Propane tanks
- Mobile props specifically designed to simulate flammable liquid and gas fires using propane

Figure 7.15 Dumpster fire props are typically fueled by Class B materials.

Flammable/Combustible liquid fires. Simulating fires in flammable/combustible liquid, LPG, and natural gas storage, production, and pipeline facilities is usually restricted to purpose-built props in permanent training facilities **(Figure 7.17, p.214)**. They require piped fuel supplies, control valves, product- and water-containment diking, high-capacity water supplies, and water-decontamination capabilities. Evolutions generally involve multiple-company training.

Wildland fires. Training fire personnel to control wildland and/or **wildland/ urban interface** (areas where structures mix with wildland fuels) fires can take the following two approaches:

1. Specialized training for organizations that are responsible only for protecting forests and wildland areas.

2. General training for structural firefighters who may be responsible for limited areas of wildland, or areas that include the wildland/urban interface.

In some areas of North America, the training for both groups focuses on the extreme dangers that wildland fires can pose. In other areas, structural firefighters may only receive limited training, involving off-road driving and pumping skills, fire attack, and exposure protection.

Wildland/Urban Interface — Line, area, or zone where an undeveloped wildland area meets a human development area. *Also known as* Urban/ Wildland Interface.

Figure 7.16 Aircraft fire props are contained in burn pits.

Figure 7.17 Foam application training is practiced with flammable/combustible liquid fires.

Training evolutions vary, depending on the skills required to meet the local dangers that wildland fires create. The nature of wildland fires makes them unpredictable and highly hazardous. A controlled burn can be affected by weather, wind direction, and other factors beyond the instructor's control, so training students on safety is even more of a concern during this type of training. The National Wildland Coordinating Group (NWCG) provides national standards for wildland training.

Additional Increased Hazard Exposure Training

The expanding role of fire and emergency services in protecting life and property has increased the demand for technical training evolutions involving activities other than fire suppression. While live-fire training remains the most hazardous, there are many other types of hazardous training that require a high level of attention to safety. Although these types of training are more likely to result in injury than fatalities, the potential for fatalities is still very real. Examples of other increased hazard exposure training evolutions include the following:

- Emergency vehicle operations **(Figure 7.18)**
- Vehicle and machinery extrications
- Surface-water, swift-water, and dive rescues
- Building collapse search and rescue operations
- Hazardous materials technician skill exercises
- High-angle rescue operations
- Trench shoring and rescue operations
- Ice rescues
- Power tool and equipment operations
- Confined-space entry rescue operations

Figure 7.18 Skid trainers like the one attached to this apparatus are designed to simulate inclement weather conditions and help driver/operators improve their driving techniques.

EMS Skill-Based Training

EMS instructors have a similar mandate to fire instructors: offering safe skills training on topics for professional certification. They must understand jurisdictional protocols and operating procedures and integrate these into their training. EMS training is similar to fire service training in that there are specific competencies that need to be taught, many of which adhere to national standards. Some of the skill topics that EMS instructors may teach are as follows:

- **Emergency vehicle operations** — Designed to meet U.S. DOT standards for EMT drivers. Includes defensive driving techniques.

- **Mass casualty and triage operations** — Typically part of a major disaster drill with simulated mass casualties, involving numerous agencies and jurisdictions. Training is coordinated between rescuers, medical aid workers, and hospitals.

- **Patient handling** — Proper techniques for safely lifting, moving, and packaging patients so that neither the EMS provider nor the patient sustain injury.

- **Bloodborne pathogens and Body Substance Isolation (BSI)** — Techniques for preventing contact with a patient's bodily fluids; intended to minimize the chance of contracting a disease or illness.

- **Invasive skill training** — Training in invasive procedures such as intravenous cannulation (IV) and endotracheal intubation (ET).

- **Patient care** — Includes trauma care, cardiopulmonary resuscitation (CPR), automated external defibrillator (AED) training, treating exposure patients, and field communications and documentation.

- **Scene safety** — Techniques for ensuring personal safety at a scene; may include information on weather conditions, hazardous materials, dealing with agitated patients, and situational awareness.

- **Equipment training** — Includes ambulance hydraulic lifts, stair chairs, and diagnostic tools.

- **Documentation** — Proper techniques for completing the patient care report (PCR) required by the state or local agency. This includes a detailed description of the patient's condition and any treatment procedures.

Legal Liability

Liability — To be legally obligated or responsible for an act or physical condition; *opposite of* Immunity.

Liability is a broad term that encompasses all aspects of legal responsibility. A person or organization can be held liable for both acts they take and actions they fail to take. A wrongful act resulting in harm is known as an *act of commission*, and the person or organization who commits such an act is responsible for correcting it. Neglecting to take an action that could have prevented harm is known as an *act of omission*, and the person or organization who failed to act is responsible for the consequences. Instructors and/or organizations may be considered liable for any of the following acts:

- Providing incorrect information or instruction

- Failing to instruct in a topic they are responsible for teaching

- Teaching a topic they are unqualified to teach

Instructors can reduce the potential for liability and legal action against themselves and their organizations in the following ways:

- Being aware of standard expectations

- Teaching to the standards

- Teaching only topics for which they meet all qualifications

- Providing a safe learning environment

Instructors are expected to foresee (predict) potential injuries that could happen during training events and prevent injuries while training personnel for appropriate performance on the job. Students are trained in a nonemergency environment for skills that will take place in an emergency environment. Students are learning how to perform high-hazard activities that they are initially not fully competent to perform. Instructors must foresee instructional problems and ensure that they can appropriately perform and demonstrate the skills in a thorough step-by-step introduction and then properly supervise the practice of those skills.

Training should be realistic but controlled. Instructors who fail to properly control hazards during training leave themselves and the training organization liable for any injuries that result **(Figure 7.19)**. Such failure could be interpreted as negligence in a court.

NOTE: Injuries that result from emergency scene situations have special legal defenses that do not apply to training environment situations.

Training in the fire and emergency services will always carry an element of risk, so even if the instructor takes every possible precaution, students may still be injured. However, if the instructor has done a good job of controlling risk, these injuries will likely be the result of unavoidable accidents or student misconduct, not of negligence.

When planning training evolutions or scenarios, instructors should consider the answers to the following questions:

- Can instructors be held liable for actions of students who irresponsibly act on their own?
- Can individuals be held personally liable for contributing to their own injuries and the injuries of others?
- To what extent are employers liable for injuries caused by their employees?

The sections that follow explain the concepts of vicarious liability and foreseeability, and list precautions to help prevent instructor liability. Along with the precautions for preventing instructor liability, steps are given that can reduce the possibility of personal liability.

Figure 7.19 Training situations should be safe and controlled while teaching students the skills they will need to know in similar situations.

Vicarious Liability

Vicarious liability means that the blame for the actions of one person can be placed on another. It is the liability that is placed on the employer for the acts and omissions of employees during the normal course of their employment. For instructors, the liability is placed on them for the acts and omissions of students. In training situations, individuals are responsible for their own negligent actions that cause injury to themselves or others if and only if it can be shown that the instructor made every effort to prevent the actions through proper training before the actions were taken.

Foreseeability

Foreseeability is the legal concept that reasonable people should be able to foresee the consequences of their actions and take reasonable precautions. For instructors, this means that based on their knowledge of the hazard/risk analysis, they should be able to predict hazardous training conditions and take steps to reduce the risk of injury. If they do not, they may be liable for any resulting injuries. Foreseeability also applies to the risks that students face once they have left the training environment and perform their daily jobs. Instructors must foresee the risk students will face there and prepare them to properly handle that risk.

What This Means to You

Consider a scenario in which you are scheduled to conduct a training session on ladder raises. On the day before training, it rains, and overnight the standing water freezes on the ground at the training structure. The training had been scheduled for months, and it would be difficult for the students to reschedule, so you decide to hold the training anyway. While raising a ladder, one of the students slips on the ice, falls, and dislocates his elbow. Because a reasonable person would have foreseen that icy conditions were a hazard during this kind of training, you as the instructor could be held liable for the student's injury. The foreseeable danger posed by the ice means that you should have cancelled training, even though rescheduling would have been difficult.

Liability Reduction

Generally speaking, the best way to reduce liability for any individual training scenario is to develop an IAP or safety plan, then follow it during training. If necessary, a safety or planning committee can help the instructor to develop the plan. More specific precautions an instructor can take to avoid liability include the following:

- Maintain written objectives and document each training session.

- Provide students with a written course description so they can understand all requirements.

- Ensure that students are physically fit for the tasks, based on the benchmarks for fitness set by the AHJ.

- Train all students how to safely operate equipment.

- Do not leave students unattended while they are practicing potentially dangerous skills.

- Do not exceed personal skill level when training students or working with other instructors.

- Do not ignore, shortcut, or exceed protocols or policies.

- Use as many ways as possible to ensure that students understand the intent and outcome of all directives or instructions, as well as the consequences for not following procedures. Never assume that they will understand without explanation. Tell them, show them, and give it to them in writing.

- Do not joke about serious situations or belittle the actions of others in any learning or service situation.

- Never disclose personal information (except to appropriate authorities) about students, other personnel, or any victim or patient who required emergency services.

- Follow your organization's policy on disclosing information to insurance companies, hospital personnel, legal representatives, news reporters, or other persons who want information about ongoing litigation. These policies also apply to issues that have the potential to be litigated.

- Maintain current certifications through credible refresher courses. *I didn't know* is never an acceptable defense.

- When in doubt, seek advice from a higher authority. Never attempt to make decisions that are beyond your personal knowledge or authority.

- Accurately document all issues of discrepancy, complaint, and injury, including details on dates, times, conversations, suggested resolutions, and follow-up plans.

State of New York v. Baird

On September 25, 2001, a 19-year-old male volunteer firefighter (the victim) died and two male volunteer firefighters (Firefighter #1 and Firefighter #2) were injured during a multiagency, live-burn training session. The victim and Firefighter #1 were playing the roles of firefighters who had become trapped on the second level of the structure. The training became reality when the fire was started and progressed up the stairwell, accelerated by a foam mattress that was ignited on the first floor. The victim died of asphyxiation and burns. Firefighter #1 was severely injured, as was Firefighter #2 when he went in to rescue the trapped firefighters.

Following this event, the lead instructor, Chief Allen Baird III, was tried in the New York court system as the party responsible for the training. He was convicted of criminally negligent homicide for violating established standards and guidelines by using his students as victims during the training. For more information about this training incident, refer to NIOSH investigative report #F2001-38.

Chapter Summary

Safety is an instructor's most critical responsibility during training, whether it is psychomotor skills training, a simple training evolution, or high-hazard training. Ensuring safety requires careful planning, inspection of training locations, and thorough knowledge of appropriate standards, especially during live-fire training at an acquired structure.

Instructors should use every resource at their disposal to plan safe training. Instructors should know what facilities are available to them for training including any remote sites, acquired structures, or permanent training facilities. They should be familiar with the standards, laws, and regulations adopted in their jurisdictions and follow them without exception. In any training situation, instructors must ensure that they are qualified to teach the subject matter. If an instructor's qualifications are in doubt or they do not comply with the local jurisdiction, training should be postponed until the instructor meets qualifications or a better qualified instructor can be located.

Instructors should understand their legal liability and take steps to minimize it. They should also know how to conduct themselves professionally when dealing with any liability cases that arise.

Review Questions

1. Where can instructors receive the most current information about safety guidelines and regulations?

2. How can instructors increase awareness and help prevent training accidents?

3. What actions are required for planning for safe training?

4. What are the elements involved with evolution control?

5. What information is needed to begin a skills demonstration?

6. What is the difference between a psychomotor skills training and simple training evolution?

7. What conditions affect safety during live-fire training?

8. What are five examples of increased hazard exposure training other than live-fire training?

9. What skills-based training should a qualified EMS instructor teach?

10. When can an instructor be considered liable?

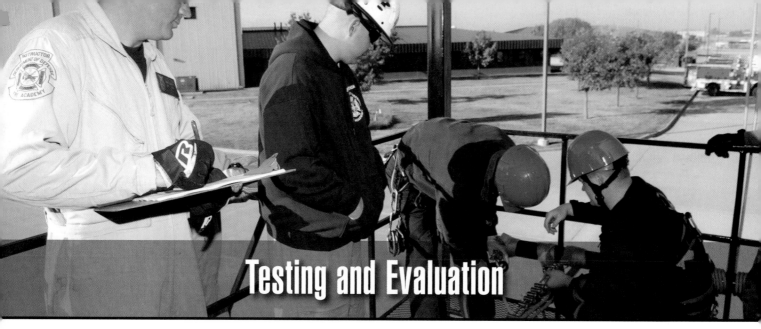

Testing and Evaluation

Chapter Contents

Key Terms

Job Performance Requirements

NFPA® 1041 References

4.5.2

4.5.3

4.5.4

4.5.5

Testing and Evaluation

1. Discuss the two ways to assess a student's success. [NFPA® 1041, 4.5.3]

2. Identify the six classifications of tests. [NFPA® 1041, 4.5.2; 4.5.3]

3. Discuss test bias. [NFPA® 1041, 4.5.2]

4. Describe the process of test administration. [NFPA® 1041, 4.5.2]

5. Explain the different processes of scoring and grading tests. [NFPA® 1041, 4.5.3]

6. Explain the importance of accurate grade reporting. [NFPA® 1041, 4.5.4]

7. Identify guidelines to reduce academic misconduct. [NFPA® 1041, 4.5.2; 4.5.3]

8. Discuss the benefits of instructor feedback on student outcomes. [NFPA® 1041, 4.5.5]

Chapter 8
Testing and Evaluation

Case History

During the administration of a written test, the instructor used his time to review the lesson plan that he intended to teach the following day and did not pay attention to the students taking the written test. The instructor rationalized this use of time because no students were talking during the test, so that must mean that security was satisfactory. Unfortunately, the instructor failed to notice that several students were using PDAs to communicate with each other. The test results had to be discarded because several students had cheated due to the instructor's lack of supervision of the test takers.

Evaluation is the last step in the four-step method of instruction (See Chapter 6, Classroom Instruction) and is accomplished through observation and testing. The purpose of student evaluations and testing is to determine how well students have learned and retained the course material. While evaluation is often used to assign grades or scores, it should also result in feedback for students. This feedback gives students a clear idea of what they have learned and what they still need to learn.

Evaluating student progress or performance requires a stated performance criterion. To determine whether this criterion has been met, instructors must either observe students directly or use testing instruments. Watching students perform skills, respond to questions, participate in discussions, and participate in practical training evolutions are all ways that instructors observe students. Evaluation instruments include quizzes, written reports or research papers, oral tests, written tests, and timed skill performance tests.

The organization may develop tests internally or purchase them from a test-writing organization. In either case, tests must be valid and reliable based on the organization's job requirements or course or class learning objectives.

This chapter focuses on the formal evaluation and testing duties of Level I Instructors as defined in NFPA® 1041, *Standard for Fire Service Instructor Professional Qualifications.* Level I Instructors are responsible for performing the following duties:

- Administering oral, written, and performance examinations
- Scoring examinations and determining grades
- Reporting examination results to the administration of the training division or organization
- Providing security for testing materials and processes
- Providing feedback to students based on both informal and formal evaluations

Approaches to Student Assessment

Examinations used to certify personnel are used to determine mastery of a subject or topic. Personnel must have a complete and thorough knowledge of the subject and the ability to recall and apply the knowledge. Assessing or evaluating student success may be accomplished either through norm-referenced or criterion-referenced assessment. Both of these approaches have their strengths and weaknesses, as described in the sections that follow.

Norm-Referenced Assessments

The traditional approach to teaching is based on **norm-referenced assessment**, which measures the accomplishment of one student against that of another. At the end of an instructional unit, an exam is given, the results are scored, and the scores are translated into grades. These grades are often based on the distribution of scores, which can be either normal or bell-shaped. This type of assessment is used for some **evaluations** in the fire and emergency services, including promotional testing and determining ranking in recruit academies.

Criterion-Referenced Assessments

A **criterion** (plural: criteria) is a standard on which to base a decision or judgment. In the context of training, a student's grade is based on whether or not they meet the criteria that are defined in the learning objectives, and all course activities should be designed to help students reach this goal.

Criterion-referenced assessment compares student performance with the criteria stated in the learning objectives, not with the performance of other students as in the case of the norm-referenced assessment. Although each student's performance varies somewhat from another's, any performance is considered acceptable as long as it meets the conditions stated in the criteria.

Using the criterion-referenced approach, test scores translate to either a passing or failing grade, depending on whether the student has met or failed to meet the criteria. For example, if the criterion for performance on an end-of-instruction exam is 70 percent, any grade of 70 or higher is a Pass, while anything below 70 is a No Pass/Fail.

A similar approach may be used to evaluate psychomotor skills, in which the student either passes or fails a manipulative skills test. In an SCBA test, for example, students are required to accurately don an SCBA in a fixed amount of time. Using a skills checklist and a timer, instructors can assess whether students have completed the skill quickly and accurately enough **(Figure 8.1)**. If they do, they pass, but if they do not, they fail. In some skills, a single step may be so critical that performing it incorrectly may result in a failing grade, even though the rest of the skill was performed perfectly.

Norm-Referenced Assessment — Form of assessment in which a student's performance is compared to that of other students. Grades are determined by comparing scores to the class average, and assigning grades based on where students scored compared to that average.

Evaluation — Systematic and thoughtful collection of information for decision-making; consists of criteria, evidence, and judgment.

Criterion — The standard against which learning is compared after instruction. Plural for the term is *criteria*.

Criterion-Referenced Assessment — Measurement of individual performance against a set standard or criteria, not against other students. Mastery learning is the key element to criterion-referenced testing.

Figure 8.1 Using a skills checklist will help the instructor evaluate skills completely and consistently.

Test Classifications

Both criterion-referenced and norm-referenced tests can be divided into more specific classifications, based on the reason for testing and the way the test is administered. No single test type is suitable for every situation, so it is important that instructors be familiar with test classifications (purpose and administration) and be able to select the one that will be the best measure of learning.

Purpose Classification

The **purpose classification** is based on the reasons a test is given and the point at which it is given during instruction. Test types include prescriptive, formative, and summative tests.

Prescriptive (Pretest)

Prescriptive tests are given at the beginning of instruction to establish a student's current level of knowledge, in order to compare it to a subsequent summative evaluation. Comparing the two scores measures the amount of learning that has occurred.

Formative (Progress)

Formative tests may be quizzes, pop tests, or question/answer periods that are given throughout the course or session. These tests typically measure improvement and give the instructor and students feedback on learning progress. When measuring improvement, the test answers the question: *Is the student achieving the objectives?* Tests can include the most important learning objectives, or all of them if possible. Each test item should be designed to a level of difficulty that matches the learning objective it is meant to measure. Doing so helps to ensure that the test is criterion-referenced.

Summative (Comprehensive)

Summative tests measure comprehensive knowledge and skills at the end of a course, or of a major segment of the course. These tests answer the question: *Has the student achieved the course objectives?*

Purpose Classification — Means of classifying tests based on when the test occurs during a course.

Prescriptive Test — Test given at the beginning of instruction to determine what students already know; alternatively, a test that is given remedially.

Formative Test — Ongoing, repeated assessment during a course to evaluate student progress; may also help determine any needed changes in instructional content, methods, training aids, and testing techniques.

Summative Test — Evaluation that measures students' learning at the conclusion of a training session or course; the test results can also be used to measure the effects and effectiveness of a course or program.

Examples of comprehensive tests would be the written and/or practical exams given at the midpoint or end of emergency medical technician (EMT), basic fire fighting, or driver/operator courses. Students who are tested must demonstrate comprehensive knowledge and skills relating to all material from the beginning of the course to the testing point.

Administration Classification

Administration Classification — Test classification based on how a test is administered.

The **administration classification** is based on how the test is administered, and includes oral, written, and performance tests. The Level I Instructor does not often determine which of these test types to use. That decision is made by the Level II Instructor or agency SOPs, based on the type of learning that is being evaluated. The Level I Instructor should still be familiar with these test types, because he or she may be assigned to administer any of these types of tests.

Oral Tests

During oral tests, the student generally gives verbal answers to spoken questions during a one-on-one interaction with the instructor **(Figure 8.2)**. These tests are not commonly used in the fire and emergency services, but they may be useful under certain circumstances, such as determining a student's understanding at the end of a lesson.

Rubric — Scoring tool that outlines criteria that must be present on exams that are more subjective such as short-answer tests, essay tests, or oral tests; the criteria should be tied to learning objectives.

Administering and scoring of oral tests should follow an established **rubric**. Instructors must listen carefully to student responses in order to prevent misunderstanding, because different students will phrase the same answer in different ways. Instructors should also be careful not to make facial expressions that might confuse or mislead students. Although oral tests can be useful evaluative tools, they should never be used as the sole means of evaluating students' terminal performance for a course or course segment.

Written Tests

Written tests evaluate the accomplishment of cognitive learning objectives. They are useful for measuring retention and understanding of technical subjects, such as fire chemistry, laws and ordinances, hydraulic principles, and medical protocols. Written tests may have numerous question types, including the following:

- **Multiple-choice** — Single question followed by multiple possible answers, of which only one is correct.
- **True/false** —Students determine whether a statement is true or false.
- **Matching** — Students match dates, events, or items from one column with appropriate definitions from a second column.
- **Fill in the blank/completion** — Statement that is missing a word or several words that students must provide.
- **Short-answer** — Question that requires a brief factual answer.
- **Essay** — Question that requires a lengthy, sometimes subjective answer.

Written tests can be administered either by reading them aloud, providing students with a sheet containing the questions, or through electronic media **(Figure 8.3)**. Students write their answers on a blank page, on a formal answer sheet, or in the electronic medium through which the test is administered. The legibility of students' handwriting can be a factor during scoring. Tests that require students to circle, check, or fill in a block reduce the potential for misinterpretation based on handwriting. Whenever possible, use answer sheets that can be read, scored, and recorded electronically.

Computers are an increasingly popular method of administering written tests. Students take the test in a testing center or computer lab, and the testing program scores the results and records them in a database. This method can be used for any type of training course, and is the only way to administer tests for Web-based and Internet training programs. One advantage of this method is that it allows the instructor to create realistic scenarios that require the student to evaluate a situation and determine the correct response.

Performance Tests

Performance tests measure students' ability to perform skills and tasks as they would on the job, based on standardized criteria and performance objectives. They are tested on their abilities rather than their future potential to complete the skill. When preparing to administer a performance test, instructors should perform the following tasks:

- Determine the materials, tools, or equipment that students must have in order to perform the skills or activities. Make sure that they are available, and in working order **(Figure 8.4)**.

- Prepare a skill checklist, along with appropriate time limits for each of the steps necessary to perform the skill. The checklist provides/establishes/defines the criteria by which to assess the students' performance and indicates any steps that must be completed in order for the student to pass.

- Determine the number of test evaluators needed to observe and measure (by checklist) the performances of students.

- Review the operation of unfamiliar equipment with all instructors and test evaluators, who may be either internal or external to the organization.

Objective-based performance checklists can help prevent inaccurate assessments that are based only on the evaluators' subjective judgment. A subjective judgment is one that is based on personal preference or bias, which some evaluators may find difficult to set aside. Some test evaluators may find it difficult to completely lay aside their personal attitudes and neutrally judge the performance of

Figure 8.2 Occasionally the instructor may employ an oral exam to evaluate a student's knowledge.

Figure 8.3 Written test booklets are a common evaluation tool.

Figure 8.4 Instructors should ensure that all equipment needed for a performance evaluation is organized and available before a performance test.

the students. The specific criteria on the checklist help to ensure that evaluators will make neutral, objective assessments of the students' performances rather than subjective ones.

Test Bias

A test is considered biased when members of different groups (age, cultural and ethnic background, gender) with the same ability level routinely score differently on a test. Bias can be difficult to prove because tests are designed to discriminate between those that know the information in the test and those that do not. Discrimination is based on ability. Bias, in contrast, is an indication that the test puts one particular group at a disadvantage to another.

Level I Instructors have an obligation to eliminate testing bias wherever they can. The best way to do this, is for Level I Instructors to suggest that tests that have any of the following qualities be rewritten or more closely examined:

- Gender references (personal pronouns and proper names) are all from the same gender.

- Ethnic references are stereotypical and/or irrelevant to the test.

- Cultural references do not reflect the cultural knowledge of the likely testing group or are irrelevant to the test.

- Regional jargon or dialects are used in the questions could put students from a different region at a disadvantage.

- Terminology and vocabulary in the test are unfamiliar to the students taking the test.

In legal terms, certification skills tests and promotional tests are grouped together under the larger title *employment tests* or *selection tests*. Typically, employment tests are either entry tests for getting a job or tests for reaching a promotion after training. In the United States, the Equal Employment Opportunity Commission (EEOC) has the responsibility of investigating any bias on employment tests. In order to avoid any legal liability, Level I Instructors should follow any scoring rubrics and answer keys that have been provided to them. They should also teach to the learning objectives in provided lesson plans.

Test Administration

Administration of a test begins before the test is given, when instructors inform students what type of test they will take, what content it will cover, and which materials they will need to bring to class (paper, pencil, pen, notes, books, etc.). The course syllabus should also contain the dates and times of major tests or periodic quizzes. On the day of the test, the instructor should consider the physical environment of the classroom, making sure that students have the following **(Figure 8.5)**:

- Appropriate lighting
- Comfortable seating
- Quiet surroundings
- Regulated temperature
- Proactive responses to performance barriers

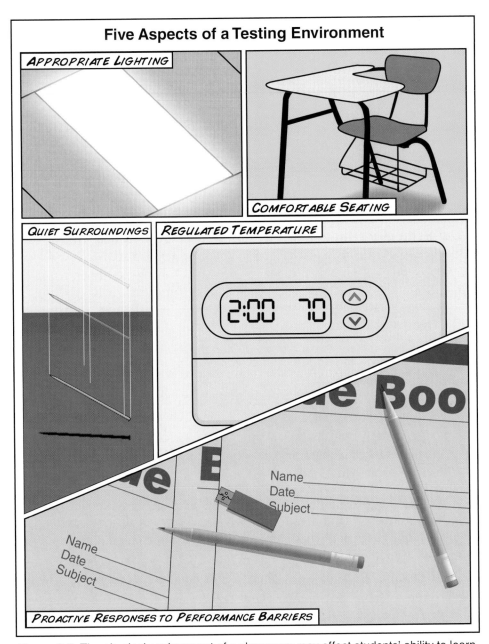

Figure 8.5 The physical environment of a classroom may affect students' ability to learn.

Administering Written Tests

Instructors should adhere to the following guidelines when administering written tests:

- Before the test:
  — Ask the testing organization or agency to determine whether there are any specific instructions or protocols for administering the test.
  — Report to the testing location an appropriate amount of time before testing begins.
  — Maintain security of tests at all times.
  — Rearrange classroom seating when necessary so that it is conducive for taking written tests.

— Eliminate loud talking or noises outside the testing room.

— Eliminate all potential distractions within the room.

— Number each page of all tests and answer sheets.

— Assign a number to each test and answer sheet, then collect them all at the end of the test.

— Ensure that all cellular phones, smart phones, mp3 players, and pagers are turned off and put away.

— Make sure that students do not bring written or electronic notes into the testing room, unless these are specifically approved by the examination guidelines.

- During the test:

  — Watch for signs of academic misconduct, such as:

    - Students whose eyes "wander" around the room.

    - Answers written on clothing, skin, or shoes, or on papers lying on the floor near students' desks.

    - Students talking to each other during the test.

  — Ensure that the environment remains quiet and safe for students.

  — Have students place all backpacks, purses, books, and other unnecessary items at the front of the room.

  — If students leave the testing area to use the restroom, refreshment area, or other rehabilitation facilities, make sure they do not take the test instrument or paper with them.

  — Supply extra paper, writing implements, and answer sheets.

  — If possible, have testing aides on hand to assist with difficult students or situations, or to perform tasks such as handing out or collecting tests and evaluation forms.

  — Ensure that students have followed instructions on the answer sheet correctly when they finish the test. Only accept students' test forms and answer sheets when they are complete.

  — Do not allow students to change their answers once answer sheets have been submitted.

- After the test:

  — Review the test (at an appropriate time) with students to clarify any objectives they may not have understood. This may occur at the following class in the case of formative tests but may not be possible with summative tests.

  — Maintain the security of tests and answer sheets, especially when scoring tests and recording grades.

  — Return test materials to the proper authority if another instructor will be scoring and grading them.

  — Identify answer sheets with identical incorrect answers or sequences of answers on multiple test sheets. These could be indications of academic misconduct.

Administering Performance Tests

Specific guidelines for administering performance tests are as follows:

Figure 8.6 Be sure to read the test instructions to the students as written to make sure they understand what is required.

- Before the test:
  - Ensure that the subject matter of the test matches the subject matter that is being tested.
  - Provide students with adequate practice time during class time leading up to the test date.
  - Provide rehabilitation facilities, such as restrooms or refreshment areas.
  - Ensure that tests are not biased through wording, timing, or unattainable criteria.
  - Include all test administration rules in the test instructions.
  - Read the instructions aloud to the students exactly as they are written. Do not paraphrase because this may alter the test results **(Figure 8.6)**.
  - Provide students with the time limits for each test and clearly state the times for emphasis.
  - Explain the purpose of each test.
  - Encourage students to ask questions if they do not understand something.
- During the test:
  - Give the test to each student in exactly the same manner.
  - Record students' scores on performance checklists as each one takes the test. Do not wait until the end of the testing period to record scores.
- After the test — Keep all test scores confidential.

Test Scoring

After administering a test, instructors collect answer sheets or performance checklists, then score and grade the tests. *Scoring* is the act of identifying which answers are right and which are wrong. Scoring should always be objective, and based on established criteria **(Figure 8.7, p.234)**. *Grading* is the act of assigning a value to the score. For example, the instructor determines that a score of 75 points is a C grade. The sections that follow describe these two steps as they relate to evaluation of student performance on oral, written, and performance tests.

Scoring Written Tests

Scoring methods for written tests can be very simple, such as assigning 1 point per test item on a test containing 100 test items. Tests may also give more weight to some test items than others. For example, a test with 52 test items (50 multiple-choice, 2 essay items) might have the points divided with 1 point for each multiple-choice item and 25 points for each essay. Tests may also assign a higher point value to questions that address more critical learning objectives. Regardless of how tests are scored, the scoring method should always be indicated on the exam.

Composite scoring used for criterion-referenced tests is based on a point system that encompasses an entire course; each scored item in the course is added to a grand total to determine a final score for the entire course. Lesson or

Chapter 6 Break a Door Lock Checklist

Name_____ Date _____

JOB STEPS	ATTEMPT NO.		
	1	2	3

Using a K-Tool

1. Size up the situation.   ___ ___ ___

    a. Status/location of fire   ___ ___ ___

    b. Windows in/near door   ___ ___ ___

2. Try the door.   ___ ___ ___

3. Examine the lock to determine the type of staple and metal.   ___ ___ ___

4. Select the appropriate tool for lock type.   ___ ___ ___

5. Adjust your protective gear.   ___ ___ ___

    a. Lowering faceshield, if not wearing SCBA   ___ ___ ___

    b. Donning gloves   ___ ___ ___

6. Using the driver, force the K-tool behind the ring and face of the
   lock cylinder.   ___ ___ ___

7. Insert a prying tool into the metal loop on the front of the K-tool. ___ ___ ___

8. Pry the cylinder from the door using the K-tool as a fulcrum.   ___ ___ ___

9. Move the locking bolt to the open position.   ___ ___ ___

    a. Inserting either end of key tool into hole made by removed
          cylinder (lock hub)   ___ ___ ___

    b. Manipulating and rotating tool until bolt moves to open position ___ ___ ___

    Note: If, for any reason, this method fails, insert the straight end
   of the K-tool through the cylinder hole and drive the lock off the
   door with an axe.

Time (Total)   ___ ___ ___

EVALUATOR'S COMMENTS

_____

_____

_____

Page 1 of 2

Figure 8.7 Scoring sheets and checklists should ask for objective information.

Using An A-Tool

1. Size up the situation.   — — —

     a. Status/location of fire   — — —

     b. Windows in/near door   — — —

2. Try the door.   — — —

3. Examine the lock to determine the type of staple and metal.   — — —

4. Select the appropriate tool for lock type.   — — —

5. Adjust your protective gear.   — — —

     a. Lowering faceshield, if not wearing SCBA   — — —

     b. Donning gloves   — — —

6. Using the driver, force the jaws of the A-tool around and behind the protruding rim of the cylinder.   — — —

7. Gouge the wood around the cylinder with A-tool chisel head for a better bite if necessary.   — — —

8. Pry the cylinder from the door, using the A-tool's curved head as a fulcrum.   — — —

9. Move the locking bolt to the open position.   — — —

     a. Inserting either end of key tool into hole made by removed cylinder (lock hub)   — — —

     b. Manipulating and rotating tool until bolt moves to open position   — — —

        Note: If, for any reason, this method fails, insert the straight end of A-tool through the cylinder hole and drive the lock off the door with an axe.   — — —

                          Time (Total)   — — —

EVALUATOR'S COMMENTS

_____

_____

_____

Page 2 of 2

course outlines establish the point value of all activities, assignments, or tests. Instructors then add the points to determine the total points earned by a student during the course.

Written tests can be scored either manually or using an electronic scoring device. Tests administered on computers are scored automatically and the results are posted to student files in the course database. While the electronic scorer is easy and fast to use, it can be costly to purchase and require the use of specific types of answer forms. Electronic scorers can also make errors that require the instructor to re-score the tests manually. Some guidelines for scoring written tests manually include the following:

- Score the same question on all of the tests before proceeding to the next question on short-answer or essay exams. This guideline improves scoring consistency and permits instructors to identify any questions that have resulted in a large number of incorrect answers.

- Read through several responses before scoring essay or short-answer tests. This technique is especially helpful when variations on answers are possible.

- Add comments to essay or short-answer questions to indicate what is missing or congratulate the student on exceptionally good work. Be specific, and avoid sarcastic or overly negative comments. Scoring is an extension of teaching, and this practice acts as positive reinforcement and motivation for students.

- Shuffle the papers before scoring the next question after scoring one set of questions on all the tests. This guideline helps offset the potential fatigue that instructors can experience and reduce the potential for scoring errors.

- Do not attempt to score large numbers of tests at one time. Take breaks or work on other projects between sets of papers.

- Indicate, using lines or arrows, which comments refer to which words or portions of the answer.

- Inform students about the meaning of scoring marks that are used in essay or short-answer question tests.

- Identify a maximum of three strengths and three weaknesses of an answer when scoring an essay or short-answer question. More than three can overwhelm the student.

- Use the provided rubric to identify the key points that should be addressed in each essay or short-answer response **(Figure 8.8)**.

Instructors who teach distance-learning courses need to take into consideration the limited contact they have with their students. Some factors to consider are as follows:

- Classes in a distance-learning format take much more preparation time for educators than the same classes in a face-to-face setting.

- Test papers and written assignments take longer to travel between students and instructors, so it will take instructors more time to return graded tests or assignments. Online courses do not have this time delay.

- Over the length of a course, student improvement takes longer because feedback is not as immediate. Instructors have to work diligently to provide effective and timely feedback to the students.

Fire Instructor I   Student Presentation Evaluation Form

Name:_____ Date:_____

This is the evaluation form for the Fire Instructor I student presentation. A 'Satisfactory' must be obtained on all nine (9) tasks for a successful presentation. Any 'Unsatisfactory' rating will require the student to repeat the presentation. Any notes or comments about the presentation are attached.

Satisfactory: The task is clearly performed without error or hesitation and the task enhanced the presentation and the communication process.

Unsatisfactory: The task is not achieved, or performed with error; the task hampered the communication process and the student's understanding of the concepts.

1. Clearly states purpose of presentation and establishes relevance and benefit to the learner.
   ☐ Satisfactory   ☐ Unsatisfactory

2. Implements motivation strategy according to the lesson plan.
   ☐ Satisfactory   ☐ Unsatisfactory

3. Incorporates appropriate verbal and non-verbal communication techniques in presentation.
   ☐ Satisfactory   ☐ Unsatisfactory

4. Asks appropriate questions to facilitate 2-way communication during presentation.
   ☐ Satisfactory   ☐ Unsatisfactory

5. Engages students in active learning process.
   ☐ Satisfactory   ☐ Unsatisfactory

6. Presents and applies all content points identified in the lesson plan.
   ☐ Satisfactory   ☐ Unsatisfactory

7. Properly uses audiovisual materials and equipment.
   ☐ Satisfactory   ☐ Unsatisfactory

8. Facilitates application of manipulative skills as identified in lesson plan in a safe manner.
   ☐ Satisfactory   ☐ Unsatisfactory

9. Summarizes presentation.
   ☐ Satisfactory   ☐ Unsatisfactory

Overall Presentation was: ☐   **Satisfactory**   ☐   **Unsatisfactory**

Oklahoma Fire Service Training
05/2006

Figure 8.8 An evaluation based on a scoring rubric will identify key points that should be addressed in a student response. *Courtesy of Oklahoma State Fire Service Training.*

- The lack of direct contact between students and instructors makes scoring written work an even more critical task. Scoring criteria, marking notations, and instructor comments must be clear, concise, and constructive. Students should have no doubt about what is expected or how to correct weaknesses in a test answer or assignment.

- When faxing tests, make sure the document you send is in black ink on white paper. Most faxes transmit only in black and white, so colored inks may be illegible, and colored paper may show up as solid black on the receiver's end. Fax transmissions can also be blurry, so format the document in a way that will be readable even if the text does not come through cleanly.

Scoring Oral Tests

Scoring oral tests depends on the purpose of the test, such as promotional exams, and the type of questions asked. The instructor should present the questions as they have been provided on the test and then follow the scoring guidelines provided. The rubric for an oral test is often very similar to performance tests.

Scoring Performance Tests

Scoring performance (psychomotor) tests can be very subjective, so instructors should closely follow the scoring sheet guidelines. These list the tasks students must perform to complete the skill, and assign a point value to each task. When the student completes the task, the evaluator gives the student credit for that task. In some cases, the instructor may give partial credit. For example, a test for an equipment inspection might give some but not all points to a student who found most, but not all, of the flaws in the equipment.

Tasks that directly relate to the life or safety of a patient, student, or other personnel cannot be skipped or performed improperly. These tasks are pass/fail items on the scoring sheets; students must be able to complete all the steps correctly in order to receive credit. In some cases, scoring for these items should also be weighted so that students who fail to perform this task adequately will fail the entire exam, even if they performed perfectly in all other aspects of the test. There are some skills for which none of the tasks can be failed. In this case, the test has a passing grade of 100% and should be scored as such.

When possible, use multiple instructors or test evaluators to observe each student during the test. Having multiple instructors or test evaluators observe each student will result in more consistent and accurate scoring. When evaluating in this fashion, the instructors or evaluators should come to a consensus before assigning the student a score. If they disagree, the student may be asked to perform the skill again or to explain how or why the activity should be performed.

Students must be given a clearly stated set of objectives and the scoring criteria. Instructors should provide immediate feedback while observing the project, especially when safety is a concern.

Grading Fire and Emergency Services Tests

Assigning a grade is very simple after scoring a test. The total number of points the student earned is divided by the total number of points possible to arrive at a percentage grade. This method usually applies to written tests but may also be applicable to performance tests.

There may be situations that require students to get every test item correct in order to pass. In these situations, tests should include questions that attentive students will answer easily. Highly difficult questions on a written test that requires 100% accuracy for completion put students at a disadvantage.

Grading Bias

Grading bias is the practice of assigning grades based not upon students' scores but upon what group they belong to or their personal relationship to the instructor. On objective tests such as multiple choice tests, grading bias is very easy to prove and is considered unethical conduct. Instructors should not deviate from scoring sheets on objective tests.

Subjective tests are more challenging for evaluators to grade. Because the evaluation is open to some interpretation, it is also an area where evaluators may try to influence grades for students that they favor. Level I Instructors who have to evaluate subjective tests should follow provided rubrics and grading checklists. They should also report fellow evaluators who they feel are being biased. In addition, instructors should not succumb to pressure to grade certain students differently than others.

Grade Reporting

Once instructors have scored oral, written, or performance tests, the scores must be recorded and reported in accordance with local procedures or agency policies. Because fire and emergency services students are graded against a set of specific criteria and not against each other, grades are recorded in individual student records and used as feedback for students. Care must be taken to accurately record the grades in student records.

An instructor should follow the provided scoring guidelines to determine a final grade for the course. Students who fail to achieve the minimum required grade should not be recognized as having completed the training.

Testing records are private and confidential, so only instructors, training division administrators, and the student should have access to them. Testing results should be retained in individual student files for the period of time that the AHJ requires and kept private in accordance with specific department/agency policies and applicable laws.

Reporting test results to the training division or organization's administration is necessary for the following two reasons:

1. The organization must know whether a student has met the minimum requirements to effectively perform a duty or task.

2. The test results for all participants in a course provide the training division or administration with an idea of the effectiveness of the course or curriculum. When test results indicate an abnormal number of students did not pass the course, the teaching style, course curriculum, or testing system should then be reevaluated and altered as appropriate.

Test Security

Security of oral, written, performance, and computer-administered tests is essential to an effective training program. While the security of the test results has been stressed to comply with privacy requirements, security of testing instruments is

Academic Misconduct — Any unethical behavior in which students present another student's work as their own, or gain an unfair advantage on a test by bringing answers into the testing area, copying another student's answers, or acquiring test questions in advance.

equally important to prevent **academic misconduct**. Academic misconduct has a broad definition in a training environment, including cheating during exams, acquiring test answers before the exam, allowing another student to complete an assignment, or copying assignments from other students. On tests, academic misconduct presents special problems for instructors — problems that may be reduced by adhering to the following guidelines:

- Follow security measures when writing, duplicating, and storing test materials **(Figure 8.9).**

- Never rely solely on questions published in the textbook or study guide.

- Revise test questions regularly.

- Use secure data storage systems to prevent unauthorized access to tests or grades.

- Require students to use assigned passwords in order to limit access to computer-administered tests.

- Number all test sheets, booklets, and answer sheets, and take inventory after each use.

- Use two or more versions of a single exam to prevent students from copying from each other during the test. The simplest way of doing this is to change the order or the wording of individual questions. When using alternate versions, instructors must take extra care when distributing, collecting, and scoring the tests.

- Store all old test sheets in a secure location.

- Destroy outdated testing materials.

Evaluation Feedback

Conducting formal evaluations based on test results gives instructors the opportunity to use student errors as the basis for reinforcing information that was addressed on the test. These evaluations can be conducted in two ways:

1. Meet individually with students to discuss the test — Individual coaching permits instructors the time to help a student understand the correct answers to missed questions and for instructors to determine whether a student's learning or studying styles were barriers to success **(Figure 8.10)**. Remedial instruction or practice can be recommended for the student or alterations in the presentation or testing methods can be made to assist the student in reaching the desired goal.

2. Review incorrect answers with the entire class — Class review of the questions that were answered incorrectly is an opportunity to review and reinforce the correct answers. Examples:

    — Questions that a majority of students answered incorrectly can be used for group discussions.

    — Class review may help an instructor to rephrase a question so that it is easier for students to understand.

    — Review of performance tests may indicate areas where additional practice can be assigned to ensure that skills are learned properly.

Figure 8.9 Security is crucial. Make sure tests are kept private.

Figure 8.10 Reviewing the test with the student allows the instructor to provide additional assistance.

Chapter Summary

Evaluation and testing allow instructors and training divisions to determine both how well students are learning and how well instructors are teaching. Instructors must know when and how to use different types of formal evaluation and testing. Critical skills for the Level I Instructor to master include properly administering, scoring, and securing tests, and determining and reporting grades. Finally, the instructor must be able to use the test results to give students helpful, accurate, and timely feedback.

Review Questions

1. What are the two ways a student can be assessed?

2. How are tests classified?

3. What is test bias?

4. What steps should an instructor take to properly administer a test?

5. What different methods are used to score tests?

6. To which individuals or agencies are instructors allowed to report grades?

7. Why is test security an important priority?

8. Why should an instructor give purposeful feedback on evaluations?

BOOTS GLOVES	PPE	PPE SCBA	SKILL STATIONS		TIME	TIME	TIME	TIME	TIME	TIME	
		X	SKILL PPE-SCBA Emergency Operations	LOCATION App Bay							
			LEAD INSTRUCTOR Dunham ASST INSTRUCTOR								
		X	SKILL PPE-SCBA-USE IN Restricted Passages	LOCATION Skills Bld							
			LEAD INST Phippen ASST INST								
		OFF X AIR	SKILL PPE-SCBA- Service	LOCATION air fill trailer							
			LEAD INST Ech ASST INST								
		X	SKILL PPE- ... Self Rescue	LOCATION							
			LEAD INST French ASST INST								

Records, Reports, and Scheduling

Chapter Contents

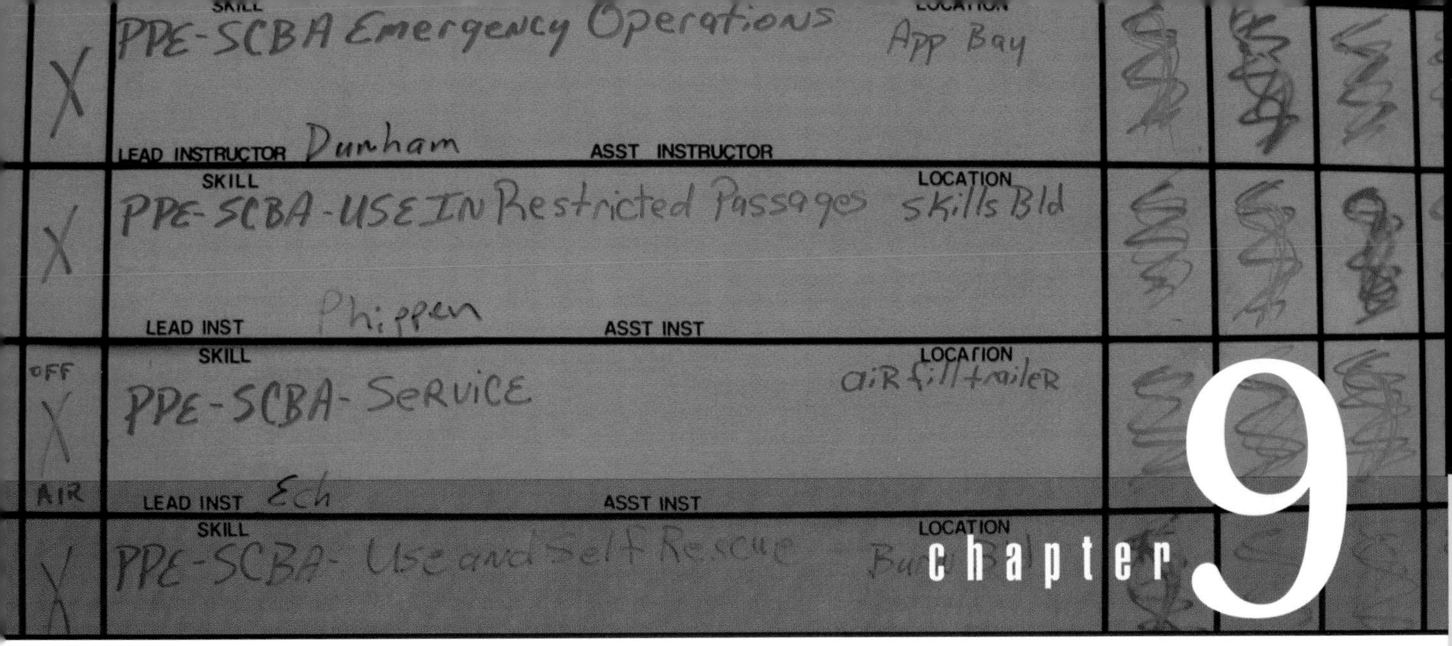
SKILL
PPE-SCBA Emergency Operations
LOCATION
App Bay
LEAD INSTRUCTOR Dunham
ASST INSTRUCTOR
SKILL
PPE-SCBA-USE IN Restricted Passages
LOCATION
skills Bld
LEAD INST Phippen
ASST INST
SKILL
PPE-SCBA-SERVICE
LOCATION
air fill trailer
LEAD INST
ASST INST
SKILL
PPE-SCBA-Use and Self Rescue
LOCATION

chapter 9

Key Terms

Job Performance Requirements

NFPA® 1041 References

4.2.3

4.2.4

4.2.5

Learning Objectives

1. Discuss the difference between records and reports. [NFPA® 1041, 4.2.5]

2. Discuss the types of training records that an instructor may be required to complete. [NFPA® 1041, 4.2.3, 4.2.5]

3. Describe the different parts of most reports. [NFPA® 1041, 4.2.5]

4. Describe the responsibilities of a Level I Instructor I when scheduling training. [NFPA® 1041, 4.2.4]

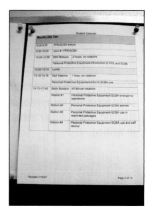

Chapter 9
Records, Reports, and Scheduling

Case History

A worker had an accident while working on the upper stories of a high rise under construction. The worker's safety line became caught in a descending elevator. The worker was pulled into the elevator shaft and fell approximately 45 feet (14 m). The worker landed on top of an elevator car, climbed onto a crossbeam, and waited for help.

Firefighters responded to the scene. The first-arriving firefighters used the elevator to reach the injured worker. The firefighters carefully helped the worker into the elevator and returned to the ground. Paramedics then treated the worker's injuries.

The Department of Labor and Industries, the state agency responsible for worker safety, reviewed the accident. In that review, the agency questioned the level of training that firefighters received in rope-rescue procedures.

The responding fire department had initiated operations-level, rope-rescue training for all firefighters and officers. The training program developed by the department's technical rescue and training divisions included a workbook, test, and specific performance objectives checklist in addition to the lesson plan.

The fire department produced these items for each of the firefighters directly involved in the rescue. The amount and scope of rope-rescue training for these firefighters was appropriate and well documented. The Department of Labor and Industries took no action against the department because the firefighters involved had well-documented training histories.

Instructors spend part of their on-duty time writing reports and maintaining records, which provide a history of the organization's training practices. Instructors must be able to write concise, accurate reports about training sessions and training incidents. They must also keep complete, accurate records given the proper record forms and the policies and procedures set forth by the AHJ and they must schedule individual training sessions.

Difference Between Records and Reports

Records are permanent accounts of past events or of actions taken by an individual, unit, or organization. For example, training records consist of the types and hours of training provided, names of personnel in attendance, learning

> **Records** — Permanent accounts of past events or of actions taken by an individual, unit, or organization.

Report Writing

Instructors must be able to write clear, concise, and accurate reports based upon witnessed events and the records that are available to them. They must also ensure that all written reports are accurately completed, properly filed, delivered in a timely fashion, and securely stored. NFPA® 1041, *Standard for Fire Service Instructor Professional Qualifications*, assigns report-writing responsibilities to instructors at each classification level. Because these responsibilities may vary between organizations, all instructors should be familiar with the types of reports for which each level is responsible. However, Level I Instructors are generally responsible only for training reports. Examples of various types of reports that instructors at each level may be required to complete are shown in **Table 9.1**.

The most difficult portion of most reports is the report narrative. A report narrative should answer to the five questions important to the report: who, what, when, where, and why **(Figure 9.2)** To keep report narratives simple and concise, organize them based upon the following parts:

- **Heading** — Contains basic information similar to the heading of a memo or electronic mail (e-mail) communication. It includes the date, name of the recipient(s), name of the sender or author, and subject of the report. Some organizations have a formal template or format that provides a space for all of this information.

- **Introduction** — Provides a brief overview of the report in a single paragraph. Includes the purpose of the report, time period covered by the report, and name or names of the people involved in writing the report.

- **Body** — Contains all information relating to the report, including the following:
  - Reason for the report
  - Specific and concrete facts based on accurate figures and data; may include visually effective graphs and tables
  - Problems that were discovered
  - Proposed solutions

- **Conclusion/summary** — A final paragraph (or two) that summarizes main points and recommends changes or other actions **(Figure 9.3, p.250)**.

After Action Reports

The following four questions taken from after action reports can be used to help organize the body section of a narrative:

1. What was planned?
2. What actually happened?
3. Why did it happen?
4. What can we do differently next time?

Chapter 9
Records, Reports, and Scheduling

Case History

A worker had an accident while working on the upper stories of a high rise under construction. The worker's safety line became caught in a descending elevator. The worker was pulled into the elevator shaft and fell approximately 45 feet (14 m). The worker landed on top of an elevator car, climbed onto a crossbeam, and waited for help.

Firefighters responded to the scene. The first-arriving firefighters used the elevator to reach the injured worker. The firefighters carefully helped the worker into the elevator and returned to the ground. Paramedics then treated the worker's injuries.

The Department of Labor and Industries, the state agency responsible for worker safety, reviewed the accident. In that review, the agency questioned the level of training that firefighters received in rope-rescue procedures.

The responding fire department had initiated operations-level, rope-rescue training for all firefighters and officers. The training program developed by the department's technical rescue and training divisions included a workbook, test, and specific performance objectives checklist in addition to the lesson plan.

The fire department produced these items for each of the firefighters directly involved in the rescue. The amount and scope of rope-rescue training for these firefighters was appropriate and well documented. The Department of Labor and Industries took no action against the department because the firefighters involved had well-documented training histories.

Instructors spend part of their on-duty time writing reports and maintaining records, which provide a history of the organization's training practices. Instructors must be able to write concise, accurate reports about training sessions and training incidents. They must also keep complete, accurate records given the proper record forms and the policies and procedures set forth by the AHJ and they must schedule individual training sessions.

Difference Between Records and Reports

Records are permanent accounts of past events or of actions taken by an individual, unit, or organization. For example, training records consist of the types and hours of training provided, names of personnel in attendance, learning

Records — Permanent accounts of past events or of actions taken by an individual, unit, or organization.

outcomes achieved, and training resources expended. From these records, raw data can be used to develop reports or demonstrate the effectiveness of the division or agency's training program.

Reports are official, factual accounts of an incident, response, or training event, presented either verbally or in writing. Following an incident, a written report is compiled, detailing all pertinent activities required to control the incident. Reports keep administrators informed of the accomplishments, problems, and daily training activities of an organization's members and divisions. Reports also provide data that enable an organization to make informed decisions about operations and strategic planning.

Records can be standardized forms, narratives, or a simple list of names. They may be handwritten, typed, or computer-generated **(Figure 9.1)**. Reports are generally in essay format and either typed or computer-generated. Both reports and records must be stored in a secure location but be easily accessible to appropriate personnel.

Training Records Completion

Level I Instructors must be able to accurately complete many types of record forms, and do so according to organizational policies and procedures. Sometimes, this may be as simple as keeping a daily attendance sheet during a course. The following are types of training records that may need to be completed as a part of the instructor's duties:

- **Attendance Records** — Evidence that an individual or unit has completed a specified number of hours of training in a specific topic, such as respiratory protection or hazardous materials incident response.

- **Applications for Certification** — Forms that students submit after a certification course; students may require an instructor's assistance and/or signature to complete these forms.

- **Incident/Injury Records** — Documentation of student injuries during training. These records may be completed by the instructor, or by an investigative team. These records may be requested for public view after they have been completed but should be kept private internally and not shared without proper authorization or cause.

- **Test Records** — Documentation of scores on individual tests given during coursework; test results must remain secure after becoming part of a student's personal training records and/or personnel files.

- **Training Reports** — Documentation of the training that the organization has conducted in the past. Training records also confirm which individuals have been accepted to courses and whether they completed those courses.

- **Scheduling Records** — Documentation about what training has been approved by the organization. Usually completed as part of the training scheduling process and may be kept as a history of training offered by the organization.

- **Resource Request** — Documentation of what resources an instructor needs to teach a certain lesson. The AHJ may have a particular form that the instructor needs to complete in order to obtain the needed resources. Instructors should follow the policies and procedures in their organizations for requesting the resources that they need for training.

In addition, instructors may be required to collect basic medical information from students as part of a course. For example, instructors may document stu-

Record

Grades

Name	Quiz 1	Test 1	Quiz 2	Test 2	Final
Billy Bob Jenson	67	88	92	96	100
Jean Clarkson	80	100	85	95	96
Richard Jones	75	76	92	85	94
Harold May	42	79	96	82	89
Kim Tanner	90	88	88	72	100
Jason Butler	85	94	95	87	100
Anthony Pitt	70	94	76	85	94
Graham Nowak	62	100	94	89	98
Hattie Cook	98	97	72	100	100
Eli Thompson	92	89	79	100	89
Hunter Rhoades	94	99	92	84	91

Report

INCIDENT STATUS SUMMARY
FS-5100-11

[Form: ICS 209 / NFES 1333 — Incident Status Summary with fields numbered 1 through 34, including Date/Time, Incident Name, Incident Number, Incident Commander, Jurisdiction, County, Type Incident, Location, Started Date/Time, Cause, Area Involved, % Controlled, Expected Containment, Estimated Controlled, Declared Controlled, Current Threat, Control Problems, Est. Loss, Est. Savings, Injuries, Deaths, Line Built, Line to Build, Current Weather, Predicted Weather, Cost to Date, Est. Total Cost, Agencies, Resources, Cooperating Agencies, Remarks, Prepared by, Approved by, Sent to.]

Figure 9.1 Both records and reports are used to store information in an established format, but they differ in how the information is presented and organized.

dents' medical vitals before live-fire training. This documentation is confidential. If this falls under the instructor's responsibility, he or she should follow all policies and procedures for completing and maintaining these records.

All training records should be considered private. Test scores and medical information are especially sensitive. Only the instructor and student should have access to test scores. Instructors should not post records publicly or report test results over e-mail. Test scores should be communicated directly to the student in writing. The same rules apply to certification records.

Finally, all training records can be subpoenaed under the United States Freedom of Information act or state sponsored open records act. Simply put, this means that the records can also be considered legal documents that track the training career of a student. Any requested records should be easy to find within the record keeping systems. Although Level I Instructors are not responsible for managing their organization's entire record system, they should become familiar with the organization's filing system and the individuals who manage it. Any records created during a course should be submitted to these individuals.

Level II Instructor Duties

Level I Instructors may be the only people available to maintain training records for the entire organization. If so, they must assume duties that are normally assigned to Level II Instructors. Instructors who find themselves in this situation may wish to consult Chapter 14, Supervisory and Administrative Duties for information on maintaining records, legal requirements, privacy information, and records management systems.

Report Writing

Instructors must be able to write clear, concise, and accurate reports based upon witnessed events and the records that are available to them. They must also ensure that all written reports are accurately completed, properly filed, delivered in a timely fashion, and securely stored. NFPA® 1041, *Standard for Fire Service Instructor Professional Qualifications*, assigns report-writing responsibilities to instructors at each classification level. Because these responsibilities may vary between organizations, all instructors should be familiar with the types of reports for which each level is responsible. However, Level I Instructors are generally responsible only for training reports. Examples of various types of reports that instructors at each level may be required to complete are shown in **Table 9.1**.

The most difficult portion of most reports is the report narrative. A report narrative should answer to the five questions important to the report: who, what, when, where, and why **(Figure 9.2)** To keep report narratives simple and concise, organize them based upon the following parts:

- **Heading** — Contains basic information similar to the heading of a memo or electronic mail (e-mail) communication. It includes the date, name of the recipient(s), name of the sender or author, and subject of the report. Some organizations have a formal template or format that provides a space for all of this information.

- **Introduction** — Provides a brief overview of the report in a single paragraph. Includes the purpose of the report, time period covered by the report, and name or names of the people involved in writing the report.

- **Body** — Contains all information relating to the report, including the following:
  — Reason for the report
  — Specific and concrete facts based on accurate figures and data; may include visually effective graphs and tables
  — Problems that were discovered
  — Proposed solutions

- **Conclusion/summary** — A final paragraph (or two) that summarizes main points and recommends changes or other actions **(Figure 9.3, p.250)**.

After Action Reports

The following four questions taken from after action reports can be used to help organize the body section of a narrative:

1. What was planned?
2. What actually happened?
3. Why did it happen?
4. What can we do differently next time?

Table 9.1
Report Writing Responsibilities

Instructor Level I	Instructor Level II	Instructor Level III
• Injuries • Training activity • Lesson outcome (grade)	• Budget requests • Budget administration • Purchase requests • Specifications • Training activities • Facility and equipment usage • Facility and equipment repair requests • Course outcome (grade) • Staff attendance • Postincident critiques • Personnel evaluations	• Division annual budget • Training activity • Accident investigation • Executive summaries • Budget justifications • Disciplinary documentation

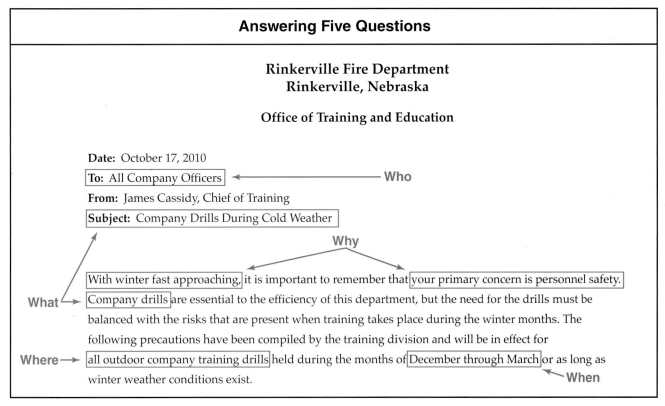

Answering Five Questions

Rinkerville Fire Department
Rinkerville, Nebraska

Office of Training and Education

Date: October 17, 2010
To: All Company Officers ◄————————— **Who**
From: James Cassidy, Chief of Training
Subject: Company Drills During Cold Weather

Why

What → With winter fast approaching, it is important to remember that your primary concern is personnel safety.
Company drills are essential to the efficiency of this department, but the need for the drills must be balanced with the risks that are present when training takes place during the winter months. The following precautions have been compiled by the training division and will be in effect for
Where → all outdoor company training drills held during the months of December through March or as long as winter weather conditions exist.
When

Figure 9.2 A report should answer the five journalistic questions.

Scheduling Training Sessions

Level I Instructors should be able to schedule individual training sessions for their organizations. Typically, the instructor will have an idea of the available resources that can be used to facilitate training. Considerations for scheduling training sessions include the following:

● **Sufficient planning period** — Instructors should schedule long enough in advance to ensure that the session is well planned.

Parts of a Report

Rinkerville Fire Department
Rinkerville, Nebraska
Office of Training and Education

Heading

Date: October 17, 2010
To: All Company Officers
From: James Cassidy, Chief of Training
Subject: Company Drills During Cold Weather

Introduction

With winter fast approaching, it is important to remember that your primary concern is personnel safety. Company drills are essential to the efficiency of this department, but the need for the drills must be balanced with the risks that are present when training takes place during the winter months. The following precautions have been compiled by the training division and will be in effect for all outdoor company training drills held during the months of December through March or as long as winter weather conditions exist.

Training evolutions will not be held when:
• Wind velocity exceeds 20 mph.
• Snow has accumulated to a depth of 3 inches.
• Horizontal surfaces are ice-coated.
• Temperatures are at or below freezing.
• Lightening, hail, or tornadoes have been predicted within the next 4 hours.

Training may be held:
• During light to medium rain conditions.
• When temperatures are above freezing.
• When snow is less than 3 inches in depth.
• During sunny conditions with temperature above freezing.

Body

Precautions that must be taken for all winter weather company drills:
• Full personal protective clothing must be worn.
• Rehabilitation must be provided at 30-minute intervals.
• Traction devices (chains) must be applied to all apparatus in snow conditions.
• Ground ladders and aerial devices must be clean and free of ice or mud.

The training division believes that these guidelines will provide company officers with a practical approach to winter weather training. Training during winter weather conditions will provide personnel with near-realistic conditions and still reduce the risk inherent during these conditions.

Conclusion

Figure 9.3 The four component parts of a report are: heading, introduction, body, and conclusion.

- **Student availability** — Attempt to schedule training sessions at a time when as many students as possible are available.

- **Mandated staffing levels** — Work within department requirements for keeping minimum personnel levels available for emergency response. It may be necessary to schedule the training session more than once in order to accommodate all students and still meet staffing levels.

- **Facilities availability** — Ensure that whatever training environment is needed for the session is available. This could include arranging for use of the apparatus bay on a certain date or scheduling the use of a local training facility. Scheduling a facility could require planning a number of months in advance.

- **Facility policies and procedures** — If another facility is selected as a training location, instructors should learn the policies and procedures for the facility and follow them during training. Part of this discovery may be determining if there are adjunct instructors at the facility who can assist with training.

- **Equipment availability** — Ensure that any equipment needed is available at the time of training. This might include arranging for the use of an apparatus or it could include the requisition of certain equipment from the department.

In addition to these considerations, instructors should become familiar with their departments' policies and procedures for scheduling and delivering training. Scheduling polices may include any of the following:

- Which personnel are authorized to schedule training

- Which areas of training are authorized and/or needed

- Which instructors are responsible for which training, for example, policies may require an EMS instructor rather than a fire instructor to teach CPR classes

- Who approves any expenses for training

Procedures may include timelines for completion of certain training or mandated training at certain times of the year. Each department has its own way of announcing training to personnel, and instructors should become familiar with these procedures. Finally, instructors should know to whom they make requests within their departments for any training resources that they need.

Chapter Summary

Although they are not responsible for all of their organization's records and reports, Level I Instructors must be able to write and keep training records, and be familiar with other record types. They should learn through practice to write accurate, concise, error-free reports and present them in a timely fashion. They should also know to whom they deliver reports and records and where the files are located and organized. Instructors should also understand the legal requirements for preserving records. Finally, Level I Instructors should be able to schedule individual training sessions.

Review Questions

1. What is the difference between records and reports?

2. What training records are the responsibility of the instructor?

3. How do instructors keep report narratives simple and concise?

4. What are the factors an instructor must consider when scheduling training?

Lesson Plan Development

Chapter Contents

Key Terms

Job Performance Requirements

NFPA® 1041 References

5.3.2

5.3.3

5.4.2

Lesson Plan Development

Learning Objectives

1. Discuss the effect that the laws of learning have on developing a lesson plan. [NFPA® 1041, 5.3.2]

2. Discuss the steps used to develop a lesson plan. [NFPA® 1041, 5.3.2]

3. Describe reasons to modify a lesson plan. [NFPA® 1041, 5.3.3]

4. Identify instructional techniques an Instructor II should use when teaching from a newly developed lesson plan. [NFPA® 1041, 5.4.2]

5. Discuss lesson plan evaluation and revision. [NFPA® 1041, 5.3.3]

Chapter 10
Lesson Plan Development

Section B: Instructor II

The first nine chapters of this manual have emphasized the job performance requirements (JPRs) of Instructor Level I. The next eight chapters will emphasize the job performance requirements of Level II and III Instructors: Chapters 10-14 will address Instructor II, and chapters 15-17 will address Instructor III. The previous chapters contain prerequisite information for understanding the remaining chapters. Several short review sections will be included in the upcoming chapters, but with a shift in emphasis toward JPRs for Instructor Levels II or III. Students or instructors who do not feel confident in their knowledge of Instructor I information should review any portions of chapters 1-9 that may help them to learn the new material. Students should also be aware that chapters 10-12 will meet the requirements for the DOT guidelines for EMS Instructor.

Case History

Two full time instructors at a state fire academy were preparing to teach an instructor development course at a department several hours drive away from the academy. Both instructors assumed that the other had packed all of the materials that were needed for the course (with lesson plans, digital presentations, handouts, and miscellaneous supplies). However, they did not double check their materials before leaving.

Upon arrival at the class location, and while setting up for the class start, the instructors realized that their lesson plans were not among the materials they had brought. While each of them was well versed in the course materials, they both felt unprepared. The instructors did the best they could using the textbook and the computer-generated slides that they did have.

Though they did their best, the class did not run as smoothly as it could have; nor did the students get the full benefit of all of the instructional materials. Fortunately, the instructors were experienced teachers. The experience reinforced with them that there is no substitute for a well written lesson plan.

According to NFPA® 1041, lesson plan development and modification are basic duties of Level II Instructors. EMS instructors share these responsibilities. This chapter provides these instructor candidates with the information needed to develop and modify lesson plans, including the following elements:

- Laws of learning applicable to lesson plan development
- Lesson plan creation
- Lesson plan modification
- Lesson plan evaluation and revision

A Reminder about Terminology

Learning objectives, instructional objectives, performance objectives, behavioral objectives, specific objectives, enabling objectives, terminal objectives, course objectives, course outcomes — all these different terms are confusing to instructors! While some education professionals may argue that there are significant differences between these terms, they are all just ways of expressing desired student performance. Terminology is important, but instructors should focus on what is most important — student performance.

Laws of Learning Applicable to Lesson Plan Development

Chapter 2, Principles of Learning, introduced Thorndike's Laws of Learning. When developing lesson plans, instructors should reacquaint themselves with the Laws of Learning and how they relate to developing effective lesson plans as follows:

- **Readiness** — Readiness means a person is emotionally, mentally, and physically prepared to learn new knowledge or skills. If students are ready to learn, instructors do not have to include "ice-breaker" or "warm-up" exercises in their lesson plans that are not related to the lesson.

- **Exercise** — Adults learn best when they are allowed to exercise skills; the more an act is practiced, the faster and surer the learning becomes. Instructors should make sure that their lesson plans include enough practice time.

- **Effect** — Adult learners need to see the positive effect of what they are learning. When developing a lesson plan, reinforce how the information is useful to the student.

- **Disuse** — Among adult learners it can be assumed that habits and memories used repeatedly are strengthened, and habits not reinforced are weakened through disuse. Training programs should force students to repeat skills at regular intervals.

- **Association** — Instructors can assume that adult learners tend to try to associate new information with information they have already learned. Lesson planners should consider what students know and connect it to the material they need to learn.

- **Recency** — Skills and information practiced or learned most recently are also the best remembered. Whatever students have learned most recently will be most prominent in their minds. If a lesson requires that students recall information from an earlier stage of the course, the lesson plan should include time for review.

- **Primacy** — Primacy is similar to recency. Primacy assumes that the first of a series of learned acts will be remembered better than others. In lesson plan development, especially skills training, the first portion of a process will be best remembered. As a result, there may need to be additional emphasis on the middle and ending of a series of skills steps.

- **Intensity** — The principle of intensity states that if a stimulus (experience) is vivid and real, it will more likely change or have an effect on the behavior (learning). The necessary equipment recommended in a lesson should be the same as equipment used on the job. Similarly, the lesson should require training that is as similar to a real world experience as is safely possible.

Lesson Plan Creation

A lesson may vary in length from a few minutes to several hours, depending on the desired learning objectives. When instructors create a lesson plan, determining the learning outcomes is the first step, which leads to the writing of the learning objectives. Using the learning objectives as a starting point, instructors then create the rest of the lesson plan by performing the following steps **(Figure 10.1, p.258)**:

Step 1: **Identify the expected learning outcomes** — Analyze the job and identify all of the expected job skills and tasks that a person would perform when doing the job.

Step 2: **Divide learning outcomes into tasks** — Consult the appropriate standards or subject matter experts to assist you in organizing and sequencing the tasks.

Step 3: **Divide tasks into steps** — Divide the tasks into the basic knowledge and skills steps required to perform them. Use this list to identify the essential knowledge and skills required to perform the task.

Step 4: **Write learning objectives for each task** — Learning objectives are generated from the knowledge and skills needed to complete each task.

What This Means to You

Let's assume that you are responsible for writing a lesson plan about inspecting SCBA equipment as part of a refresher course on basic skills. Your first step is to decide precisely what it is you want your students to know how to do when they complete the class. This skill is the learning outcome for the course, and can be described using a simple statement about student behavior. In this example, it might be something like: *Students will be able to inspect SCBA and identify any flaws or deficiencies that could lead to malfunction of the device.*

This learning outcome must now be divided into separate tasks. Think very methodically about the tasks involved in completing an SCBA inspection, and check that these tasks match the appropriate standards. Next, organize the tasks in an appropriate sequence, and divide each task into a series of steps. For each step, determine what information students will need to successfully complete it. For example, if students have to examine the SCBA's faceplate, they should be shown what damage to look for (information) and also what skills steps should be followed to find the damage (demonstration). Next, create a learning objective for each step, such as: *Students will identify the damage on the faceplate of an SCBA.*

These early steps of the lesson plan creation process require the most thought. Matching outcomes, objectives, tasks, and steps to the appropriate standard involves abstract thinking, which can be difficult and confusing. However, doing this hard work at the beginning of the process makes the entire lesson more effective.

Figure 10.1 Following a step-by-step process is an excellent way to create effective lesson plans.

Step 5: **Write test items or design practical assessments for each lesson objective** — Make sure that these match the requirements from the relevant standard and reflect the skills that the student will have to perform on the job.

Step 6: **Determine the sequence in which you will present the material** — Determine the order in which knowledge and skills will be taught. Identify the prerequisite knowledge and skills students need to learn the new material.

Step 7: Conduct research to become more familiar with the topic — Use sources such as the following:

— Standard operating guidelines and procedures

— Current literature

— Current accepted practices

— National consensus standards

Step 8: Write the outline — Develop the lesson plan using any one of the following formats:

— Outline with only major points

— Detailed outline

— Outline featuring major points supported with explanatory information (considered the best type of format for the fire and emergency services Level I Instructor to use; see Chapter 4, Instructional Materials and Equipment)

What This Means to You

Instructors may confuse creating computer-generated slides with creating a lesson outline, but the difference should be easy to remember. An outline provides the structure of the lesson, and from this the instructor creates a lesson plan based on the desired learning objectives. In contrast, computer-generated slides are training aids that help teach the learning objectives — they serve the lesson plan, but are not the plan itself.

If all you create for a lesson is a series of slides, you will probably not give enough consideration to other important issues, such as the learning objectives, additional activities that could aid learning, or safety. Though it seems like the simplest way to create a training lesson, simply creating slides for viewing and then reading the slides does not provide students with the best training opportunity possible.

Step 9: Develop lesson activities — Develop activities that reinforce objectives and provide students the opportunity to apply what they have learned. Indicate where during the lesson that the activity should occur.

Step 10: Identify and develop training aids to support instruction — List all the appropriate media, props, equipment, materials, facilities, costs, and time that will be required to present the lesson.

Step 11: Write or develop the planning components of the lesson plan — Include title, level of instruction, list of instructional references, and a list of required resources including human, physical, and instructional elements.

Step 12: Write ancillary and reference materials:

— Identify and develop assignments (when required).

— Develop course and instructor evaluation instruments that will be used to determine the effectiveness of the course.

— Write a bibliography of references that you referred to when creating the lesson plan. Use an accepted method of citing sources, such as American Psychological Association (APA) formatting.

Step 13: Write the lesson summary — Emphasize important, critical, or key information, especially by reviewing or previewing it. Provide a logical, effective conclusion to the lesson.

Some of these steps are self-evident, such as listing the needed materials, but others require more detail to understand. The sections that follow discuss the steps that require more explanation.

Lesson Plan Components: Review

The components of a lesson plan were introduced in Chapter 4, Instructional Materials and Equipment. It is important for instructors to review these components before developing lesson plans. In the most basic format, lesson plans consist of the following components:

- **Job or topic** — Short descriptive title of the information covered.
- **Time frame** — Estimated time it takes to teach the lesson.
- **Level of instruction** — Desired learning level that students will reach by the end of the lesson.
- **Learning objectives** — Descriptions of the minimum acceptable behaviors that students must display by the end of the lesson.
- **Resources/materials needed** — List of all items (including quantity) needed to teach the number of students in the class.
- **Prerequisites** — List of information, skills, or previous requirements that students must have completed or mastered before starting this lesson.
- **References** — List of specific references and resources (textbooks and other instructional materials) that will be required reading during the course of the lesson.
- **Lesson summary** — Restatement or reemphasis of the key points (sometimes referred to as the conclusion) of the lesson.
- **Assignments** — Readings, practice, research, or other outside-of-class requirements for students.
- **Lesson outline** — Summary of the information to be taught.
- **Evaluations** — Type of evaluation instrument the instructor will use to determine whether students have met lesson objectives.

In addition to this information, Chapter 4 also has information on sources for additional resources to be used in the classroom. This information can also be useful in the lesson plan development process.

Eliminating Bias in Instructional Materials

Lesson plans should be designed so that a wide variety of students can learn from the materials. If the materials – lesson plans, learning activities, ancillary components – show bias to one group or another, then only some students will learn well from those materials. The materials may offend other students or otherwise hinder their learning experience. Bias in instructional materials may be based on gender, racial, or cultural stereotypes. It may also be a result of using terminology or regional jargon that students do not understand.

The best way to avoid bias when creating instructional materials is to adhere very closely to the source material that is being taught. If the source material is an NFPA® standard, for example, whatever terminology is used in the standard is what should appear in the materials. This same guideline applies if the materials are created from an approved textbook or training manual.

In addition to terminology, instructors creating instructional materials should be very careful in the wording that they use. For example, gender specific names and pronouns should be used in roughly equal amounts throughout the materials. When in doubt, words like *firefighter*, *fire officer*, or *paramedic* can be used instead of *he* or *she*. Any references to specific cultural backgrounds should be avoided unless they are relevant to the materials. If they are included, stereotypes are strictly prohibited.

Learning Objective Development

Learning objectives are specific statements (also referred to as performance objectives, behavioral objectives, or competencies) that describe desired learning results. They describe the knowledge or skills that students should have acquired by the conclusion of a lesson. Written learning objectives represent the learning outcomes and, therefore, learning objectives and learning outcomes are directly related. Learning objectives also provide students with a self-assessment tool. By having a list of the learning objectives with the lesson plan or lesson outline, students are able to determine whether they are accomplishing the requirements of each learning objective as they complete the course. They are also better prepared for success in comprehensive final or summative tests.

Learning Objective — Specific statement that describes the knowledge or skills that students should acquire by the end of a lesson. *Also known as* Behavioral Objective, Competency, or Performance Objective.

Learning objectives focus on the specific, measurable results of instruction. Learning objectives are basic components of instructional development and have the following key purposes:

- Provide a foundation for instructional design, and aid in overall course development.

- Help instructors select content and instructional materials and develop an appropriate instructional strategy.

- Provide a basis for measuring and evaluating student learning through appropriate assessment and testing.

- Inform students of expected performance standards and criteria.

- Allow instructors flexibility in teaching and make teaching more efficient.

- Help the instructor facilitate instruction.

Learning objectives can be developed or written in various ways. Although each individual instructor may approach developing learning objectives with a different perspective, all learning objectives should communicate the intended learning outcome and be clearly stated, measurable, specific, and detailed. The learning objective statement may also be student-centered so that the learning objective focuses on the student as the person displaying the observable behavior. The learning objective may be written to include the phrase, *the student will*..., although the active participation of the student is understood when the phrase is not used.

Effective learning objectives should adhere to the following guidelines:

- Avoid terminology such as understand, know, comprehend, or learn. For example, *The student will understand the principles of fire behavior* does not indicate a measurable result. Learning objectives must contain an action verb and a specific description of the lesson content. A measurable outcome example: *The student will state the principles of fire behavior.*

- Make learning objectives short and focused on a single result. Example: *Match U.S. Department of Transportation (DOT) symbols to their meanings.*

- Make learning objectives specific and objective. Example: *Apply an occlusive dressing to a sucking chest wound.*

Mager Model of Learning Objective Development: Review

The Mager Model for writing learning objectives was introduced in Chapter 4, Instructional Materials and Equipment. Whenever an instructor is writing learning objectives it is important to review this method. According to Mager, learning objective statements should contain the following three components:

- **Performance (behavior) statement** — Identify what the student is expected to do in clearly observable terms using clear action verbs.

- **Conditions description** — Describe the situation, tools, or materials required for a student to perform a single specific action or behavior.

- **Standards criteria** — State the acceptable level of student performance which may be based upon measurable criteria from an existing standard.

In addition to the guidelines already described, instructors should understand how the levels of learning apply to developing learning objectives in the cognitive, psychomotor, and affective areas. Instructors should also understand how internationally-standardized job performance requirements (JPRs) can be used as a model for creating learning objectives.

Cognitive Levels of Learning

The levels of learning in the cognitive domain follow an ordered progression or hierarchy of instructional outcomes. Each level builds upon the previous level and is progressive in its format. Emphasizing one level over another in a learning objective indicates the specific outcome desired from that objective. The levels of learning in the cognitive domain are as follows **(Figure 10.2, p.264)**:

- **Remember (Knowledge)** — Students remember, recall, and recognize previously learned facts and theories. They can describe, define, label, list, and match terms and items.

- **Understand (Comprehension)** — Students understand, compare, and contrast information, and estimate future trends. They give examples and explanations, make predictions, and summarize information and ideas.

- **Apply (Application)** — Students apply information, rules, and concepts that they have learned to new situations. They compute, demonstrate abilities, solve problems, modify ideas and actions, and operate equipment.

- **Analyze (Analysis)** — Students divide information into its component parts to understand how the parts relate to one another and to the whole.

- **Evaluate (Evaluation)** — Students judge the value of materials or actions based on defined criteria using elements from all other levels. They compare, conclude, contrast, discriminate, and justify decisions based on standards and criteria.
- **Create (Synthesis)** — Students put parts together to form a new whole. They categorize, create, design, organize, revise, and integrate parts to invent something new.

NOTE: The names for these levels of learning contained in the parentheses are the names used in the seventh edition of Fire and Emergency Services Instructor. They are also the older terms used to describe the levels before the terms were revised in 2000. The older terms are included here and in other places throughout this book as a bridge between the old terminology and the new.

Because effective learning objectives depend on the use of action verbs, instructors should find or create a list of appropriate verbs to help them develop learning objectives in a variety of learning levels. Some appropriate action verbs for use in the cognitive domain include those in **Table 10.1, p.265**. Note that some words are applicable to a variety of learning domains and emphasis.

Wording of Cognitive Domain Objectives

The following are examples of learning objectives that might be written about a lesson teaching the fire tetrahedron:

- **Remember (Knowledge)** —Define the combustion elements of the fire tetrahedron.
- **Understand (Comprehension)** —Explain how the fire tetrahedron combustion elements interact to create or sustain combustion.
- **Apply (Application)** —Demonstrate how fire extinguishment can occur when one of the combustion elements of the fire tetrahedron is eliminated.
- **Analyze (Analysis)** —Analyze the relationships among the combustion elements of the fire tetrahedron.
- **Evaluate (Evaluation)** —Justify the use of various extinguishing agents to disrupt the combustion elements of the fire tetrahedron.
- **Create (Synthesis)** —Show how combining various chemical compounds in the absence of oxygen can result in combustion.

Examples that might be common in an EMS environment are as follows:

- **Remember (Knowledge)** — List the possible locations to obtain a pulse on a patient.
- **Understand (Comprehension)** — Explain how a pulse is generated.
- **Apply (Application)** — Demonstrate how to obtain a patient's pulse.
- **Analyze (Analysis)** — Analyze the pulse rate and strength of the patient and compare findings with patient history and overall presentation.
- **Evaluate (Evaluation)** — Determine if an intervention is necessary based on patient's history, presentation, and assessment.
- **Create (Synthesis)** — Create a treatment plan based on findings, and periodically reassess to determine if intervention is achieving the desired effect.

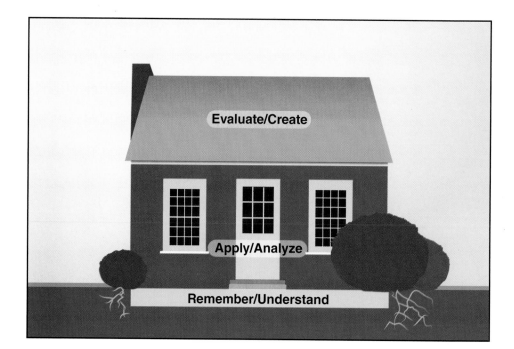

Figure 10.2 The levels of learning begin with the foundational (Remember/Understand) and build toward the more complex (Evaluate/Create).

Psychomotor Levels of Learning

Like the cognitive domain, the levels of learning in the psychomotor domain progress through a series of steps, with each one more complex than the previous. Action verbs, such as those listed in **Table 10.2, p.266**, are usually included to define the activity in a psychomotor learning objective. Learning objectives may be written based upon any of the following psychomotor levels:

- **Observation** — Witness the motor activity as the instructor demonstrates it.
- **Imitation** — Imitate this activity in a step-by-step process.
- **Adaptation** — Modify and personalize the motor activity.
- **Performance** — Practice the activity until the steps become habit.
- **Perfection** — Improve the performance until it can be completed without error.

Instructors first demonstrate the skill correctly as students watch. Students develop a sense for performing the motions and mentally prepare themselves to take action. As they begin to practice, they imitate the instructor's motions. Instructors guide the students, correct their mistakes, and reinforce desired performance.

Affective Domain

Desired changes in attitude (affective domain) must be determined in advance and planned into the lesson. Instructors then emphasize the correct behavior that the student must learn and exhibit. When wording learning objectives, use of words in the affective domain such as *confident* or *satisfied* can help to emphasize correct attitude or emotional state: *The student will be confident navigating the driving course in the time required.* Affective changes in attitude likely develop alongside cognitive and psychomotor learning. Learning objectives in this domain are difficult to measure objectively.

Table 10.1
Useful Words for Expressing Objectives

Remember	cite cite rule count spell define state trace find identify	list name quote read repeat recite recognize review point	indicate write tell recall describe select gather data show
Understand	associate conclude convey meaning of compute deal with describe in own words distinguish	extrapolate give reasons interpret predict differentiate discriminate translate	reformulate restate rewrite summarize tell why discuss
Apply	employ illustrate compare classify administer adopt a plan utilize demonstrate	contrast solve construct put in action apply carry out plot complete	use result perform make use of calculate practice detect use
Analyze	analyze check detect	explain deduct separate	infer designate criticize
Evaluate	assess appraise ascertain assay assize	determine diagnose recommend test grade	judge fix value of evaluate
Create	combine compose design develop devise	fabricate form specify propose prescribe	prepare plan integrate formulate

Source: Permission given to reprint from *Instructional Techniques For Company Officers,* 1983, National Fire Academy, Emmitsburg, Maryland: Government Printing Office, pp. 1–12.

Table 10.2
Possible Action Verbs for Psychomotor Objectives

stand	grasp	watch
sit	crawl	catch
dance	write	open
turn	balance	close
select	stop	run

Lesson Outline Development

Writing a basic lesson outline is a skill that all Level I Instructors should be able to perform (see Chapter 4, Instructional Materials and Equipment). Level II Instructors are required to go beyond writing outlines to writing lesson plans. For them, the outline is only one step in the process.

After establishing learning objectives, the development of an outline is the next step in the lesson planning process. A good way to create an outline is to organize the learning objectives into the order that the instructor should teach them. For each objective, the instructor determines an instructional method and time frame, and possibly a learning activity or discussion questions.

When developing a course for other instructors, remember that a lesson outline is not enough. A complete lesson plan based on the desired learning objectives is required, as the other instructors may not be qualified to develop an effective plan.

Instructional Method Selection

When writing lesson plans, instructors should consider which instructional methods best match the learning objectives in the lesson. An illustrated lecture, for example, might be the best method for conveying information while a demonstration is necessary when teaching skills. If the instructor attempts to teach the skill with a lecture format without the use of demonstration, instruction will not be as effective.

Lessons should also employ a number of different instructional methods in order to reach a variety of learning styles. **Table 10.3** provides a cross-reference depicting how different instructional methods emphasize interactions, skills, and learning styles.

Lesson Activity Development

Activities that address specific learning objectives should always be included in lesson plans. The sections that follow describe some learning activities that instructors may want to include in their lesson plans.

NOTE: Skills practice is one variety of lesson activity. When a lesson requires students to master a skill, the practice is considered a mandatory lesson activity that the instructor must include.

Table 10.3
Instructional Method Characteristics

	Interaction	Visual	Auditory	Kinesthetic	Skills
Illustrated Lecture	Yes	Yes	Yes	No	No
Discussion	Yes	No	Yes	No	No
Demonstration	No	Yes	Yes	Yes	Yes
1-on-1	Yes	No	Yes	Yes	Yes
Case Study	Yes	No	Yes	Yes	Yes
Simulation	Yes	Yes	Yes	Yes	Yes
Mentoring	Yes	No	Yes	No	No
Company Drill	No	Yes	No	Yes	Yes

Whole Group Discussion Development

Preparing for classroom discussions and including them in lesson plans requires careful planning. When including a whole group discussion in a lesson plan, the instructor should take the following actions:

- **Define the purpose** — Know in what direction the discussion should go and what students should understand after completing the discussion.

- **Set goals** — Establish the goals or outcomes of the discussion. If possible, ensure that goals are measurable so that the discussion can be evaluated for its effectiveness.

- **Establish ground rules** — Establish rules that govern interpersonal relations, because discussions are social as well as educational. Explain in the lesson plan any rules that instructors need to communicate to students. Include how students who wish to speak are recognized, how to be respectful of others, and how long each speaker may control the discussion.

- **Recommend questions** — In the lesson plan, provide opening questions for the instructor to ask.

Small Group Discussion Development

Small group discussions are different from whole group discussions because the instructor is not part of the group. A student is selected to facilitate or lead

Training Evolution Supervision

Chapter Contents

The revised lesson plan should be reviewed by other instructors, the training division or agency administration, or other experts. When possible, it should be presented to the original group of students to determine whether the revisions were effective. Ultimately, the revised lesson plan will be evaluated based upon student test scores and course evaluations after the revised plan has been taught for the first time.

Chapter Summary

Level II Instructors are responsible for creating lesson plans that other instructors will follow. They should write these lessons with an emphasis on reinforcing the laws of learning. They should also ensure that they address all applicable components of a lesson plan and that sufficient practice time is included. They should incorporate questions and activities that are appropriate to the lesson, and that will generate interaction and discussion.

Finally, Level II Instructors should be able to evaluate and revise lesson plans. New or newly revised lesson plans should be evaluated after their first use, based on analysis of students' performance, and feedback from instructors, students, and administrators. If revision is necessary, it should adhere to the same criteria used in creating new lesson plans.

Review Questions

1. What effect do the laws of learning have on the development of a lesson plan?

2. What steps should an instructor take to create a lesson plan?

3. Why would an instructor have to make lesson plan modifications?

4. What might an Instructor II anticipate when teaching a newly developed lesson plan for the first time?

5. How does an instructor evaluate a lesson plan?

Training Evolution Supervision

Chapter Contents

- **Determine presentation factors** — Determine how to present the case study to students, how to conduct the question-and-answer process, and whether or not any visual aids will be necessary. It is also important to set a time frame, otherwise presentation and discussion can take up much more time than is necessary.

- **Write the case study** — The final step includes the following actions:
  - Write the story.
  - Write questions that students must answer to guide their research and analysis.
  - Prepare any audiovisual aids.
  - Write the instructions for presenting the case study during the lesson (time frame, rules for discussion, explanations of audiovisual aids, etc.).

  Case studies can come from any of the following settings:

- Private business community
- Local, regional, state/provincial, or national training agencies
- Professional training associations
- Other government agencies, such as National Institute for Occupation Safety and Health (NIOSH) investigations and warnings
- Fire and EMS trade journals

Role Play Development

Role-playing is particularly effective for teaching or reinforcing concepts in the affective domain (values, beliefs, and emotions) or basic interpersonal communication. Instructors should take the following steps when creating a role-play activity:

- Ensure that scenarios apply to the course materials, and clearly explain learning objectives.

- Explain the purpose of the activity at the beginning of the role-play, and ensure that students fully understand the scenario, character roles, time frame, and expected results.

- Limit the number of character roles, but involve all students in some part of the activity. Students who do not play a character should be assigned to critique, take notes, or observe, and prepare to discuss their observations or conclusions with the rest of the class.

- Have several role-plays prepared if there will be a large number of students to provide many (if not all) individuals the opportunity to act a role. These role plays may be performed in small groups to save time.

Ancillary Components

Ancillary components are any supplementary materials, such as informational handouts, study guides, skills sheets, work or activity sheets, and assignment sheets. They provide students with background or resource information that is neither available in the text nor easily reprinted from copyrighted standards or protocols. Ancillary components are aids that an instructor can use as desired. They often serve as important and useful instructional adjuncts as well as helpful guides that reinforce learning.

Ancillary Components — Supplemental written materials that help students meet the learning objectives; may include information sheets, study guides, skills sheets, work or activity sheets, and assignment sheets.

NOTE: Ancillary components may be presented under a variety of names in different lesson plans. They may be referred to under the broader term learning activities, for example.

In addition, some ancillary components list performance steps that students can follow while practicing skills or evolutions. The overall purpose of ancillary materials is to enable students to apply, study, and practice the lesson content. The following sections describe several types of ancillary components, including information sheets, skills sheets, work sheets, study sheets, and assignment sheets. **Appendix I** includes examples of each of these different sheets.

Information Sheet

An information sheet is a handout that addresses a topic not covered in the course textbook or other course materials. It might be an outline summarizing key ideas, or a reproduction of computer-generated slides used during a lecture. It might also provide a list of references or include suggestions for further research.

Information sheets are usually created for one of the following reasons:

- The information is unavailable to some students because texts or other learning resources are limited.
- To get the information, students would have to find and consult a number of texts, which may be time-consuming.
- The information is not available in any text.

Information sheets should be designed to encourage students to learn. Steps for developing information sheets are as follows:

Step 1: Create a title that indicates the subject area and relates the title to the lesson.

Step 2: Introduce the information with a brief description that explains its importance, relating it to the course textbook or part of the lesson. Present the information in a form that creates interest in the student to read, study, and learn.

Step 3: Present the information so that it is easy to read and follow. Include appropriate charts, tables, or illustrations, and label them for easy referral.

Skill Sheet

Skill sheets are appropriate for tasks that require both psychomotor skills and cognitive knowledge. They divide a task into **operational steps**, **critical criteria**, and the **key points** or steps for completing each operation. Skill sheets give Level I Instructors the information they need to teach the task successfully. Depending upon the skill, students may be able to use an approved skill sheet as a guide for unsupervised practice when an instructor allows it. Unsupervised practice time is important because even during supervised practice time, instructors cannot oversee every student's efforts.

Other skills, especially those in which there are hazards that could lead to injury or fatality, should never be practiced unsupervised. Instructors should follow AHJ regulations, training safety standards, or departmental procedures to determine which skills may be practiced without supervision.

Operational Step — The smallest aspect of performing a task; to complete the task, students perform a series of operational steps in sequential order.

Critical Criteria — Step or steps on a practical skills test that must be completed accurately in order for the student to pass the test.

Key Point — Important cognitive information on a skill sheet that students need to know in order to perform a task or operational step; generally appears on right-hand side of a skills sheet.

Skill sheets provide the steps students need to know and practice. Students can use them to practice in groups on their own, coach each other, discuss and think about the activities, and develop higher level (analytical and synthesis) cognitive skills. These self-practice exercises allow students to prepare for performance evaluations where they perform without instructor guidance, exercise thinking skills, and perform at the mastery level for an evaluator. Students can use a skill sheet to prepare for a performance evaluation.

Steps for developing a skill sheet are as follows:

Step 1: Provide a title for the sheet. The title should be the name of the task.

Step 2: Divide the page into two columns.

Step 3: Provide a heading for the left column: either *Operations* or *Performance* units. This column will contain the psychomotor skills.

Step 4: Provide a heading for the right column: either *Key points* or *Knowledge units*. This column will contain any cognitive information necessary to perform the task accurately and safely.

Step 5: List the steps of the task, in order, in the left column. Use action verbs such as grasp, push, turn, lift, or don.

Step 6: List cautions, warnings, safety factors, critical criteria, and conditions essential for performing the task operations in the right column.

Worksheet

Worksheets are assignments that students will complete during class. The assignments will vary widely but could include answering open-ended questions, writing a short narrative, or researching a topic.

A worksheet or activity sheet provides students opportunities to apply rules, analyze and evaluate objects and situations, or use multiple skills while completing activities. Instructors create student worksheets from the information content of the lesson plan. Any worksheets that the instructor develops must support the learning objectives and provide activities that enable students to meet those objectives.

The completion of a worksheet may also be a learning objective. In this case, the knowledge and skills learned in class are applied to the particular task of completing the worksheet. Worksheets can be used to generate discussions on a topic and generally contain optional activities. Worksheets typically do not need to be scored or graded.

Worksheets that require students to exercise abilities in the affective domain may support more than one learning objective. Recall that the affective domain has students change or adjust, develop, practice, and adapt attitudes, values, beliefs, and appreciations.

Steps for creating a worksheet are as follows:

Step 1: Create a title that reflects the subject or topic.

Step 2: List all the materials and resources that students need in order to complete the activity. List titles and page numbers of books, journals, or other reference material. Provide enough information so that students can locate resources quickly and easily.

Step 3: Write a brief introduction that generates interest and motivates students to complete the activity. Explain how the skill or activity relates to the topic, the learning objectives, and students' job performance. Show how the activity will help students to master the relevant skill.

Step 4: Provide clear directions that explain how to complete the worksheet.

Step 5: Provide answers or solutions on a separate page. Distribute the answer sheet either with the worksheet or after the worksheet is completed.

Study Sheet

A study sheet explains the specific areas students will need to study before an exam or certification test. Instructors may want to distribute study sheets for students to use during instruction or for them to use as self-study aides. It is also helpful to include a practice test with the study sheet, which enables the instructor to measure and provide feedback on how well students understood the material. Steps for creating study sheets are as follows:

Step 1: Create a title that reflects the subject or topic and is related to the lesson.

Step 2: List all the materials and resources that students need to complete the study sheet. List titles and page numbers of books, journals, or other reference material. Provide enough information so that students can locate resources quickly and easily.

Step 3: Write a brief introduction that generates interest and motivates students to complete the study sheet.

Step 4: Present the information in a format that enables students to use and learn the material.

Step 5: Put a study-sheet test (if one is included) on a separate sheet of paper.

Step 6: Design study questions to make students think about all aspects of the topic. Include enough questions to thoroughly address the material.

Assignment Sheet

An assignment sheet contains information about a specific activity or project that the student is expected to complete without supervision. The activity may occur within the class period or outside of class. Generally, an assignment sheet contains the three components of the Mager Model (performance, conditions, and criteria) and some of the same material listed for the lesson plan. Assignment sheets differ from worksheets in that the assignment is required and will be graded. Steps for creating assignment sheets are as follows:

Step 1: Create a title that reflects the subject or topic, and is related to the lesson.

Step 2: List all the materials and resources that students need to complete the assignment. List titles and page numbers of books, journals, or other reference material. Provide enough information so that students can locate resources quickly and easily.

Step 3: Write a brief introduction that generates interest and motivates students to complete the assignment.

Step 4: Present the information in a format that enables students to use and learn the material.

Step 5: Include the scoring and grading criteria for the assignment.

Step 6: Describe the form that the final product (essay, table, graphic, etc.) should be in as well as the format (handwritten, typed, model, etc.) and the due date.

Audiovisual Components

In addition to creating lesson plans, the Level II Instructor may also be required to create or select audiovisual components for use with lesson plans. The instructor may have to do research to find illustrations, photos, video recordings, or audio recordings that enhance a lesson. Instructors rarely create these items by themselves, but sometimes they are able to use photographs that they took during training evolutions or at the scene of an incident. Usually, instructors will be responsible for creating computer-generated slides to accompany lectures.

When selecting audiovisual components, instructors should remember that good audiovisual training aids have the following purposes:

- Show abstract concepts through the use of charts or diagrams.
- Aid memory through the use of eye-catching, humorous, or colorful images.
- Illustrate real environments using plans, maps, photographs, or videos.
- Reinforce key points through the use of quotes, tables, or figures.
- Tie complex ideas together through diagrams, outlines, and headings.
- Compare information through the use of charts and graphs.
- Introduce the lesson through the use of a title slide or image **(Figure 10.3)**.
- Illustrate a process through the use of artwork, photographs, or cutaway models.
- Define terms or words through the use of glossaries or examples.
- Provide motivation through images, logos, or slogans.

New instructors often have difficulty making effective computer-generated slides. For example, they have a tendency to overuse animation effects. To create effective computer-generated slides, instructors should apply some generally accepted presentation guidelines, such as the following **(Figure 10.4)**:

- Keep visual aids simple and easy to understand.
- Take the time to ensure that all slides look professional and convey their messages effectively.
- Use typeface or fonts that are consistent, easy to read, and large enough to

Figure 10.3 Title slides that express lesson or course goals are good ways of introducing a lesson to students.

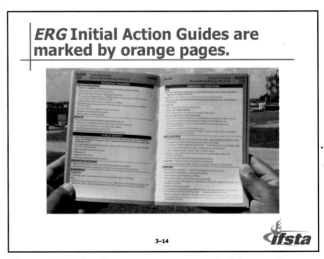

Figure 10.4 Simple computer-generated slides can be very effective.

read at a distance. Font size depends on the size of the presentation room and projection screen. One guideline is to never use less than 24-point type.

- Make text concise, emphasizing phrases and lists when possible. The text helps the audience focus on the key points of the presentation. The oral presentation expands on these phrases.

- Create one heading for each slide or image. Use subheadings or illustrations when appropriate.

- Keep the backgrounds simple so they do not conflict with the text or graphics.

- Use a background color that contrasts with the color of the text or graphic, but does not clash with it. Never use colors that will distract the audience's attention.

- Use transition effects sparingly because they can overpower the message that a slide or image is attempting to convey.

- Use graphs, charts, photographs, and clipart to create interest.

- Use parallel structure on each slide or image; starting phrases with nouns and bullets with verbs make points easier to link together.

- Use one style of transition effect for the major topics and a different one for the subtopics.

- Provide handouts of some slides or images. Handouts can be particularly helpful when presenting complex or detailed concepts. The audience can make appropriate notes on the handouts; however, handouts can also distract the audience by taking their attention away from the presentation.

What This Means to You

Simple computer-generated slides are the most effective. You may find it tempting to create fancy, involved, and visually stimulating transitions and animations. But this can be distracting, causing students to focus on the visual effects and not the information. The sound effects that are included in most presentation software are also inappropriate for training sessions and should not be used unless they are necessary to convey the message.

You might feel as though you aren't working hard enough if your slides are straightforward and avoid sound and visual effects. But simpler slides lead to better instruction. Make sure your slides meet the guidelines included in this section, but don't waste time building elaborate transitions, sound effects, and animations.

Lesson Plan Modification

Training divisions and agencies either create lesson plans based on local needs or purchase commercially available curriculums that contain prepared lesson plans. Even though these lesson plans may include all the necessary component parts and information, an instructor may still be required to modify the plan to the needs of a specific class or situation. The instructor should review the lesson plan to determine if any modifications are required in the format or content (**Figure 10.5**). Components may need modifications for the following reasons:

- To ensure thorough coverage of the course material and effective use of available resources

- To include updated information or changes in operating policies and procedures

- To address particular groups of students

Figure 10.5 When revising old curriculum, check current standards to make sure that lesson plans contain only the most up-to-date information.

When creating a lesson plan, the first step is to determine the learning outcomes. The same is true when modifying a lesson plan. Subsequent steps for modifying a lesson plan closely resemble the subsequent steps for creating a lesson plan. If modification is necessary, refer to the steps described in the Lesson Plan Creation section of this chapter.

Instructors should keep records of any modifications they make to lesson plans. Lesson plans and curriculum content should be reviewed by the training division or agency periodically to determine whether the materials are current and ensure that all instructors are familiar with the modifications that have been made. Old versions of curriculums or lesson plans should be retained in archives for future reference and as documentation that the organization met the training requirements during a particular time in its history.

Lesson Plan First Use

Once a lesson plan has been developed or modified, it can be put into use in the classroom. Level II Instructors should be able to teach from a newly developed lesson plan while at the same time evaluating their work in a real world situation.

Teaching from a newly developed lesson plan is no different than teaching from a previously prepared lesson plan. The instructor should still use the skills included in Chapter 6, Classroom Instruction and Chapter 7, Skills-Based Training Beyond the Classroom. The only difference is that there may be items in a new lesson plan that appear effective on paper but do not meet expectations in practice. Experienced instructors should be the first to use newly developed lessons plans because they are more likely to make smooth transitions when one portion of a lesson is not meeting expectations.

Finally, instructors using a newly developed lesson plan for the first time should take notes on what was and was not effective during instruction. Doing so provides feedback for lesson plan evaluations and can be early indicators of areas of the lesson plan that require revision.

Lesson Plan Evaluation and Revision

Course evaluations evaluate the knowledge and skills of the students, the performance of the instructor, and the effectiveness of the lesson plan. Administrators, employers, course or curriculum developers, and instructors can judge whether the course or curriculum accomplished its objectives by assessing the results of

instruction. After this evaluation, it may be necessary to revise the lesson plans to correct any deficiencies that are discovered. A thorough course evaluation is based on input from students, instructors, and administrators.

Lesson Plan Evaluation

Review of student and instructor evaluations can help course planners determine how effective a lesson plan has been. The following steps assist the instructor in evaluating a lesson plan:

Step 1: **Review student test /course scores** — Analyze test results. Situations:

— When the majority of students met the evaluation criteria, lesson plan alterations may not be required.

— When the majority of students did not perform satisfactorily, a review of the instructor and course evaluations may help determine the cause.

— To determine the cause of unsatisfactory performances, review the students' training records and interview those who did not meet the criteria.

Step 2: **Review the instructor and course evaluations** — Look for a consistency in comments concerning the presentation style. Considerations:

— Determine whether environmental factors such as lighting, noise, or temperature could have created a barrier to learning.

— Determine whether any other factors could have affected the teaching or learning environment.

— Training aids and devices are appropriate to the topic.

Step 3: **Review the lesson plan** — Determine whether the learning objectives are clear, concise, and attainable. Factors:

— Time frame is sufficient to cover the required material in sufficient detail.

— Testing criteria are appropriate to the topic and teaching style.

— Testing criteria and learning objectives were properly explained to the students.

— Support materials and personnel were adequate to meet the lesson plan requirements.

— The instructor was familiar with the topic and lesson plan.

— Unforeseen elements (such as weather, equipment malfunction, or site conditions) caused a problem in the presentation

If the lesson plan has significant flaws, the instructor or the training division may need to revise it – but only if the changes would be cost- and time-effective. If it is not effective to revise a flawed lesson plan, instructors may seek prepared lesson plans that better help students meet the desired learning objectives.

Lesson Plan Revision

Revising a lesson plan generally follows the steps shown in the Lesson Plan Creation section of this chapter. The evaluation should provide a definite list of revisions to be made. The instructor should make the revisions, and then compare the revised lesson plan to the revision list and course curriculum requirements. It may be necessary to further refine the changes to meet all requirements. The modification of fire or EMS lesson plans may require approval from the AHJ.

Table 10.3
Instructional Method Characteristics

	Interaction	Visual	Auditory	Kinesthetic	Skills
Illustrated Lecture	Yes	Yes	Yes	No	No
Discussion	Yes	No	Yes	No	No
Demonstration	No	Yes	Yes	Yes	Yes
1-on-1	Yes	No	Yes	Yes	Yes
Case Study	Yes	No	Yes	Yes	Yes
Simulation	Yes	Yes	Yes	Yes	Yes
Mentoring	Yes	No	Yes	No	No
Company Drill	No	Yes	No	Yes	Yes

Whole Group Discussion Development

Preparing for classroom discussions and including them in lesson plans requires careful planning. When including a whole group discussion in a lesson plan, the instructor should take the following actions:

- **Define the purpose** — Know in what direction the discussion should go and what students should understand after completing the discussion.

- **Set goals** — Establish the goals or outcomes of the discussion. If possible, ensure that goals are measurable so that the discussion can be evaluated for its effectiveness.

- **Establish ground rules** — Establish rules that govern interpersonal relations, because discussions are social as well as educational. Explain in the lesson plan any rules that instructors need to communicate to students. Include how students who wish to speak are recognized, how to be respectful of others, and how long each speaker may control the discussion.

- **Recommend questions** — In the lesson plan, provide opening questions for the instructor to ask.

Small Group Discussion Development

Small group discussions are different from whole group discussions because the instructor is not part of the group. A student is selected to facilitate or lead the discussion in each of the small groups, because students are more likely to express their ideas when the instructor is not present. Small group discussions work best under the following conditions:

- The task is structured.
- Students are experienced in working with others.
- The outcome is clearly defined.
- Students have time to prepare for the discussion.

The following actions are important for planning small group discussions:

- **Select a topic** — Select a topic for the discussion. As students become more familiar with small group discussions, more controversial topics can be chosen.
- **Define group goals** — Define goals for the group such as:
  - Generate a new process or policy, or create a plan for completing a task.
  - Determine an appropriate course of action or a solution to a problem.
  - Negotiate a dispute and come to a consensus.
  - Compete with other groups in a planned activity.
- **Establish time frames** — Set time limits to help students stay on task. Divide class time between research (if necessary), discussion, and summary. Remind the groups a few minutes before they should move into the next phase of their work.
- **Gather closing summaries** — Reconvene into the larger group when each of the small groups has completed its work. Have the facilitator or recorder for each present their conclusions and summarize their discussion. Before returning to the large group, the instructor should post the small groups' conclusions and summarize the results, making connections between each group's findings.

Case Study Development

When selecting or developing a case study, the instructor should ensure that the problem is similar to one that students will face in performing their duties. The case study should also be relevant to the lesson plan in which it appears and support the learning objectives of the lesson. Whether selecting an existing case study or developing a new case study, instructors should take the following steps:

- **Identify a story or event** — Locate an event that relates to the learning objectives contained in the lesson.
- **Research the story or event** — Locate as much information on the event as possible and ensure that all information is readily available to students. For example:
  - When the event occurred locally, the instructor may choose to interview participants to gain an insight into their decision-making process. This information can be used following student presentations to compare the actual approach taken to the students' suggestions.
  - When the story is hypothetical, the instructor should then research similar actual events and use pertinent elements to create the fictional event.
- **Develop an outline** — An outline provides students with all the facts in the story and ties the details and visual aids (if any are used) to the timeline of the story. Key elements in the outline should include those that had a direct effect on the outcome of the event.

chapter 11

Key Terms

Job Performance Requirements

NFPA® 1041 References

5.4.3

Training Evolution Supervision

Learning Objectives

1. Describe the safety challenges an instructor faces during a training evolution. [NFPA®1041, 5.4.3]

2. Summarize the use of the ICS model to supervise training. [NFPA®1041, 5.4.3]

3. Discuss environmental regulations that affect training evolutions. [NFPA®1041, 5.4.3]

4. Discuss the roles and responsibilities of the instructor during accident investigation. [NFPA®1041, 5.4.3]

Chapter 11
Training Evolution Supervision

Case History

Instructors were conducting an early spring firefighter recruit training at a state fire academy. During evening drills covering interior fire attack to the second floor of a burn building, a light freezing rain began. As the evolution progressed, and the freezing rain continued, students and instructors began to experience problems with using ground ladders as a part of the evolution. The ladders kept sliding away from the building, and the students who were attempting to stabilize the ladders were also slipping on the wet ground.

There were many students involved in the evolution working with a number of instructors. The lead instructor had appointed one of these instructors to function as a safety officer. The safety officer observed that the students had begun having difficulties keeping the ladders grounded during the light rain. She reported to the lead instructor that the evolution either had to be stopped altogether or modified so that the participants could continue in safety. The lead instructor called the evolution to a halt, gathered the participants together, and adjusted the training program for the remainder of the evolution so that ground ladders were no longer needed. The safety officer's vigilance and the lead instructor's flexibility allowed training to continue without compromising the safety of the students.

In Chapter 7, Skills-Based Training Beyond the Classroom, Level I Instructors were introduced to the basics of smaller scale training situations. Level II Instructors should be able to supervise these evolutions as part of their job performance requirements. This chapter expands on the information in Chapter 7 to include instructors' supervisory duties during larger scale training evolutions.

The Safety Challenge

The challenge for the instructor is to provide realistic training situations that are similar to actual emergencies while still providing the maximum level of safety. The sections that follow describe various aspects of the challenge of providing safe training evolutions for students and instructors.

Organizational and Administrative Support

In addition to instructors incorporating safety into the training curriculum, changes in organizational policy can reduce the number of training accidents. Some of the recommendations provided in the USFA report, *Trends and Hazards in Firefighter Training, Special Report-0 May 2003 (TR-100)* include the following:

- Follow established guidelines and currently accepted organizational procedures as well as training and safety standards.

- Conduct live-burn evolutions in a variety of structure types to provide realistic fire fighting experiences.

- Train firefighters and emergency responders to recognize the visual and physical clues to impending danger (such as changes in smoke conditions) and anticipate fire behavior in a variety of building types (**Figure 11.1**).

- To reduce the potential risks to personnel, all fire and emergency services organizations regulated by legally adopted NFPA® standards are required to have a risk-management plan. After implementing the plan, instructors must monitor its effectiveness. Risk-management plans are designed to accomplish the following objectives:

  — Identify risks.

  — Evaluate the potential for injury or damage, based on the frequency and severity of risk.

  — Establish appropriate controls to minimize or eliminate the risk.

Risk-Management Plan — Written plan that identifies and analyzes the exposure to hazards, selects appropriate risk management techniques to handle exposures, implements those techniques, and monitors the results.

The **risk-management plan** includes all job-related activities in which fire and emergency services personnel normally participate, including emergency, nonemergency, training, and support activities. NFPA® 1500, *Standard on Fire*

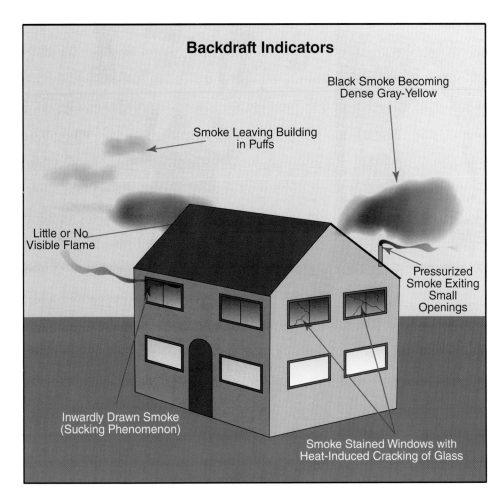

Backdraft Indicators

Black Smoke Becoming Dense Gray-Yellow

Smoke Leaving Building in Puffs

Little or No Visible Flame

Pressurized Smoke Exiting Small Openings

Inwardly Drawn Smoke (Sucking Phenomenon)

Smoke Stained Windows with Heat-Induced Cracking of Glass

Figure 11.1 Backdraft indicators are visual clues that firefighters must be able to recognize.

Department Occupational Safety and Health Program, provides detailed guidelines for developing a risk-management plan. IFSTA's **Occupational Safety, Health, and Wellness** manual is also an excellent resource for establishing safety and health programs.

The organization's administration plays a role in supporting and enforcing safety, fitness, health, and wellness programs in all aspects of the organization's operations. It is the administration's responsibility to perform the following actions:

- Provide adequate personal protective equipment (PPE).
- Ensure that all apparatus and equipment are maintained.
- Ensure that all safety equipment is properly installed and operating.
- Provide policies and procedures for the safe use of the apparatus and equipment.
- Address the fitness, health, and wellness of personnel by providing the following **(Figures 11.2 a-c, p.284)**:
  — Employee assistance programs
  — Job-related physical fitness testing
  — Annual medical evaluations and periodic examinations
  — Health and wellness related information and training

Figures 11.2 a-c Fitness, health, and wellness programs are an important aspect of fire fighter safety and should be supported by organizations.

Review: NFPA® 1403, *Standard on Live Fire Training Evolutions*

An essential element for planning live-fire training is NFPA® 1403. Instructors must be familiar with the requirements of this standard for all live-fire training in purpose-built burn buildings, acquired structures, and burn props. Safety requirements must be enforced by the instructor-in-charge of any training evolution, the designated safety officer, and the organization's administration. For more information on NFPA® 1403, see Chapter 7, Skills-Based Training Beyond the Classroom.

Unsafe Behavior

Injuries and fatalities during training are usually the result of unsafe acts by persons who are unaware or uninformed of potential hazards, who are ignorant of the safety policies, or who fail to follow safety procedures. Casualties may also be caused by conditions in the physical environment that were not examined or considered as potential hazards. Almost all accidents are predictable and preventable.

Human factors generally lead to unsafe behavior in fire and emergency services training. Before allowing participation in a training scenario, an instructor should determine whether any of the following factors apply to an individual student and take the appropriate action:

- **Improper attitude** — Address unsafe attitudes or behaviors so that the individual does not create or become involved in an accident. Instructors should monitor their classes for signs of high-risk behavior, such as students who are:

  — Irresponsible or reckless

  — Inconsiderate or uncooperative

  — Fearful of, or phobic about, the situation

  — Egotistical or jealous

  — Intolerant or impatient

  — Excitable or oversensitive

  — Obsessive or absentminded

- **Complacency** — Students may perceive some safety procedures as unnecessary, perhaps because they have been so well-practiced. Instructors should ensure that students are not avoiding or overlooking safety steps during any training evolution.

- **Lack of knowledge or skill** — If students are unprepared for an evolution, instructors must address the situation by providing additional training, including supervised practice time. Instructors must be sure that students are:

  — Sufficiently informed about the training

  — Capable of interpreting the training and convinced of its need

  — Experienced in requisite knowledge and skills, and capable of decisive actions

  — Properly trained and able to recognize potential hazards/risks

- **Physical limitations** — Instructors should be aware of any physical limitations that could lead to training injuries or fatalities. These limitations could include any of the following:

  — Inability to see or hear well enough for the situation

  — Physical characteristics that reduce a student's ability to perform safely

  — Limited strength or aerobic capacity

  — Effects of a medical condition, allergy, illness, or mental condition

  — Reduced reaction times due to substance abuse or legally prescribed medications

Hazard and Risk Analysis

A **hazard and risk analysis** identifies potential problem areas and is the foundation for any risk-management plan. For example, a planned driver/operator training evolution may require novice or inexperienced personnel to drive apparatus on public streets or highways. This situation creates a potential risk to both personnel and the public. The instructor should search for a more suitable location and use cones to simulate traffic; after personnel have gained experience in this setting, subsequent evolutions can be held on public streets.

Hazard and Risk Analysis — Identification of hazards or risks and the determination of an appropriate response; combines the hazard assessment with risk management concepts.

When creating a lesson plan for skills training, instructors perform a task analysis to determine the necessary tasks and the order in which they should be performed. An instructor should examine these tasks and ensure that they can be safely performed on the available training ground. For example, if the roof at an acquired structure looks unlikely to support the weight of multiple firefighters, then roof ventilation training cannot occur without reinforcing the roof or acquiring a new structure.

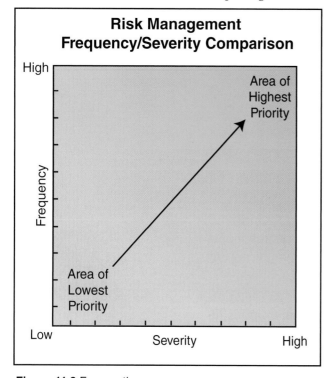

Figure 11.3 Frequently encountered hazards that result in serious injuries should be given top priority.

Instructors should follow all aspects of risk-management plans established by their organizations. They should also heed any potential risks outlined in prepared lesson plans before teaching lessons and assess potential risks in the training environment. Instructors must eliminate hazardous environments near training areas. If hazards cannot be eliminated or sufficiently minimized, instructors must move the training to another location.

NOTE: Even with good policies in place and good instructions to work from, skills training can be unpredictable.

When reviewing injury records, investigators should prioritize potential hazards that have led to injuries in the past while considering the following two factors **(Figure 11.3)**:

1. Frequency of the hazardous activity, and how this relates to the frequency of accidents or injuries

2. Relative severity of the potential loss

A type of minor injury may be a higher priority than a more serious injury type if the minor injury is more frequent because it occurs during a more frequently performed task. Thus a common, minor hand injury may be more important to address than a serious, infrequent shoulder injury, because it may be more important to address a hundred minor injuries than a single more serious injury. Ideally, all hazards are addressed as high priorities, but prioritizing hazards is often a necessity imposed by limited resources. See **Appendix J**, Risk-Management Formulas, for the frequency/severity table and calculation formulas.

Hazards and Risks

In everyday conversation, the terms *hazard* and *risk* are often used interchangeably; however, technically, they describe two different things. *Hazard* usually refers to a condition, substance, or device that can directly cause an injury or loss. A risk, on the other hand, is the likelihood of suffering harm from a hazard. Risk can also be thought of as the potential for failure or loss. In other words, risk is the exposure to a hazard, and a hazard is the source of a risk.

Using ICS to Supervise Training

The ICS model adopted by many jurisdictions in North America is based on NFPA® 1561, *Standard on Emergency Services Incident Management System*. It provides guidance and direction for the management and control of all types of emergency incidents, ranging from single company responses to multiple agency and jurisdiction incidents. These guidelines can also be applied to large-scale skills-training exercises and operational training evolutions. Using ICS also increases the safety and accountability of students.

The ICS model should be used at all types of training evolutions, whether they involve live fire or not. Students and instructors will then become familiar with ICS roles and procedures. The sections that follow describe topics related to implementing an ICS during large-scale skills exercises and operational training evolutions.

Incident Command System Duties and Functions

Level II Instructors should have a working knowledge of incident command systems, and they should implement the ICS that their agency has adopted. ICS is adaptable to a wide variety of situations and is therefore a useful tool for organizing training evolutions.

Figure 11.4 ICS positions should be filled based on the scope of the training evolution.

The instructor in charge should staff the ICS positions that are necessary to effectively manage the training evolution. Examples of ICS positions that may need to be staffed include the following **(Figure 11.4)**:

- Incident Commander (IC) or Lead Instructor
- Safety Officer
- Logistics Officer
- Staging Officer
- Division or Group Supervisor
- Communications Officer
- Ignition Officer
- Water Supply Officer
- Public Information Officer (PIO)

ICS span of control redommends that the number of instructors reporting to the lead instructor should be between 3 and 7 individuals.

Training Plan or Incident Action Plans (IAP)

Every lesson requires a lesson plan, and operational training evolutions can be described as large-scale lessons. The lesson plan for these evolutions must be based on either the plans used at actual incidents, an agency approved training plan, or an **incident action plan (IAP)**. Instructors can adapt the various IAP forms in the NIMS-ICS system to create the training evolution IAP. Like operational IAPs, training plans usually contain the following elements:

- **Objectives** — Clearly stated and measurable objectives to be achieved in a specific time interval
- **Organization** — ICS-defined units and agencies that are involved, and the roles they will play in the command structure

> **Incident Action Plan (IAP)** — Written or unwritten plan for the disposition of an incident; contains the overall strategic goals, tactical objectives, and support requirements for a given operational period during an incident.

- **Assignments** — Specific unit tactical assignments for students and instructors; usually divided by branch, division, and group

- **Support materials** — Includes site plans, access or traffic plans, and locations of support activities such as staging, rehabilitation, and logistics

- **Safety message** — Information concerning personnel safety at the training incident, including a site-safety plan

At the end of the training evolution, the training plan is used as part of the postincident analysis and critique. It is an instrument for evaluating both the students' learning achievements and the overall effectiveness of the training.

What This Means to You

Skills Training with a Large Number of Students

You have been assigned to be the lead instructor for a weekend training exercise on basic skills for fifty students. To make the best use of the time needed to complete the training, you divide the skills that will be taught into ten exercise sections, so that students can be divided into groups of five for each section.

When planning the exercise, you locate enough qualified instructors to supervise each of the five sections. You also enlist three additional instructors for other command structure positions. The first is a safety officer whose task is to travel among the training sections, ensuring that safety procedures are being followed. This officer will report to you in the event of safety violations. The second is a logistics officer whose task is to ensure that the students and instructors have the equipment and supplies that they need to train safely. The third functions as a staging officer who maintains a rehab area and the common area where students go between training assignments. The instructors at each training section report problems up the chain of command to these command positions, who then report to you. The clear-cut roles and responsibilities dictated by the NIMS-ICS and IAP ensure that the training runs smoothly, and that students focus solely on learning basic skills throughout the weekend **(Figure 11.5)**.

Operational Training Evolutions

You are planning an operational training evolution that simulates a response to a three alarm fire while applying ICS management methods. One of the learning objectives for the evolution is to teach ICS to students who meet the prerequisites for command training. All the students will assume ICS-dictated roles for extinguishing a live fire, issuing commands, and conducting all communication within the ICS framework.

You first develop a training plan based upon the IAP that would normally be written for an operational incident; one that is similar to the one in the training evolution **(Figure 11.6)**. You assign instructors to the various command positions needed for the evolution. You then identify students to act as command officers and pair them with instructors who will monitor their decisions during the training. Some will lead units who will enter the live-fire area while others will function in support operations, as safety officers, or the communications officer.

At the time of the training, you review the training plan (IAP) with all the students and instructors who will be involved. You brief non-fire agencies on the communication structure you will use for the evolution. You tell command students who they will be paired with during the training. At the end of the training session, you use the IAP to debrief all participants and focus on how the training did or did not meet their expectations.

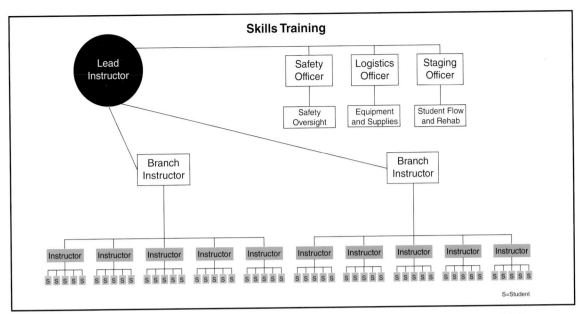

Figure 11.5 Skills training with a large number of students requires clear-cut roles and responsibilities.

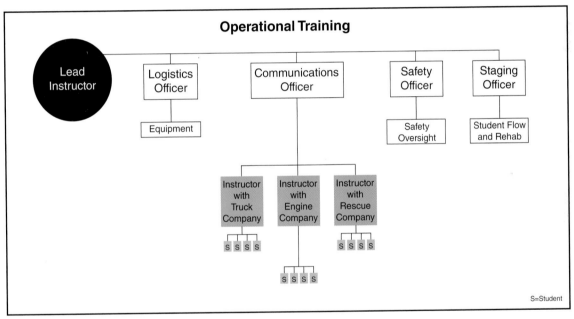

Figure 11.6 Roles and responsibilities assigned during operational training should reflect the roles and responsibilities required at the scene of an incident.

Training Evolution Evaluation

At the termination of the practical training evolution, a **post-incident critique or analysis** should be held. The post-incident critique fulfills the following purposes:

- Evaluates student skills and learning
- Evaluates the practical training evolution
- Determines safety problems that need to be corrected
- Trains students in the post-incident critique process
- Evaluates the instructor's supervisory and teaching skills

If the critique determines that students have not attained the learning objectives for the evolution, further training should be provided and the evolution

Post-Incident Analysis — Overview and critique of an incident by members of all responding agencies, including dispatchers. Typically takes place within two weeks of the incident. In the training environment it may be used to evaluate student and instructor performance during a training evolution.

restaged. If the evaluation determines that the evolution did not provide the level of training necessary to meet the learning objectives, then the evolution should be redesigned to provide that level.

If safety problems are discovered, they should be corrected immediately before the evolution is used again. If the instructor did not provide adequate supervision or instruction, he or she should pursue additional professional development.

Along with the IAP, the post-incident critique should be used to generate a report on the training evolution. That report should contain the recommendations for changes to the evolution and be sent to the organization's leadership. All reports should be maintained in the organization's record system.

Environmental Issues at Training Evolutions

In the United States, the Environmental Protection Agency (EPA) regulates activities that affect the nation's water, atmosphere, and soil. In addition, in each of the individual states, similar agencies enforce their own rules and regulations that may affect training evolutions. Instructors and administrators must be familiar with federal, state, and local environmental regulations, so that they can apply for the necessary permits before conducting any training that may release harmful agents into the environment.

NOTE: Canada also has laws that protect the environment. Instructors conducting training in Canada should become familiar with Canadian law and take the appropriate measures to train safely and legally.

Water

Rivers, streams, lakes, ponds, and other bodies of water can be contaminated by runoff water from training evolutions. Training facilities should have systems that trap, contain, and clean contaminated water from training props, especially when using flammable liquids **(Figure 11.7)**. Some municipal fire and emergency services organizations may also have storm drains that are equipped with filtration systems. However, the vast majority of training divisions do not have the ability to clean contaminated materials from runoff water before it reaches streams, rivers, or lakes.

Instructors and administrators should contact the local environmental AHJ or enviornmental protection to determine the specific regulations they will have to follow. Sometimes an evolution will release such a diluted level of contaminant that it will not cause any environmental damage. But even in such cases, permits may be required.

Atmosphere

Live-fire exercises may involve the intentional release of hydrocarbons into the atmosphere, which may be controlled or prohibited by local open-burning ordinances **(Figures 11.8 a and b)**. These ordinances may require acquiring a permit and displaying it at the training site. To ensure that training does not pose a threat to the environment, instructors should take the following steps:

Step 1: Adhere to all environmental rules and regulations imposed by all levels of government.

Step 2: Meet environmental protection guidelines for the use of Class B (flammable/combustible) liquids.

Figure 11.7 Training facilities should include systems for trapping and cleaning contaminated water.

Figures 11.8 a and b Training fires that produce thick smoke (a) are generally considered atmospheric hazards. Fires that produce less smoke (b) are more likely to meet local open-burning ordinances

Figure 11.9 Instructors must comply with investigators after any training accident.

Figure 11.10 Witnesses and parties who were involved in training accidents should be interviewed immediately.

Step 3: Ensure that weather conditions do not spread contaminants into populated areas.

Step 4: Provide spark and cinder control for adjacent areas.

Soil

Soil can be contaminated from water runoff that contains byproducts of combustion, fuels, and nonbiodegradable extinguishing agents. Large quantities of these materials are considered hazardous waste, but even small quantities must always be removed after training, along with any contaminated soil. Because this can be costly and could result in litigation, training agencies must take steps to avoid soil contamination. Instructors and administrators should consult either the *EPA* or their local environmental agency about the relevant rules and regulations.

If it is not possible to meet these requirements for containing water runoff, training should be performed on a nonporous concrete surface that can be cleaned with inert materials. Training agencies should also consider using training-type foam extinguishing agents that are nontoxic and biodegradable.

NOTE: See Chapter 7, Skills-Based Training Beyond the Classroom, for more information about the environmental impact of fuels used in live-fire training. Additional information on Class B fuels can be found in IFSTA's **Aircraft Rescue and Fire Fighting** and **Industrial Exterior and Structural Fire Brigades** manuals.

Accident Investigation

Instructors and students who are involved in or witness an accident are often afraid to provide information, thinking that they may get someone in trouble. But an investigation cannot be resolved and future accidents cannot be prevented when personnel withhold valuable information. After any injury or fatality, investigators must determine the sequence of events and their cause. Their job is about fact-finding, not fault-finding; they try to determine only what caused the accident, not who to blame for it. After any training accident, instructors should do the following:

- Report the accident according to their organizational policies.
- Answer any questions asked by investigators about the accident **(Figure 11.9)**.
- Complete any appropriate forms.
- Decide whether or not the training evolution can continue after the accident has occurred.
- Obtain statements immediately after the accident from persons involved and potential witnesses **(Figure 11.10)**.

Chapter Summary

Level II Instructors are responsible for supervising large-scale, skills-based training and operational training evolutions. They need to understand the safety challenges involved with supervising a large number of students during training. They must also understand the uses of ICS as a tool for organizing training evolutions. Instructors should take into account how their training might affect the environment when they train at acquired structures. Finally, Instructors should understand how accidents are investigated.

Review Questions

1. What safety challenges does an instructor face when supervising a training evolution?

2. How does an instructor use ICS to supervise training?

3. What environmental issues may arise during all phases of training evolutions?

4. What are the roles and responsibilities of the instructor during accident investigation?

Test Item Construction

Chapter Contents

Key Terms

Job Performance Requirements

NFPA® 1041 References

5.5.2

Test Item Construction

Learning Objectives

1. Describe common considerations for test instruments. [NFPA® 1041, 5.5.2]

2. Discuss the three types of tests used in fire and emergency service training. [NFPA® 1041, 5.5.2]

3. Explain the steps for test planning. [NFPA® 1041, 5.5.2]

4. Describe the process to select a test scoring method. [NFPA® 1041, 5.5.2]

Chapter 12
Test Item Construction

Case History

In an effort to cover each objective of the lesson, an instructor developed a test by basing questions on exact phrases from the lesson plan. She felt confident that her lessons had been a success because the scores on the tests were very high. However, another instructor pointed out that constructing test items directly from the lesson plan had resulted in questions that provided clues to other items on the test. It was determined that it was possible to use the clues to pass the test without having knowledge of the subject. The test was not an adequate measure of knowledge due to this poor test construction. After revising questions so that they were not word-for-word duplications of text in the lesson plan, the new test item produced more realistic results.

This chapter expands on Chapter 8, Testing and Evaluation. In general, the information found there about tests that the AHJ has purchased or prepared applies to Level II Instructors as well. When prepared tests are not available or do not measure the learning objectives that the AHJ wishes to evaluate, Level II Instructors may have the following two additional responsibilities:

1. Creating new testing instruments and test items for their organizations.

2. Modifying existing test items or creating replacement test items that more appropriately measure the learning taking place in their jurisdictions.

This chapter describes how to plan and create new testing instruments.

Evaluation Terminology

NFPA® 1041 refers to testing instruments as "student evaluation instruments." In order to avoid confusion with other types of evaluation instruments referenced in NFPA® 1041 (such as class evaluations, instructor evaluations, and course evaluations) this chapter uses the more common terms "testing instrument" and "test item" to describe student evaluation instruments that are designed to measure a student's knowledge or mastery of learning objectives.

Test Instruments

Instructors should be able to select appropriate **testing instruments** that address all of the following:

- The three domains of learning – cognitive, psychomotor and affective
- Levels of learning ranging from basic (Understand) to advanced (Create)
- The level of difficulty presented in a course – beginner, intermediate, or advanced

The sections that follow describe common considerations for all test types and provide specific information about the following three basic types of test instruments **(Figure 12.1)**:

- Written tests, which measure cognitive ability
- Oral tests, which measure either cognitive or communicative ability
- Performance tests, which measure psychomotor skill ability

Common Considerations for All Tests

Test items must always be based on specific learning objectives. Level II Instructors must consider the following additional criteria when designing any test:

- Test formatting
- Arrangement of test items
- Test item level of cognition
- Difficulty of test items
- Test instructions
- Time requirements

Testing Instrument — Series of test items that are based on learning objectives and collectively measure student learning on a specific topic.

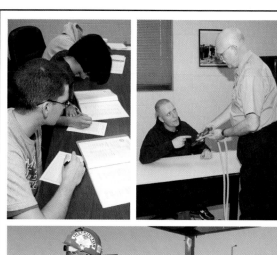

Figure 12.1 The most common test types are written, oral, and performance tests.

Test Item — Single question on a testing instrument that elicits a student response and can be scored for accuracy.

Test Formatting

Proper layout and formatting of the test sheet will make any test easier to take, administer, and score **(Figure 12.2)**. Consider the following guidelines for test formatting:

- Provide space for students to write their name and the date on either the test sheet or a separate answer sheet.
- Provide a title or label at the top of the first page.
- Number all tests and label different versions of the test. This will help with score reporting and test security.
- Provide clear instructions at the beginning of the test, and at the beginning of each section that uses a different type of test item (such as multiple-choice, matching, true-false, or fill-in-the-blank).
- Provide a sample test item, along with a sample answer, to show students how to respond to each item.
- Number all items consecutively (1, 2, 3, 4, etc.).
- Single-space each test item, but double-space between items.

- State the point value of each test item (for example, *Multiple choice: 1 point each; Short-answer: 2 points each*).
- Use commonly understood terms; for example, do not use abbreviations unless they are placed in parentheses following the common term

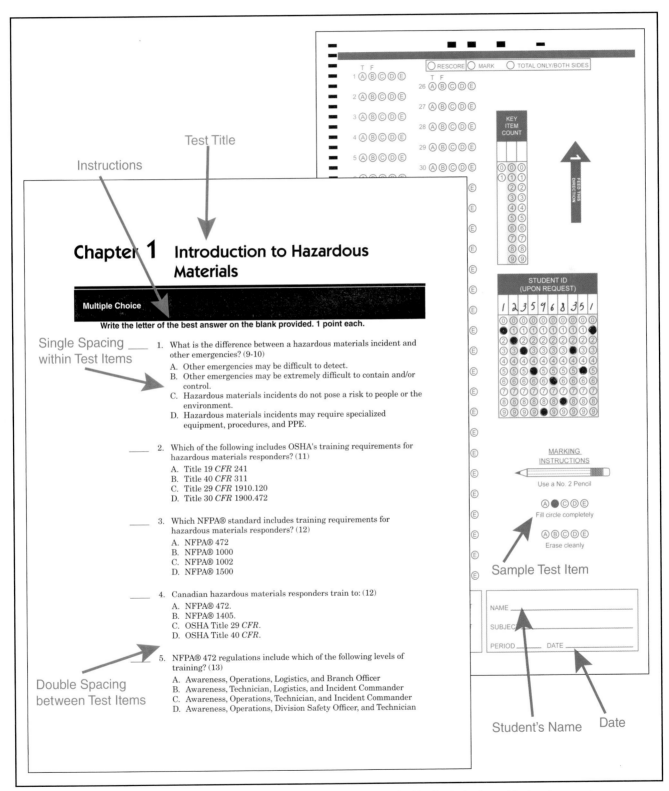

Figure 12.2 Proper layout and formatting of the test sheet makes the work of both students and instructors easier.

Test Item Arrangement

Test items must be arranged in a logical sequence. They can be grouped either by learning domain outcome (such as knowledge, comprehension, or application) or type of test item (such as multiple-choice, matching, or short-answer). Instructors must make sure that the wording of one test item does not reveal the answer to another test item. On computer-adaptive tests, such as those used in EMS, sequencing may be organized so that students can only progress to a more difficult question after correctly answering a simpler one.

Test Item Level of Cognition

The levels found in Bloom's Taxonomy may be categorized from low to high as follows:

- Remember (Knowledge)
- Understand (Comprehension)
- Apply (Application)
- Analyze (Analysis)
- Evaluate (Evaluation)
- Create (Synthesis)

Test items should evaluate the student's ability at the level within the taxonomy that corresponds to the learning objective being evaluated. A variety of levels can exist within any course. For example, an advanced level class will still need test items written to lower levels of the taxonomy for new information that students are meant to remember and understand. These points will be further reviewed later in this chapter.

Test Difficulty

The actual determination of test difficulty does not occur until the test has been taken and scored. At that time, students' performance on individual questions will determine the level of difficulty. A test is considered appropriately difficult if most of the students answered between 65 and 85 percent of the questions correctly.

Test Instructions

Test designers should include clear instructions at the beginning of the test that explain the following:

- Purpose of the test
- Method and means for recording answers
- Suggestion on whether to guess when undecided on an answer (in some cases, incorrect answers are penalized more than not answering the question)
- Amount of time available to complete the test

Additional instructions should be provided at the beginning of each section that uses a different type of test item (such as multiple-choice, matching, true-false, or fill-in-the-blank).

Time Requirements

The average time it takes a student who knows the material to complete a given type of test item is as follows:

- **True-false (true answer)** — 15 seconds for true answers
- **True-false (false answer)** — 30 to 45 seconds
- **Seven-item matching** — 60 to 90 seconds
- **Multiple choice (with four possible responses)** — 30 to 60 seconds
- **Problem solving, analyze, create, or evaluate level questions** — 30 to 60 seconds
- **Short-answer** — 30 to 60 seconds
- **Essay** — 60 seconds for each major point that students must include

Instructors can use these estimates to calculate how much time students will need to complete the test. It may also be helpful to ask another member of the organization (but not a student) to take the test, to see how much time he or she needs to finish. The most important criteria is that tests should be written to the appropriate length to address the learning objectives the test is intended to evaluate.

When time is a restrictive factor, tests can be written that emphasize the most critical learning objectives and include a sampling of less important objectives to complete the rest of the test. This method of test construction is called sampling. When the instructor uses sampling, the plan must be documented. The most critical objectives must be tested in each version of the test while the less critical objectives tested are included in a certain rotation (that is, tested on a series of tests during the lesson or course).

Testing Bias

As described in Chapter 8, Testing and Evaluation, test items and testing instruments should not be biased toward any particular group of students. When writing test items, instructors should avoid including biases in their questions. Ensuring that test questions very closely reflect the materials being tested – standards, textbooks, training manuals – is the best way to avoid bias. In addition, when students recognize that test items closely resemble the information that they have studied, they are more likely to perform confidently on tests regardless of their gender, cultural, ethnic, or regional backgrounds.

When instructors find evidence of these biases, the questions associated with the bias should be revised or, if necessary, rewritten. In the fire and emergency services, bias is generally limited to use of regional jargon and differences in terminology. For example, small governments in the U.S. and Canada may be referred to as counties or parishes or referred to in legal terms as jurisdictions. Similarly, some fire apparatus may be referred to as a tanker or a tender depending on geographical region or the differences between departments. The terminology on the test should reflect the terminology of the students and the materials from which they studied.

Written Tests

Written tests measure students' understanding and retention of technical information and evaluate their accomplishment of the cognitive learning objectives. Written test items fall into one of two categories, either objective or subjective. These are defined as follows:

- **Objective** — An objective test item is a question for which there is one, and only one correct answer. The judgment of the instructor or evaluator is not relevant and has no effect on assessment. Objective items measure cognitive learning, but typically only at the lower levels of remembering and understanding. However, properly constructed objective test items can also be used to measure higher levels of cognitive learning such as evaluation or creation. There are three main types of objective questions:

  — Multiple-Choice

  — True or False

  — Matching

- **Subjective** — A subjective test item is one that has no single correct answer. The evaluator's judgment may therefore affect assessment. Subjective items are an effective way of measuring higher cognitive levels, (analyze, evaluate, and create) because subjective test items allow students the freedom to organize, analyze, revise, redesign, or evaluate a problem. The strength of a student's response to these items depends on a variety of factors, such how well they communicate their ideas, and the personal opinions of the evaluator. There are three main types of subjective test items:

  — Short-Answer or Completion

  — Essay

  — Interpretive Exercise

The sections that follow describe objective test items in detail and also present information about subjective tests that instructors may encounter in the fire and emergency services.

Study Guides and Workbooks

Questions that are published in study guides, test preparation guides, textbooks, and manuals should not be used for certification or summative tests. These questions have not been validated and should only be used to help students determine how well they understand the material in a particular coursebook.

Multiple-Choice

A multiple-choice test item consists of either a question or an incomplete statement, called the **stem**, plus a list of several possible responses, which are referred to as *choices* or **alternatives** (**Figure 12.3**). Students must read the stem and select the correct response from the list of alternatives. The correct choice is known as the *answer* and the remaining choices are called **distractors**. Distractors discriminate between students who understand the subject matter well and those who know only a little and are therefore uncertain of the correct answer. Distractors are not meant to trick, confuse, or mislead students.

When creating multiple-choice test items, it is important to adhere to the following guidelines:

- Write the stem in the form of a direct question or an incomplete sentence that measures only one learning objective.

Stem — The question or introductory statement in a multiple-choice test item.

Alternatives — Possible answers in a multiple-choice test item.

Distractors — Possible answers in a multiple-choice test item that are incorrect but plausible.

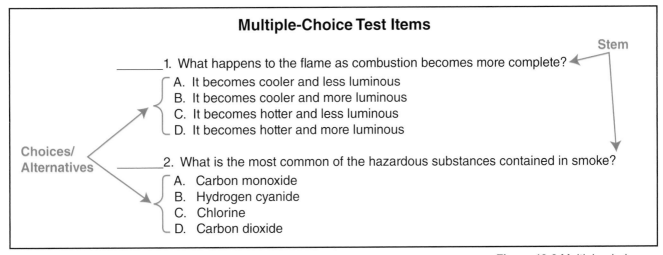

Multiple-Choice Test Items

Stem

_____ 1. What happens to the flame as combustion becomes more complete?
    A. It becomes cooler and less luminous
    B. It becomes cooler and more luminous
    C. It becomes hotter and less luminous
    D. It becomes hotter and more luminous

Choices/Alternatives

_____ 2. What is the most common of the hazardous substances contained in smoke?
    A. Carbon monoxide
    B. Hydrogen cyanide
    C. Chlorine
    D. Carbon dioxide

Figure 12.3 Multiple-choice test items consist of a *stem* and *alternatives* (possible answers). Incorrect alternatives are known as *distractors*.

- Write a clear, brief stem that contains most of the wording for the test item; doing so helps to avoid placing repeated words in the alternatives.

- Write positive questions, but if and when negative statements are used, negative words should be emphasized consistently.

- Provide at least three plausible, attractive distractors.

- Phrase the choices so that they are parallel with each other and grammatically consistent with the stem.

- Place correct answers in varied positions among the A, B, C, and D choices.

- Place each choice on a separate, indented line and in a single column.

- Begin responses with capital letters when the stem is a complete question.

- Begin responses with lowercase letters when the stem is an incomplete sentence.

- Do not include choices that are obviously wrong or intended to be humorous.

- Make sure that stems and alternatives do not give students grammatical clues as to the correct response. For example, a stem that calls for a singular response (by using *a/an* or a singular word ending) would automatically rule out alternatives that are plural, and a stem phrased in the present tense would rule out alternatives phrased in the past tense.

- Make all alternatives close to the same length.

- Avoid using the phrases *all of the above* and *none of the above* as the fourth choice.

- Do not test trivial ideas or information.

- Use correct grammar and punctuation.

Instructors should be aware of the disadvantages of multiple-choice tests, such as the following:

- They are not well suited to measuring some cognitive skills, such as organizing and presenting ideas. Essay tests are more effective for this purpose.

- It can be very difficult to construct multiple-choice tests that include different difficulty-level test items that measure a variety of cognitive learning levels.

- It is often difficult to create enough appropriate and plausible distractors for each stem.

- Students who do not know the material may still be able to guess the correct answer.

True-False

The true-false test item is a single statement that the student must determine to be either true or false (**Figure 12.4**). The difficulty in constructing this type of test is creating a statement that is completely true or completely false. True statements should be based on facts, while false statements should be based on common misconceptions of the facts. In addition to the traditional true-false test items, there are also modified true-false test items. Modified true-false items ask the student to explain why an item is false or to rewrite the item to make it true.

One limitation of true-false questions is that students tend to remember the false items on the test as being true, a phenomenon known as the negative suggestion effect. Instructors should review the correct answers to true-false questions with students after scoring the test to help combat this effect.

Alternative-Response Questions

The alternative-response question is based on the premise that the question has only one correct answer out of two possible choices. Although the true-false test item is the most common, other options include agree-disagree, yes-no, or right-wrong.

Another approach is to use the alternative-response approach to determine whether the student can categorize information based on alternatives such as awareness-operational, Level I-Level II, or line-staff. These alternatives can overcome some of the disadvantage to the true-false approach that exists when the student can guess the answer and has a 50-50 chance of getting it correct.

When creating true-false tests and test items, instructors should consider the following guidelines:

- Write the words *True* and *False* at the left margin if students must mark their answers on the test paper. On computer scored answer sheets, *True* may be assigned to *A* while *False* is assigned to *B*.

- Provide clear instructions so that students know how to respond to each statement (for example, by writing *True* or *False*, by writing *T* or *F*, by circling either *True* or *False*, or by marking *A* or *B*).

- Create enough test items to provide reliable results. For reliability purposes, more true/false items are needed than the number used for multiple-choice items. A large number of test items minimizes the possibility of guessing the correct answers.

- Distribute *true* and *false* items randomly. Avoid having several questions in a row be *true* (or *false*), or any pattern of distribution (such as T-T-F, T-T-F, T-T-F) that students might be able to recognize.

- Avoid determiners (words that indicate a specific answer) that provide unwarranted clues. Words such as *usually, generally, often,* or *sometimes* are most likely to appear in true statements. The words *never, all, always,* or *none* are more likely to be found in false statements.

- Avoid creating items that could trick or mislead students into making a mistake.

- Avoid double-negative test items; they are very confusing to students and do not accurately measure knowledge.

- Avoid using personal pronouns such as "you".
- Do not use test items that test trivia or obscure facts.
- Develop test items that require students to think about what they have learned, rather than merely remember it.
- Avoid unusually long or short test items, because the length may be a clue. Test developers tend to make true items longer than false items, because they include a justification of why the statement is, in fact, true.
- Create brief, simply stated test items that deal with a single concept. Avoid lengthy, complex items that address more than one concept.
- Avoid quoting information word-for-word from the textbook.

Matching

Matching test items consist of two parallel columns of words, phrases, images, or a combination of these. In the most common example, students must match a word from the left column with its definition from the right column. The content of a matching test item must consist of similar material, items, or information. For example, a matching section that should evaluate whether students know the component parts of a tech rescue rig should not include information about other topics. Some examples of matching test items are shown in **Figures 12.5 a-c, p.306**.

A partial list of test items that can be easily made into matching test items includes the following:

- **Short questions** — With answers
- **Events** — With dates
- **Parts** — With their functions
- **Terms** — With their definitions
- **Objects** — With their names
- **Machines or tools** — With their uses
- **Problems** — With their solutions
- **Causes** — With their effects

It is important to consider the following guidelines for matching tests and matching test items:

- Avoid placing each group of prompts (words, phrases, or images) and the list of responses on more than one page.
- Separate matching sections into sets of five problems and responses when using computer or mechanically scored answer sheets.
- Consider preparing one more response than there are prompts. The extra response requires more precise knowledge and prevents students from eliminating all the other possible answers.
- Arrange problem statements and responses into two columns: problem statements on the left side of the page and responses on the right. Columns may be

---

True-False Tests

Example 1:

Identify accurate statements about fuel characteristics. Circle the word *TRUE* before each correct statement, and the word *FALSE* before each false statement.

TRUE   FALSE   1. The shape and size of a fuel affects its ignitability.

Example 2:

Identify accurate statements about fuel characteristics. Place a check mark under the column marked *TRUE* for each correct statement and under the column marked *FALSE* for each false statement.

TRUE   FALSE

_____   _____   1. The shape and size of a fuel affects its ignitability.

Example 3:

Identify accurate statements about fuel characteristics. Write TRUE for each correct statement and FALSE for each false statement on the blank.

_____   1. The shape and size of a fuel affects its ignitability.

Example 4:

Identify accurate statements about fuel characteristics. Fill in circle A for each TRUE statement and circle B for each FALSE statement on scantron.

Ⓐ   Ⓑ   1. The shape and size of a fuel affects its ignitability.

Figure 12.4 Students can respond to true/false questions by circling the correct choice, placing a check in the correct column, writing out the word, or filling in a circle.

Matching

Match the correct statement to each term.

_____ 1. Can vary from moderate (unable to see, breathless) to severe (convulsions)

_____ 2. Lowest concentration of a gas or vapor capable of killing a specified species over a specified time

_____ 3. Minimum concentration of an inhaled substance in the gaseous state that will be fatal to the test group (usually within 1 to 4 hours)

_____ 4. Lowest administered dose of a material capable of killing a specified test species

_____ 5. Statistically derived single dose of a substance that can be expected to cause death in 50 percent of animals when administered by the oral route

_____ 6. Minimum amount of solid or liquid that when ingested, absorbed, or injected through the skin will cause death

A. Incapacitating dose (ID)

B. Lethal concentration (LC)

C. Lethal concentration low (LC$_{LO}$ or LCL)

D. Lethal dose (LD)

E. Lethal dose low (LDLO or LDL)

F. Median lethal dose (LD$_{50}$)

A

Matching Test Items

Objective 16:
Match DOT hazards to their placard colors.
Write the correct letters on the blanks.

_____ 1. Nonflammable gas

_____ 2. Health hazard

_____ 3. Water reactive

_____ 4. Explosive

_____ 5. Oxidizer

_____ 6. Flammable

A. Green
B. Orange
C. Blue
D. Yellow
E. White
F. Red
G. Black

B

Pictorial Matching Test Item

Objective 16:
Match DOT placard illustrations to their hazards.
Write the correct letters on the blanks.

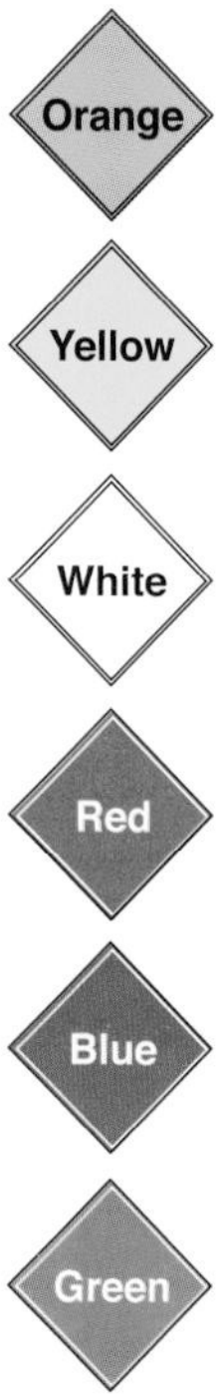

_____ 1. (Orange)

_____ 2. (Yellow)

_____ 3. (White)

_____ 4. (Red)

_____ 5. (Blue)

_____ 6. (Green)

A. Nonflammable gas
B. Oxidizer
C. Flammable
D. Chemical hazard
E. Explosive
F. Health hazard
G. Water reactive

C

Figures 12.5 a-c Several examples of matching test items. Note that in b and c additional alternatives have been included to discourage students from guessing.

titled with appropriate headings, such as Tools and Uses, or Symptoms and Treatments. Details:

— Number the problem statements. Place an answer line to the left of each number unless a separate answer sheet is used.

— Use letters for each response (A, B, C, etc.).

- Arrange responses alphabetically, chronologically, or numerically, in either ascending or descending order.

- State whether a response may be used once, more than once, or not at all.

- Avoid giving clues to answers in either problem statements or responses.

- Do not include responses that are obviously wrong.

NOTE: Instructors should be advised that matching test items may be more effectively and efficiently written as a series of multiple-choice questions.

Short-Answer/Completion

These test items require students to supply the correct answer themselves, without a list of possible choices. A short-answer item is a question for which students must provide a correct response. To do so they must recall previously learned information, apply relevant principles, or understand methods or procedures **(Figures 12.6 a and b)**. Short-answer items are often subjective. A completion item is an incomplete statement in which omitted key words are represented by an underlined blank space that students must fill in. Completion items should be objective.

When creating short-answer/completion tests items, instructors should consider the following guidelines:

- On completion test items, create short, concise, and direct statements so that only one answer is possible.

- Avoid long, involved statements with a string of blanks to fill; they tend to be confusing.

- Start with a direct question and change it to an incomplete statement.

- Make sure that the desired response is a key point in the lesson.

- Arrange the statement in order to place the blanks at or near the end of the sentence.

- Avoid statements that call for answers with more than one word, phrase, or number.

- Eliminate unnecessary clues, such as answer blanks that vary in length or the use of the words "a" or "an" preceding the blank.

- Write a rubric or detailed answer sheet so that the scorer understands the full extent of possible, acceptable answers to the questions.

Short-Answer Test Items

1. Laws arranged systematically and usually pertaining to one subject area are known as _____.

2. What is a local law that applies to persons, things, and activities in a jurisdiction?

   _____

A

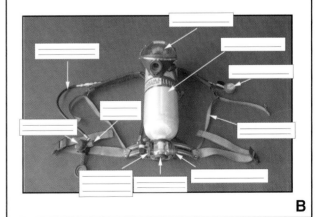

Picture Identification

Objective 11:

Identify components of positive-pressure SCBA.

B

Figures 12.6 a and b Short answer test items (a) should be written so that only one correct answer is possible. Completion items (b) require that students provide a correct answer without being given a list of possible choices.

Awareness-Level First Responder

Comprehensive Exam

Answer the following questions completely in the space provided. Each question is worth 10 points. Allow a maximum of 10 minutes for each question.

1. Explain the difference between initial isolation distances and protective action distances.

2. Describe the limitations of using the senses to determine the presence or absence of hazardous materials.

Figure 12.7 Essay questions require students to display in-depth knowledge.

Essay

Like short-answer test items, essays are subjective. Students must construct an in-depth answer on a topic or question related to a key aspect of the course material **(Figure 12.7)**. The strength of this item type is that it tests the higher level cognitive processes. Students are expected to demonstrate the ability to analyze a topic, create a solution to a problem, or evaluate a system or process. Essay tests also eliminate guessing, because students must know the material thoroughly in order to write an effective essay. Creative students prefer this type of test item because it allows them to express everything they know about a topic. However, there are disadvantages, such as the following:

- Essays are time-consuming, both for students to complete and for instructors to score.

- Differences in students' writing ability, penmanship, spelling, and grammar may affect an instructor's ability to score the test.

- Students who have difficulty writing or write slowly will be at a disadvantage, especially in a timed test.

Although essay test items are generally easy to construct, instructors should be aware of the following guidelines:

- Choose essay topics that reflect key aspects of the course material.

- Create a rubric that establishes clear scoring guidelines.

- For each essay question, provide clear instructions that define how students should respond, how much time they should spend responding, and how long each response should be.

- Provide sufficient time for students to respond to all questions.

Interpretive Exercises

The interpretive exercise is another subjective test item that measures higher level cognitive processes. An exercise consists of introductory material, typically numerical data, a graph, or a paragraph of text, followed by a series of test items. Students read the text or look at the illustrations, then answer the questions posed in the test items, which may be any of the types described in this chapter: multiple-choice, true-false, short-answer/completion, matching, or essay.

Instructors should apply the following rules when creating an interpretive exercise:

- Make sure that all introductory material relates to key learning objectives, and is as concise as possible.

- For each test item, apply relevant guidelines for effective item construction.

- Use test items that require the same type of performance that is listed in the test specifications for the various learning objectives.

- Create introductory material that is unfamiliar to students. For instance, create an original scenario that requires them to apply a set of learned responses from a similar situation.

- Make sure that the introductory material does not give away the answer to any of the test items.
- Make sure that students must read the introductory material to be able to answer test items.
- Provide enough test items, using a variety of item types, to effectively measure students' understanding of the material.

Oral Tests

Oral tests consist of either open or closed questions. When the purpose of the test is to determine knowledge, then the questions should be closed, requiring only a single brief answer. When the purpose is to determine how a student responds under pressure, then the question should judge both accuracy and presentation. In this case, the questions should be open, permitting longer answers that may lead to further questions.

Oral tests can be very stressful for some students, so it is important that instructors provide a relaxed, comfortable atmosphere. Otherwise, students' emotional response to the testing conditions may make it difficult for them to express what they have learned. Important aspects of designing and conducting oral tests include the following:

- **Development** — Base oral questions on standard criteria and performance objectives.
- **Validation** — Before using oral test items on actual testing candidates, pose the questions to other instructors, technical experts, or students in other training programs. Revise inappropriate or ineffective questions, and modify questions as needed to meet updated criteria.
- **Evaluation** — When administering the test, listen carefully to students' responses. Assess responses based on learning/performance objectives and standard criteria. Scoring should be based on the difference between what students express and what the standards and objectives require.

Oral tests are highly subjective, especially when the questions are open. To reduce evaluator bias against any particular student's responses, test developers should provide a scoring rubric that lists all possible correct answers.

Even though scoring is subjective and testing conditions may cause anxiety, an oral test is the most valid and reliable way to test a student's ability to verbally communicate ideas, concepts, and processes. It may also be the best measure of a student's judgment and thought processes.

Performance (Skills) Tests

A performance or skills test measures a student's proficiency in performing any task that involves a psychomotor objective. Examples include demonstrating care of tools and equipment, driving and operating apparatus, and performing emergency care steps and techniques **(Figure 12.8)**. Assessment is based on either a speed standard (timed performance), a quality standard (minimum acceptable performance), or both.

Figure 12.8 Performance tests measure psychomotor skills.

Performance tests require students to demonstrate psychomotor proficiency after appropriate practice or drill sessions. Tests must take place under controlled conditions, so that instructors can make reliable, valid judgments about student performance. Instructors and test developers should consider the following guidelines when creating performance tests:

- **Specify performance objectives to be measured** — All test items should be directly related to the relevant objectives. To save time, each item should then require that students perform several basic skills. For example, a test item that requires ventilating a pitched roof also requires students to demonstrate proper use of ground and roof ladders, cutting tools, safety ropes, and hoselines.

- **Select rating factors on which the test will be judged** — Rate students against a standard, not against the performance of other students **(Figure 12.9)**. Design a rating form that includes the following:

  — Student's approach to a stated job or procedure

  — Care shown in handling tools, equipment, and materials

  — Demonstration of accuracy

  — Time required to complete a job or procedure safely

- **Provide written instructions that clearly explain the test situation** — Review these instructions orally and give students the opportunity to ask questions if necessary so students understand how to proceed.

- **Try a new performance test on other instructors before administering it to students** — Conduct a trial test to uncover problems that can be corrected.

- **Use more than one test evaluator** — Ask other instructors or officers to be test evaluators. For certification testing, use more than one test evaluator. However, make sure that instructors do not evaluate their former students on material they covered together during the course. Provide instructions to evaluators about what they should look for during the test and how to use the rating scales and forms. Calculate an average score from all evaluators for each student or student team. Examples:

  — A student or team who receives three scores of 97, 94, and 94 percent from three evaluators receives an average score of 95 percent.

  — Scoring for performance tests that are criterion-referenced are typically pass/fail or satisfactory/unsatisfactory, although this scoring may be coupled with a minimum-points-earned requirement.

- **Follow established procedures when administering the test** — All necessary apparatus and equipment must be ready before beginning the tests. Evaluators must use the same equipment, follow the same task sequence, and rate performance on the same basis for each student. Eliminate all distractions from the testing area so that evaluators can concentrate on observing and evaluating, and students can concentrate on demonstrating their proficiency.

- **Make a score distribution chart after tests have been administered** — Evaluate students with low scores. Students with difficulty performing manipulative skills must receive immediate attention.

- **Rotate team members to every position for team evaluation ratings** — Ensure that each student is observed and evaluated in each position in an evolution.

Performance tests have many of the following advantages:

- **Validity** — A performance test is the only valid method of measuring a student's ability to perform manipulative skills.

LPFD SKILLS CHECK-OFF (2000)

FIREFIGHTER NAME: _____ DATE: _____

SKILL STATION	EVALUATION CRITERIA	PASS	FAIL
Bunker Gear/Airpack	Proper donning of bunker gear		
	Proper donning of airpack within 90 seconds		
	By-pass, "buddy breathing," trouble shooting		
	Proper bottle exchange/replacement		
	Proper bottle filling		
	Proper cleaning and placement back in service		
	Skill Station Overall Pass/Fail		
Evaluator Signature:			
Radio Seat	Proper radio usage (portable and apparatus)		
	Proper radio channel knowledge/usage		
	Proper map book usage		
	Proper pre-plan book usage		
	Proper radio transmission (en-route, arrival, clear)		
	Knox Box key usage		
	Skill Station Overall Pass/Fail		
Evaluator Signature:			
EMS	Location of EMS equipment		
	Proper Bio Hazard protective equipment use		
	Proper vital signs skills		
	Proper oxygen administration skills		
	Proper spinal immobilization skills		
	Proper CPR skills		
	Proper S.A.E.D. operation skills		
	Skill Station Overall Pass/Fail		
Evaluator Signature:			
Haz Mat	Proper DOT reference guidebook usage		
	Proper understanding of DOT book guidelines		
	Proper oxygen detector usage		
	Proper CO detector usage		
	Skill Station Overall Pass/Fail		
Evaluator Signature:			

continued on next page...

Figure 12.9 Using checklists for evaluation helps to ensure that students are rated against a standard and not against one another. *Courtesy of Scott Bryant & Linden-Peters Fire District.*

continued from previous page

SKILL STATION	EVALUATION CRITERIA	PASS	FAIL
Extrication	Proper cribbing technique?		
	Proper set up of extrication rescue tools?		
	Proper demonstration of extrication tools?		
	Proper return to service of extrication tools?		
	Skill Station Overall Pass/Fail?		
Evaluator Signature:			
Ladders	Proper removal and laddering of building?		
	Proper accent of ladder?		
	Proper placement back in service of ladder?		
	Proper accent of ladder?		
	Skill Station Overall Pass/Fail?		
Evaluator Signature:			
Hydrant	Proper supply line selection?		
	Hydrant tools and fittings?		
	Proper wrap of line around hydrant?		
	Proper connections made?		
	Remove supply line kinks and check for tight connections?		
	Skill Station Overall Pass/Fail?		
Evaluator Signature:			
OVERALL	**2000 SKILLS CHECK-OFF**		
Training Div. Signature			

- **Reliability** — A properly constructed performance test using specific criteria is a reliable measure of performance when coupled with an appropriate rating scale.

- **Skills-based** — Students who may not express themselves well orally or in writing may be able to perform a set of skills as well as or better than other students.

- **Student motivation** — Performance tests are an excellent means of motivating students. Knowing that they are expected to demonstrate skills in performance tests usually motivates students to practice, both in and out of class.

- **Sense of accomplishment** — Students who successfully complete well-prepared and carefully administered performance tests will be proud of their accomplishments.

- **Job related** — Students recognize that the psychomotor skills they are being tested for are directly related to the performance of their duties as fire and emergency services personnel.

Affective Domain Test Items

Test items are not normally written to evaluate the affective domain because affective objectives are often difficult to measure. But if learning objectives include a change in affective behavior, this can be evaluated in other ways besides testing. For example, instructors can rate behavioral performance based on what they observe during training.

Test Planning

Test planning consists of three major steps:

Step 1: Determine test purpose and classification.

Step 2: Define learning objectives or learning outcomes.

Step 3: Construct appropriate test items.

Constructing appropriate test items (Step 3) can be fairly easy when the instructor pays attention while completing the first two steps of the planning process. The sections that follow describe the three test-planning steps.

Determining Test Purpose and Classification

Instruction must be based on learning objectives, and any test must match those objectives. On a written test, it is usually important to have at least one question based on each course learning objective. For a psychomotor skills test, the students must have already learned the proper performance of the skill as stated in the learning objectives. They should also have had ample time to practice that skill prior to the test **(Figure 12.10)**. The test must evaluate each student's performance of that skill and not require a cognitive written test on it.

However, there are other considerations when determining the purpose of a test. Test developers must ask: *Should the test assess student performance against a set criterion or rank individual performance against other students?* The answer to that question determines whether test developers create a criterion-referenced or norm-referenced test.

Figure 12.10 Students should be given time to practice skills under the direction of an instructor before psychomotor skills tests.

Norm-referenced tests should never be used as end-of-course or certification tests. However, they are very effective for promotional examinations, when ranking applicants is desirable. Outside of this particular use, norm-referenced tests are rare in the fire and emergency services, so the majority of tests are criterion-referenced, using criteria that have been established through the following sources:

- NFPA® professional qualifications standards
- Federal, state/provincial, or local requirements
- Other professionally accepted requirements

  When planning tests, the instructor should also consider the following factors:

- Whether the test is designed to determine readiness for instruction or placement in the appropriate instructional level (prescriptive or placement test)
- Whether the test is designed to measure improved progress or identify learning problems that are hampering progress (formative or progress test)
- Whether the test is designed to rate terminal performance (summative or comprehensive test)
- Whether the test measures technical knowledge retention and recall in the cognitive domain, which requires the use of written or oral tests
- Whether the test measures manipulative skills in the psychomotor domain, which requires the use of performance or skill tests
- Whether the test measures behavioral changes in attitude, values, or beliefs in the affective domain, which requires written or oral tests

Identifying Learning Objectives

After determining the purpose and classification of the test, the instructor must identify the learning objectives the test will evaluate. Learning objectives reflect the course outcomes, which are broad statements explaining what students should have learned at the end of a course. For example: *Upon completion of the High-Angle Rescue Course, the student (given proper equipment) will be able to perform a high-angle rescue.* The test should be based upon the specific learning or behavioral objectives taken from each part of the course or individual lesson plans because they are specific, detailed, and measurable. Learning objectives and the level of proficiency each student must achieve are indications of what the test should measure.

Review: Cognitive Levels of Learning

Test questions, like learning objectives, are often based upon the cognitive levels of learning originally described in Chapter 10, Lesson Plan Development. The levels of learning in the cognitive domain, ranked from the simplest to the most complex, are as follows:

- **Remember (Knowledge)** — Students remember, recall, and recognize previously learned facts and theories. They can describe, define, label, list, and match terms and items. Sample Question: *Which of the following is an indication that a victim is in shock?*

- **Understand (Comprehension)** — Students understand, compare, and contrast information, and estimate future trends. They give examples and explanations, make predictions, and summarize information and ideas. Sample Question: *If one point of the fire tetrahedron is removed during combustion, which of the following will occur?*

- **Apply (Application)** — Students apply information, rules, and concepts that they have learned to new situations. They compute, demonstrate abilities, solve problems, modify ideas and actions, and operate equipment. Sample Question: *How would you approach a fire scene if smoke had been reported coming from under the eaves of the house?*

- **Analyze (Analysis)** — Students divide information into its component parts to understand how they relate to one another and to the whole. Sample Question: *Based on the case study included in the chapter, what is the role of Truck Company B at this fire scene?*

- **Evaluate (Evaluation)** — Students judge the value of materials or actions based on defined criteria using elements from all other levels. They compare, conclude, contrast, discriminate, and justify decisions based on standards and criteria. Sample Question: *Given the information provided about a residential fire in the narrative above, what actions should the responders have taken to prevent the incident from escalating beyond the first residence.*

- **Create (Synthesis)** — Students put parts together to form a new whole. They categorize, create, design, organize, revise, and integrate parts to invent something new. Sample Question: *Describe how you would organize the command structure at a mass casualty incident.*

All instruction should be based on this hierarchy of cognitive levels, first exposing the student to simpler information before moving on to more challenging material. Testing may or may not follow this progression, but should include test items that are written at a cognitive level that corresponds to the learning objectives in the course.

Constructing Appropriate Test Items

After determining the purpose and type of test and identifying the specific learning objectives, test developers and instructors are ready to meet the challenge of matching the specifications with individual test items. Writing effective tests requires that the instructor completes the following tasks:

- Selecting proper level of test item difficulty
- Determining appropriate number of test items
- Eliminating language and comprehension barriers
- Avoiding giving clues to test answers
- Matching test items to learning objectives
- Ensuring test usability (ease of testing and scoring)
- Ensuring validity and reliability

Selecting Proper Level of Test Item Difficulty

Test item difficulty is determined by whether the test is norm-referenced or criterion-referenced. Norm-referenced tests rank the members of the class. Criterion-referenced tests determine how well the individual student has achieved the learning objectives established for the lesson or course. A wide range of test item difficulty does not ensure that there will be a wide distribution of scores. Test items with better discrimination create a wider range of scores. On a criterion-referenced test, the test items should be designed so that knowledgeable students should be able to pass the test.

In addition, criterion-referenced test items determine how well all students have learned the material. Test items are written to correspond to the clearly defined learning objectives established for the lesson or course. In addition, the test items should match the cognitive level of the learning objectives in the course.

Norm-referenced tests, however, must include test items that have a wide range of difficulty. The desired test result is a wide spread of test scores. Test items that can be answered by the majority of students should not be included. The most desirable test items are those with an average or greater level of difficulty that can be easily answered correctly by only half of the class, or less. This level of difficulty ensures that the test reveals a clear separation between students who know the information and those who do not. This separation allows evaluators to rank students against one another's performance.

Determining the Appropriate Number of Test Items

The appropriate number of items for any test depends on the following factors:

- Purpose of the test
- Types of test items or performance items
- Desired level of reliability

A test should measure students' abilities in all phases of a course. However, it must also fit within the time constraints for administering the test. Determining the appropriate number of test items may be accomplished by using either an established set of guidelines or a mathematical approach as follows:

1. **Guideline approach** — Write questions to address each difficulty level or multiple levels of learning in the cognitive domain based upon:

   — The length of time allowed for the test

   — The number of learning objectives to be tested

   — The importance (weight) of the learning objectives (learning objectives considered more important should receive more questions)

2. **Mathematical Approach** — Instructional time for each learning objective determines the percentage of test items that address that objective. For example, an objective that took 30 minutes to teach in a 120 minute course would be addressed by 25 percent of the test items.

Eliminating Language and Comprehension Barriers

Instructors should eliminate, or at least minimize language and comprehension barriers. One approach is to use words that students would use during training or on the job. Avoid test items that include the following:

- Higher reading level than students possess
- Lengthy, complex, or unclear sentences
- Vague directions
- Unclear graphic materials
- Obsolete words or terms (for example, carbon copy)

Avoiding Giving Clues to Test Answers

Test items should not give clues on how to answer the question correctly. Some areas to avoid include the following:

- Word associations that give away the answer.
- Plural or singular verbs, or use of the words "a" or "an," that may hint at the answer or eliminate an answer.
- Words that make some answers more likely (such as sometimes) or less likely (such as always or never). Never and always are appropriate when the student should absolutely know the information, for example, questions that emphasize safety.
- Correct answers that are consistently placed in the same location, such as the Choice B answer in multiple-choice questions.
- Correct answers that are consistently longer than distractors, such as true statements that are always longer than false statements.
- Stereotypical answers.
- Test items that give the answer to other test items.

Ensuring Test Usability

A usable test is one that is easy for instructors to give, easy for students to take, and convenient and cost-effective for the training organization. Usability is an important factor to consider when developing a test, or when selecting a test developed by another organization. Tests that are difficult to administer or score, or that are difficult for students to understand should be avoided. A usable test has the following characteristics:

- **Easy to administer** — Tests should include simple, clear instructions for administering the test. Instructions should be easily understood, even for an instructor with no experience administering a test.

- **Easy to take** — Tests should include clear directions that tell students how to take the test, including sample questions and answers.

- **Appropriate length** — Test length should be sufficient to provide accurate assessment of student learning. Tests should be long enough to obtain valid and reliable results, but not longer.

- **Cost-effective** — Internally-developed tests may seem at first to save money, but they often require personnel to spend many hours developing them properly. It may be more cost-effective to purchase tests from an outside publisher.

- **Contains multiple testing instruments** — Some test-preparation firms offer multiple tests with different sets of test items on the same subjects or learning objectives. Different tests over the same subjects may allow instructors to use of a variety of textbooks, skills sheets, or other ancillary materials. Multiple tests also make it more difficult for students to cheat.

- **Easy to score** — Answer sheets should be easy to read and easy to use. Ideally, instructors should be able to score and grade tests electronically. This method is not only faster, it is also more accurate.

Ensuring Validity and Reliability

The two most important characteristics of a well-designed test are validity and reliability. Validity is the extent to which a test measures what it is supposed to measure. It is built into the test by selecting an ample number of test items for each learning level and content area. To validly measure whether students have achieved the desired learning objectives, test items should require students to display specific knowledge of the appropriate learning objectives.

A reliable test is one that provides consistent, accurate measurements of student achievement. A reliable test should have the following characteristics:

- Clear instructions
- Clear, well-written test items
- Specific scoring criteria

Devoting attention to each of the test characteristics, analyzing a test each time it is given, and discarding or rewriting test items that do not meet requirements aid in improving test reliability and validity. Instructors should take the following steps to help ensure that the tests they write are valid and reliable:

Step 1: Select a representative sample of learning objectives.

Step 2: Select enough test items to represent the skills required in the learning objectives.

Step 3: Select test-item formats that reduce the potential for guessing.

Step 4: Use only the number of test items that an average student can complete in the available time.

Step 5: Determine methods to maintain positive student attitudes toward testing.

Finally, bias is an important factor that can invalidate a test instrument. No tests should be biased toward one group or individual. Bias means that the words or cultural references are unknown or difficult to understand for a group or individual because of ethnic, economic, social, or cultural influences and background. Tests should use universally understood terminology.

Test Scoring Method Selection

The final step in creating a test instrument is determining how to score it, which includes establishing the criteria for either passing or failing. Scoring systems vary depending upon the type of test and the importance (weight) of the questions on the exam.

For written tests, a point value should be assigned to each question. All questions of the same type (for example, all multiple-choice items) can be given the same value, or different questions can be weighted with differing values. For example, items that address the most important learning objectives may be worth more than other items of the same item type. Short answer and essay items may also be worth more than other item types, because they take more time to complete and require greater understanding of the course material. However an instructor chooses to weight the scoring of different items, the scoring system should always be explained on the test sheet.

Oral tests should have scoring sheets that indicate what the proper responses are and how many points those responses are worth. Oral tests are very subjective, and scoring is subject to the interpretation of the instructor. Scoring sheets should remove this subjectivity to the greatest extent possible.

Scoring performance or skills tests can also be very subjective. Instructors or test evaluators may each have their own opinion on how a particular evolution or activity should be performed. To overcome this subjectivity, the training division should do the following:

1. Train instructors or test evaluators in the steps of the skills to be tested. This training is especially important when instructors represent a variety of jurisdictions.

2. Develop checklists for each tested skill and use them for scoring students' performances. Checklists ensure that the instructors are scoring each step against the same criteria **(Figure 12.11, p.320)**. Fire and emergency services skills must be accomplished completely, accurately, and confidently because there is no margin of error during an emergency.

As discussed in Chapter 8, Testing and Evaluation, some tasks in some skills may be considered mandatory. When creating scoring sheets with mandatory tasks, those tasks should be indicated as pass/fail. The instructions should also indicate that, regardless of the student's performance on other tasks, skipping or failing mandatory tasks will result in a failing score.

Finally, criteria for passing the test should be included in the test instructions and on the scoring sheet, so that both the student and the test evaluator are aware

Skills Evaluation Checklist

Obtain information about a hazardous material using the *Emergency Response Guidebook (ERG)*.

Task Steps: Using the U.N. Identification Number	Yes	No
1. Identify the four-digit U.N. identification number.		
2. Refer to the appropriate yellow-bordered pages to find the correct reference guide number.		
3. Refer to the orange-bordered page with the appropriate guide number for information on managing the incident.		
4. For highlighted chemicals, refer to the green-bordered pages for initial isolation by looking up the identification number.		

Task Steps: Using the Material Name	Yes	No
1. Identify the name of the material.		
2. Refer to the name of the material in the blue-bordered pages to locate the correct guide number.		
3. Refer to the orange-bordered page with the appropriate guide number for information on managing the incident.		
4. For highlighted chemicals, refer to the green-bordered pages for initial isolation by looking up the identification number.		

Task Steps: Using the Material Name	Yes	No
1. Identify the profile of the container and locate the profile in the white pages of the *ERG*.		
2. Refer to the appropriate guide number in the circle and go to the appropriate orange-bordered page.		

Task Steps: Using the Material Name	Yes	No
1. Identify the placard and locate it in the white pages of the *ERG*.		
2. Refer to the appropriate guide number in the circle and go to the appropriate orange-bordered page.		

Figure 12.11 Another value of checklists is that they ensure that instructors score each step against the same criteria.

of them. Depending upon the type of test and the learning objectives it addresses, the criteria for passing may be different. For example, a written, multiple-choice test may have a passing score of 75%, while a performance test of highly hazardous skills may require a score of 100% to pass.

Chapter Summary

Level II Instructors should be able to create testing instruments or modify existing testing instruments for their jurisdictions. In order to meet this responsibility, the instructor must understand various types of test items and how those items may be used to assess whether or not a student has met the learning objectives for a course. Instructors must also understand how tests are to be scored and graded and what criteria will be used to determine whether a student has passed or failed a course or test.

Review Questions

1. What are the common considerations for test instruments?

2. What type of ability does a written test assess?

3. What type of ability does an oral test assess?

4. What type of ability does a performance test assess?

5. What are the steps for test planning?

6. How does an instructor select a test scoring method?

Supervisory and Administrative Duties

Chapter Contents

chapter 13

Key Terms

Job Performance Requirements

NFPA® 1041 References

5.2.2	5.2.6
5.2.3	5.3.2
5.2.4	5.3.3
5.2.5	

Supervisory and Administrative Duties

Learning Objectives

1. Discuss techniques for supervising other instructors. [NFPA® 1041, 5.2.6]

2. Describe the tasks necessary for scheduling instructional delivery and resources. [NFPA® 1041, 5.2.2]

3. Explain the process used for formulating budget needs. [NFPA® 1041, 5.2.3, 5.2.4]

4. Discuss the components of the purchasing process. [NFPA® 1041, 5.2.4]

5. Explain the aspects of keeping training records. [NFPA® 1041, 5.2.5]

6. Describe information and skills that instructors can use to perform basic research. [NFPA® 1041, 5.3.2, 5.3.3]

Chapter 13
Supervisory and Administrative Duties

Case History

A training agency was having some morale issues with part-time instructors; the part-time staff felt that they were offered less attention and respect than full-time instructors. Some of the full-time instructors felt that the part-time instructors were inferior to full-time staff.

To try to address this problem, the training agency developed a quantitative evaluation process to measure instructor performance. This data was collected from course evaluation forms and stored in a database. Annually, the training agency would process this data in a report to view instructor performance. The intention of the program was to offer quantitative data showing that part-time instructors performed in many cases as competently as full-time instructors.

As part of the evaluation program, the agency decided to create an *Instructor of the Year* award. Unlike some awards which were based on popularity, the agency used data from the evaluation report as part of the criteria for its *Instructor of the Year*. The agency provided the *Instructor of the Year* with a plaque, created a plaque in their office to list past recipients, provided the recipient with a flag flown over the Fallen Firefighters Memorial, and covered expenses for a major instructor conference for them to attend.

Over the next several years, the collection of quantitative data of instructor performance improved. Fire departments started to inform the agency of improved instructor performance, and morale among part-time instructors also improved.

Besides developing and presenting instructional material, the Level II Instructor is assigned duties associated with the administration and supervision of the training division. This chapter concentrates on the knowledge and skills required to perform instructional resource management duties. They include the following:

- **Supervisory Techniques** — Applying sound supervisory skills to create a positive work environment and resolve conflicts between instructors and students

- **Resource and Instructional Delivery Scheduling** — Ensuring that courses, instructors, and resources are scheduled in such a way that instruction is delivered efficiently

- **Formulating Budget Needs** — Creating program and division budgets
- **Purchasing Process** — Procuring equipment, materials, apparatus, and facilities for training
- **Training Records Management** — Maintaining training records in accordance with all legal, agency, and jurisdictional requirements
- **Conducting Research** — Applying effective research techniques to both administrative and instructional duties

NOTE: For the purposes of this chapter, a supervisor is anyone who is responsible for the activities of one or more instructors. The term supervisor should also be considered synonymous with the phrase *Level II Instructor.*

Supervising Other Instructors

Level II Instructors may be responsible for supervising other instructors. The number of instructors who are directly supervised varies according to the following factors:

- Size of the training division or department
- Supervisor's position and duties
- Abilities of the instructors
- Complexity of the specific training environment or learning scenario

In addition to demonstrating effective leadership skills, supervisors should know how to do the following:

- Encourage instructors to participate in the decision-making process.
- Delegate and involve instructors in planning.
- Respect the judgment of instructors.
- Teach, enforce, and follow health and safety rules.
- Coach and mentor instructors.
- Show consideration for diversity among instructors.
- Acknowledge instructors' accomplishments.
- Treat each instructor fairly and equitably.
- Keep accurate records.
- Keep lines of communication open at all times.
- Build and maintain a professional work environment.
- Resolve conflicts between instructors or between students and instructors.

Above all, the supervisor must apply these techniques consistently. Lack of consistency undermines the supervisor's authority and ability to accomplish organizational goals.

Level II Instructors must always be leaders, regardless of their level of experience. However, leadership is a topic that is beyond the scope of this manual. Level II Instructors with supervisory duties should seek out other sources to help hone their leadership skills. They should also remember that they lead by example and must adhere to a standard of ethical, moral, and legal behavior that will motivate their peers and other instructors to do the same.

The sections that follow detail a supervisor's primary responsibilities within a training organization. Supervisors are encouraged to seek out other sources that illustrate good supervisory techniques and leadership skills to supplement the basic information included here.

Review: Supervision

This section contains information about supervision of instructors as a general skill for Level II Instructors. Supervision information that pertains directly to training can be found in Chapter 7, Skills-Based Training Beyond the Classroom, and Chapter 11, Training Evolution Supervision.

Establishing and Communicating Goals and Objectives

Level II Instructors set the training objectives for instructors under their supervision. The training agenda is only as worthwhile as the communication between a supervisor and his or her instructors. Objectives and their timelines can be communicated to instructors in two ways:

1. Communication through group meetings where information is shared and discussed

2. Written task sheets, including personalized assignments and deadlines, that are provided to each instructor

Supervisors should involve instructors in decision-making, including setting goals and timelines, tracking progress, and establishing a plan for evaluation. Supervisors who communicate goals and objectives clearly and provide periodic progress reports will find that instructors function more efficiently and effectively. In addition, supervisors who involve instructors in establishing the objectives will find that their instructors have more incentive to fulfill the objectives.

Promoting Professional Development

It is vitally important that instructors maintain and develop their professional skills. Instructors benefit from having a supervisor who actively recommends or provides opportunities for such development. In some cases, a well-informed supervisor can provide this training directly, but in other cases, training must come from other sources. By emphasizing instructors' professional development, supervisors demonstrate their commitment to developing well-trained, highly qualified instructors.

Empowering Instructors

Instructors should always feel that they have authority over their own jobs. Granting them this authority shows confidence in their skills, judgment, and abilities. This support also helps to motivate instructors and improve their morale. To effectively empower instructors, supervisors must relinquish some of their authority **(Figure 13.1)**. Supervisors should avoid micromanaging instructors. Instead, the

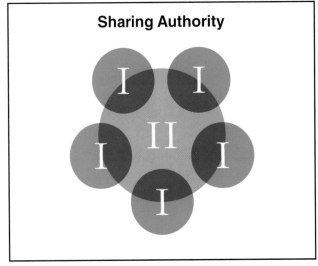

Figure 13.1 To achieve greater effectiveness, supervisors must share authority with instructors.

supervisor should focus on celebrating instructors' accomplishments, offering incentives for quality performance, resolving conflicts, setting a good example, and maintaining a positive attitude.

Celebrating Instructor Accomplishments

While most Level II Instructors do not have authority to grant raises or bonuses or to give time off for those they supervise, they should still provide positive reinforcement for good work. When their personnel meet objectives or achieve significant accomplishments, a supervisor should celebrate the accomplishment as soon as possible. This acknowledgement signals the completion of the project and shows that individual and team contributions are important to the success of the organization. A supervisor should announce the accomplishment to the rest of the department/organization and congratulate the participants on the results.

Offering Incentives for Quality Performance

Incentives are rewards that can be earned through effort or participation. Incentives are used as a motivational tool. The following actions are examples of ways to reward instructors that could be considered incentives:

- Make public acknowledgements of accomplishments.

- Hold group gatherings or parties to encourage unit cohesiveness and spirit.

- Make positive statements about the skills and abilities of instructors, whether individually or as a team.

- Make appropriate comments on the instructor's job performance evaluation, which can result in future raises or promotion **(Figure 13.2)**.

The size or value of the incentive is not the most important feature of positive feedback. The mere fact that the supervisor made an effort to acknowledge an individual's contribution to a group or project may be a significant incentive. If the organization already has an established incentive program, a supervisor should use it whenever possible. However, incentives must be awarded carefully. When supervisors give out rewards that were not truly earned, it shows disrespect to both the person who received it and to other personnel who may have deserved recognition.

Resolving Conflicts

One of a supervisor's most important roles is to resolve conflicts between two or more instructors or between instructors and students. In any conflict, the supervisor has to function as an intermediary in the dispute. Ideally, a conflict should be resolved to the satisfaction of all parties involved, although this may not always be possible. Resolving conflicts takes practice, but the following guidelines may be helpful **(Figure 13.3, p.330)**:

- Focus on the conflict, not the individuals involved.

- Speak to the parties of a dispute individually and privately.

- Allow the parties of the dispute to express themselves freely.

- Make decisions based on policies and procedures, and avoid personal bias.

Field Instructor Performance Evaluation Form

The purpose of this form is to evaluate the performance of an OSU FST field instructor. It may be used for an annual evaluation, or for performance during a specific training event. A signed copy must be provided to the instructor within 5 business days following the evaluation, and a copy must be placed in the instructor's personnel file.

Name: Jon Smith   **Date of Evaluation:** June 30, 2011
Purpose of Evaluation: Annual ☑   Other ☐ _____
Period Covered: 7/1/10 to 6/30/11   **Evaluator:** Richard Davis

Strengths
Jon is an outstanding instructor. He takes the time to learn the needs of the department and then delivers the training needed to meet those needs. He is well prepared for every class. Jon actively engages the students in the content and ensures all learning objectives are achieved. Comments from fire chiefs and students are always positive. Jon is an exemplary ambassador for OSU FST.

Areas for Improvement
Patience with low-motivation students. Jon, at times, displays a lack of patience for students who are not committed to training being conducted. He has dismissed several students from a training session who were not actively participating and following instructors. Jon should work with the fire chiefs and supervisor of those students to correct any behavior or performance which does not meet his expectation.

Improvement Plan/Expectations
Attend the OSU professional development workshop "Generations in the Classroom". Jon is to attend the next available offering, which should be in August before the start of the fall semester. A workshop certificate is to be provided to me on completion of the training.

Comments of Field Instructor (Optional)
I understand the issue with my patience. I will work on my response to students who lack motivation.

RICHARD DAVIS   6/30/11
_____   _____
Evaluator Signature   Date

Jon Smith   6/30/2011
_____   _____
Field Instructor Signature   Date

Figure 13.2 Comments on instructor performance evaluation forms should be appropriate and include strengths and areas for improvement. *Courtesy of Oklahoma State Fire Service Training.*

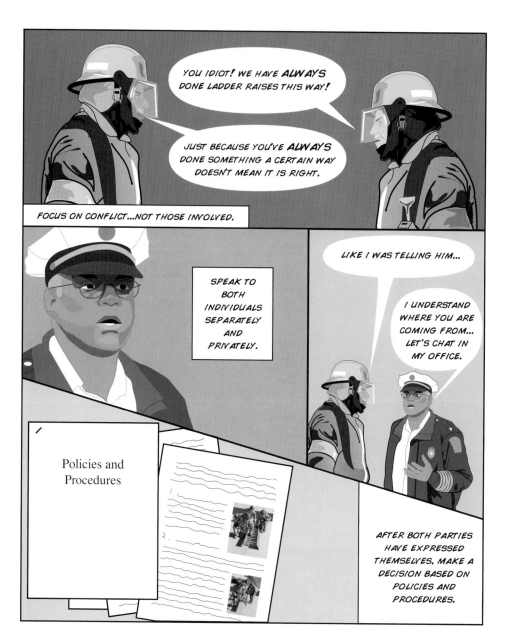

Figure 13.3 Supervisors must learn to resolve conflicts professionally, with a focus on results instead of personalities.

Maintaining Positive Examples/Attitudes

A supervisor should always express a positive attitude toward all personnel. This attitude is reflected through personal actions that set a good example for others, which fosters mutual respect in other working relationships within the organization. A supervisor's positive attitude will also encourage instructors to remain positive in their jobs.

Scheduling Resources and Instructional Delivery

Another basic task for a Level II Instructor is scheduling resources and instructional delivery. Training resources include all the elements needed to present a course or curriculum: personnel, funding, facilities, materials, information, and time.

For any course or curriculum, at any level of the organization, a supervisor should follow these steps when creating a schedule:

Step 1: Assess factors that affect scheduling

Step 2: Determine needs

Step 3: Determine requirements

Step 4: Determine availability

Step 5: Coordinate training

Step 6: Create a schedule

Step 7: Publish the schedule

Step 8: Revise the schedule (as needed)

Assessing Factors That Affect Scheduling

A supervisor has to prioritize several factors when creating a schedule, including the following:

- **Training requirements** — These include government mandates for all covered topics, and the minimum amount of time to be spent on each. Local and state/provincial mandates may also apply.

- **Physical resources** — Supervisors must always reserve classroom and training space, and may need to reserve props and apparatus. They may also have to order student workbooks and other instructional texts.

- **Instructor availability** — Instructors may serve multiple roles within an agency in addition to providing training. Supervisors should arrange the schedule to minimize conflict with their other duties and with any holidays or scheduled leave **(Figure 13.4, p.332)**.

- **Student availability** — It is best to schedule training when the largest possible number of students is available. Work schedules, personal obligations, and other conflicts to training must be considered. If personnel cannot attend because of a preapproved scheduling conflict, the organization may need to provide alternative sessions.

- **Minimum staffing levels** — Training must be planned in such a way that attendance at the training will not reduce the level of personnel below the minimum number needed for emergency response in any department wishing to attend.

- **Budgetary considerations** — Funds must be available to pay instructors, purchase materials, and rent training aids or space. If funds are unavailable, training may have to be postponed.

- **Environment** — Adverse environmental conditions may create a safety hazard for students, so specific types of training should not be scheduled in unprotected areas during those conditions. Similarly, training that is weather-related, such as ice rescue, should take advantage of appropriate weather conditions **(Figure 13.5, p.333)**.

Determining Needs

The next step in establishing a training schedule is to determine the organization's training needs. This determination is often referred to as **needs analysis**. Needs analysis or assessment determines the types of services that an organization is currently delivering and compares them to the services that are likely to be needed in the future. These needs will change over time, based on the following factors:

Needs Analysis — Assessment of the gap between the training an organization provides and the training it should provide, either currently or in the future.

Firefighter I & II Course
Fire Fighting Operations Block

DAY: __THURSDAY__	I/S: __Captain Rogers__	DATE: __10 MAY 12__

CLASS #: 0301	CLASS #: 0304	CLASS #: 0309	CLASS #: 0314
Day: 13	Day: 10	Day: 7	Day: 4
OBJ: CAR FIRES	OBJ: UNIT III	OBJ: LADDERS	OBJ: Hose Ops
PRIMARY INSTR(s)	PRIMARY INSTR(s)	PRIMARY INSTR(s)	PRIMARY INSTR(s)
Parker	Monroe	Gordon	Richards
Kent	Danvers	Stark	Wayne
MULTI-INSTRS	MULTI-INSTRS	MULTI-INSTRS	MULTI-INSTRS
Mason		Lane	Hall
Kord		Barton	Lance
Rhodes			
STUDENTS: 16	STUDENTS: 14	STUDENTS: 15	STUDENTS: 17

CLASS #: 0317	CLASS #:	LEAVE / TRAINING	APPOINTMENTS
Day: 1	Day:	Curry – SL – 5/11	0930 – Blake – Dr Appt
OBJ: UNIT I	OBJ:	Dibney – Veh Extr Trng	1330 – Kord – Cert Test
PRIMARY INSTR(s)	PRIMARY INSTR(s)	Grey – AL – 5/7 to 5/11	
Maximoff		Logan – Instr II Trng	
Blake		Prince – AL – 5/7 to 5/18	
MULTI-INSTRS	MULTI-INSTRS		
STUDENTS: 18			

INSTRUCTOR ROSTER: 24 ASSIGNED			
0 Barton	0 Hall	0 Monroe	AVAILABLE
0 Blake	0 Kent	0 Parker	Foster
0 Curry	0 Kord	0 Prince	
0 Danvers	0 Lance	0 Rhodes	
0 Dibney	0 Lane	0 Richards	
0 Foster	0 Logan	0 Rogers	
0 Gordon	0 Mason	0 Stark	
0 Grey	0 Maximoff	0 Wayne	

NOTES:
Foster to fill in for Blake and Kord, as needed.

Figure 13.4 Careful scheduling will enable instructors to fully prepare for their teaching responsibilities.

- Equipment or technology
- Personnel
- Legal concerns
- Observations at emergency incidents
- Requests from the public

The supervisor should create a list of training courses or programs required to provide the minimum level of training. The schedule should reflect both the short-term and long-term needs of the organization in order to establish recurring and projected training needs. Recurring needs include recertification or annually mandated training. Projected training needs are based on increases in service levels, expansion of coverage areas, or changes in staffing.

Figure 13.5 Seasonal weather variations create unique training opportunities.

Any training that the supervisor considers scheduling should be classified based on the following priority levels:

- **Priority 1: Training that is mandated by federal, state, or provincial agencies**— Examples may include the following:
  - Certification and recertification of fire service personnel
  - Certification and recertification of emergency medical service providers
  - Hazardous materials responder competency requirements
  - Emergency responder respiratory protection recertification
  - Continuing education that is required by the federal, state, or provincial government

- **Priority 2: Training that is required to meet goals determined by the organization or jurisdiction** — For example, an organization may want to expand its ability to respond to technical rescue incidents. In a given year a priority could be set to certify all emergency responders to the Operations Level of structural collapse and a select group of emergency responders to the Technician Level.

- **Priority 3: Training that is not mandated or required but would benefit the agency or service** — While an organization may have required all emergency responders to meet the Operations Level of structural collapse, resources may also allow it to certify everyone at the Technician Level. Other types of Priority 3 training may include the following:
  - Attending state or national conferences
  - Additional training that does not address specific organizational goals

Determining Requirements

Local jurisdictions and other governmental authorities usually mandate specific types of training. However, Level II Instructors may have to determine these training requirements themselves rather than follow mandates from the local jurisdiction. Required training includes the following elements:

- Specific topics to be taught
- Certification or testing criteria
- Minimum number of contact or teaching hours

The supervisor should determine the type of required training, the amount of time to be allocated to each course, and the sequence in which the courses must be taught. Because training mandates have a tendency to change over time, the supervisor should research the requirements annually.

Determining Availability

Supervisors should determine the availability of instructors and facilities before creating the training schedule. This determination can be made through the use of surveys that list the required training types and possible allocation of time. Instructors and facility managers complete the surveys, indicating the best times for providing the training.

The availability of students is the next determination that a Level II Instructor should make. Training should be scheduled when students are most likely to be able to attend. Students from career and combination organizations are typically available during the course of their work cycles. The only challenge is to maintain staffing requirements for emergency response which may require that training be scheduled during the evenings and on weekends. In addition, instruction may be delivered remotely over the Internet or closed-circuit television at a time that is convenient for the organization. However instruction will be delivered, supervisors should always consider scheduled leave patterns in each affected jurisdiction.

Volunteer organizations usually schedule training in the evenings and on weekends and make attendance a mandatory part of membership in the organization. However, specialized or individual training may require that volunteers attend training sessions provided during the workday by other agencies. This scheduling places a burden on students and requires students and their organizations to be flexible.

Coordinating Training

Larger classes are generally more cost-effective **(Figure 13.6)**, so supervisors should contact other fire and emergency service organizations to see if joint training sessions can be scheduled. In addition, training for nonemergency services organizations may also be coordinated with the planned training. For example, the American Red Cross can provide CPR training for emergency services responders at the same time they are providing training for the general public. The training division could also offer similar training for civilians during internal CPR classes.

National, state/provincial, and regional training schedules should also be consulted to take advantage of their course offerings. This consultation is especially appropriate when a small number of students require training in a specialized topic that the local training division does not normally provide.

Creating a Schedule

After determining needs, requirements, availability, and alternate sources for training, supervisors can create their training schedule, on either a 12-month cycle or a more long-term plan. They can use one of many available tools to help organize their thoughts, such as computer software, dry erase boards, or easel pads. Before publishing the final schedule, they should distribute a draft with

Figure 13.6 Larger class sizes may lower training costs.

times, topics, names of assigned instructors, and locations to all members of the organization. Providing this information to instructors before the schedule is published allows them to inform the supervisor of any conflicts.

Alternative dates should also be included in the schedule where possible. Supervisors should consider providing makeup sessions because of inclement weather, instructor or student absences, emergency incidents, and other situations. They should remain as flexible as possible to ensure that courses can be provided with the greatest possible efficiency.

A table or chart listing courses, dates, and instructor assignments should also be distributed to the teaching staff **(Figure 13.7, p.336)**. One effective format is to list instructors' names in the left-hand column, with dates across the top row, and course names in the appropriate intersecting box.

Publishing the Schedule

Once a schedule is created, prospective students can access the completed schedule in a number of ways. Printed versions of the schedule and catalog can be distributed at all worksites and facilities. Registration details, course prerequisites, and other information should be provided in a course catalog. The schedule can be sent to a predetermined email list, posted to the training organization's website, and/or managed using computer calendar programs **(Figure 13.8, p.337)**. Combining all of these features on a single website is the most effective way to allow students to locate and register for courses. Supervisors may wish to provide an entire year's training schedule or release training opportunities on a monthly or quarterly basis.

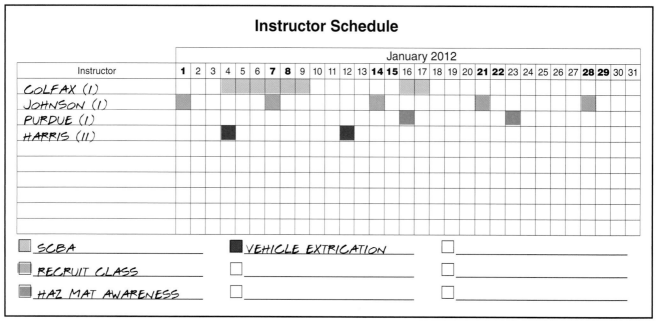

Instructor Schedule

Instructor	January 2012																														
	1	2	3	4	5	6	**7**	**8**	9	10	11	12	13	**14**	**15**	16	17	18	19	20	**21**	**22**	23	24	25	26	27	**28**	**29**	30	31
COLFAX (I)																															
JOHNSON (I)																															
PURDUE (I)																															
HARRIS (II)																															

☐ SCBA   ■ VEHICLE EXTRICATION   ☐ _____

☐ RECRUIT CLASS   ☐ _____   ☐ _____

☐ HAZ MAT AWARENESS   ☐ _____   ☐ _____

Figure 13.7 A chart listing instructors and their teaching times will give a good overview of the upcoming teaching schedule.

Revising the Schedule

Both short- and long-term training schedules may require revision, for any of the following reasons:

- Instructor availability conflicts
- Inclement weather
- Lack of funds
- Lack of equipment or materials
- Lack of facilities
- Unforeseen situations
- Changes in the amount of time required to present courses
- Creation of newly mandated courses

The supervisor and training staff should review the schedule periodically to make any necessary changes. Schedule changes should then be communicated to the teaching staff and members of the organization.

Formulating Budget Needs

In their role as supervisors, Level II Instructors may be responsible for formulating the budgetary needs for training in their jurisdictions. Typically, instructors submit budget requests to the supervisor, who then submits an official budgetary form to the organization. The line items on a budget form may include the purchase of new materials and equipment, salary and benefit costs, other costs such as travel expenses, and a justification for each budget item. If any line item contains an unusual request or proposes a funding increase, the justification should include a summary of the training need, and any relevant background research should be included in the justification. The sections that follow introduce Level II Instructors to the process of formulating budget needs.

2011 COMPANY TRAINING SCHEDULE

	Instr.	Subject
JANUARY		
Monthly Subject:	C.O.	Infection Control SOP
Other:	A.T.O.	Annual Respirator Fit-Testing
HazMat:	A.T.O.	Hazmat TECH Annual Refresher Training
Officer's Class:	T.O.	Suspicious White Powder SOP
MultiCompany Drill:	T.O.	Suspicious white powder incident
Rescue Drill:	A.T.O.	Ice Rescue
EMS CEU:	T.O.	All Shifts: Infection Control Refresher
FEBRUARY		
Monthly Subject:	C.O.	Ch. 17, Loss Control (Essentials 5th ed.)
	C.O.E.	Annual Respirator Refresher training
Driver Training:	A.T.O.	Autry Tech Driving Simulator [Refresher and New Driver Training]
Officer's Class:	T.O.	Administrative Policies & Procedures SOP
Rescue Drill:	T.O.	Confined Space Rescue
EMS CEU:	E.M.S.	A-Shift: Ryder- The Obese Patient
	E.M.S.	B-Shift: Compton- The Obese Patient
	E.M.S.	C-Shift: McDevitt- The Obese Patient
MARCH		
Monthly Subject:	C.O.	Ch. 18, Protecting Fire Scene Evidence (Essentials 5th ed.)
Officer's Class:	T.O.	FF Safety & Health SOP
Other:	T.O.	Emergency Services Instructor Course (Prerequisite for Lieutenant) Dates: March 7-11, 2011
	T.O.	ERG & Hazardous Communication Annual Refresher
	P.F.I.	Quarterly physical fitness review
HazMat:	A.T.O.	Quarterly HazMat Drill
EMS CEU:	E.M.S.	A-Shift: Palmer- Head Injuries
	E.M.S.	B-Shift: Gates- Head Injuries
	E.M.S.	C-Shift: Craig- Head Injuries
APRIL		
Monthly Subject:	C.O.	EFD Rules and Regulations Annual Refresher
Other:	C.O.	Hydrant Flowing
Driver Training:	A.T.O.	EVDT Course [Refresher and New Driver Training]
Officer's Class:	T.O.	Special Situations SOP
Rescue Drill:	T.O.	Grain Bin Rescue
EMS CEU:	E.M.S.	A-Shift: Copeland- Chest Trauma
	E.M.S.	B-Shift: Williams- Chest Trauma
	E.M.S.	C-Shift: Jenkins- Chest Trauma

Figure 13.8 All instructors should be given a full instructional schedule. *Courtesy of Oklahoma State Fire Service Training.*

Funding Needs Determination

Supervisors must provide an accurate estimate of training cycle costs. Research may be necessary to present these costs accurately. For any course, there are a number of typical operating expenses, including the following:

- **Instructor Pay** — Salary and benefits for all instructors
- **Equipment** — Includes audiovisual equipment, computers, and training gear
- **Course Materials** — Purchase price of externally created lesson plans, or the labor cost of internally created plans
- **Student Manuals** — Textbooks, workbooks, and student guides for each student
- **Audiovisuals** — Purchase price of computer-generated slides, video, and audio, or the labor cost of their internal production
- **Training Ground Expenses** — Fees for using a training ground or remote site, and the labor and construction cost of overhauling acquired structures
- **Travel Expenses** — Costs incurred if instructors have to travel to training sites

Operational Budget — Document that outlines operating expenses for any course, curriculum, or training program.

Supervisors should estimate the cost of each resource need in their **operational budget** request, and do research to make sure their estimates are accurate. With manuals for example, supervisors should consult the publisher's catalogue to determine the price of a single book, and multiply that amount by the number of expected students. The number of students and the title of the manual would also be included in the budget request.

Capital Budget — Budget intended to fund large, one-time expenditures, such as those for fire stations, fire apparatus, or major pieces of equipment.

Sometimes a course or curriculum will require that organizations make a large, one-time purchase like those found in **capital budgets**. These budget requests may require greater justification, or other sources of funding outside of the operational budget.

Most of the time, the funding items that instructors identify are meant to be included as part of the department's operational budget. Completing an operational budget often involves the relatively simple process of updating the requests from the previous year's budget to reflect the current needs. A percentage is usually added to the request that represents the rate of inflation based on the federal government's cost-of-living estimate.

Agency Budget Policies

Supervisors must become familiar with their agency's budgetary policies. As previously stated, agency budget policies typically involve completing budget request forms **(Figure 13.9)**. Supervisors should also include justifications for the line items in their budget requests as dictated by agency policies.

Agency policy may require supervisors to compare their budget requests to the previous year's budget. Similarly, the agency may create a projected budget and ask the supervisors to compare what they see as their training needs against what the agency is prepared to budget, then justify any differences. In some budget cycles, supervisors are asked to determine their training needs based on a fixed amount of money that the agency has already determined. When there is not enough funding to cover all training needs, supervisors must offer strong evidence that their requests are justified, and may also have to search for additional sources of funding.

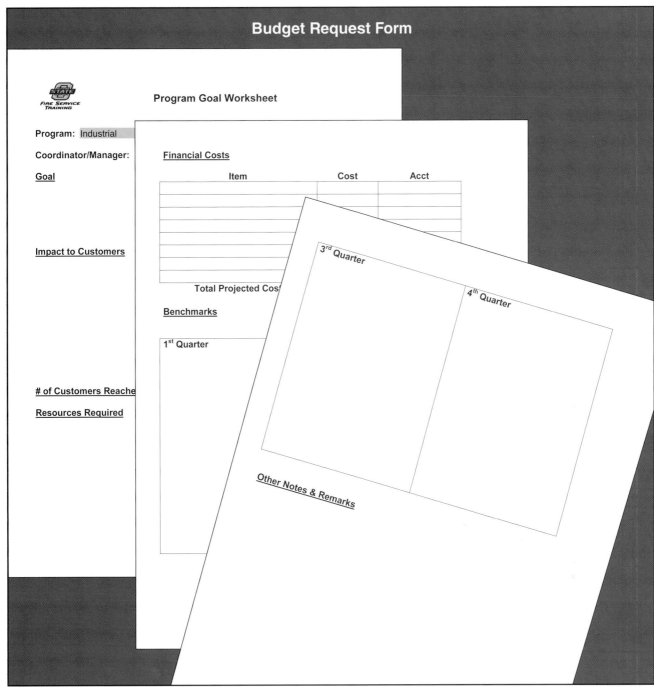

Budget Request Form

Program Goal Worksheet

Program: Industrial

Coordinator/Manager:

Goal

Impact to Customers

# of Customers Reached

Resources Required

Financial Costs

Item	Cost	Acct

Total Projected Cost

Benchmarks

1st Quarter

3rd Quarter

4th Quarter

Other Notes & Remarks

Figure 13.9 Instructors must understand the procedures and forms necessary for making budget requests. *Courtesy of Oklahoma State Fire Service Training.*

Sources of Funds

All governmental jurisdictions require revenue in order to provide necessary services. Typically this revenue comes from a combination of property taxes, sales taxes, and income taxes, but other sources include trust funds, enterprise funds, bond sales, grants/gifts, and fundraising **(Figure 13.10, p.340)**.

Although instructors may not have any control over the majority of these funding sources, they can be directly involved in grants/gifts and fundraising. Instructors who write grants or are responsible for accepting gifts must be aware of the budgetary and reporting rules of the AHJ.

Public Funding Sources

Property Taxes

Trust Funds

Fundraising Events

Grants/Gifts

Fees

Income Taxes

Bond Sales

Enterprise Funds

Sales Taxes

Special Purpose Tax Levy

Figure 13.10 Public funds for emergency services come from a variety of sources.

Figure 13.11 The emergency services may sponsor training that is accessible to the public.

Grant — Donated funding from a government or private source, typically secured through a competitive application process; funds do not have to be repaid, and may be separate from an organization's operational or capital budget.

In some municipal departments, even if the supervisor raises additional revenue, he or she cannot spend more than the budget has already authorized. However, smaller independent departments may have contracts with local governments that allow them to spend whatever money they can raise as part of their contracts with local governments.

Many fire and emergency services organizations supplement their general budgets with grants and charitable contributions, from either corporations or private citizens. This type of funding is usually intended to address a specific organizational need. For example, in some states a portion of all fire insurance premiums paid into the insurance industry is returned to local fire and emergency services organizations to pay for training and training-related materials.

Charitable Contributions

In many jurisdictions, service clubs and other civic organizations have donated funds to purchase specialized equipment such as hydraulic rescue tools or semiautomatic defibrillators (AEDs). It is important that funds donated for capital purchases are used for that purpose only — not for operating expenses.

Grants

Grants to address specific organizational needs are available from both governmental and nongovernmental organizations (NGOs). In the U.S., grants from the USFA, DHS, and Department of Transportation (DOT) provide local emergency responders with training and equipment to deal with a variety of incidents. The U.S. Department of Agriculture also provides many grants to rural fire departments. NGOs or nonprofit organizations also provide grant money to fund programs such as fire prevention training that are open to the public through the fire and emergency services organizations **(Figure 13.11)**.

The application process for securing grants can be challenging, especially for small organizations. Grant writing is a specialized skill that requires a skilled professional grant writer to be successful. Supervisors would be wise to either assign the task to staff members who have the necessary skills and time or contract it to a professional service.

While many grants are based on specific needs, such as hazardous materials training, some government programs provide funding for defined purposes but with few restrictions. These consolidated funding streams are known as **block grants**. They provide organizations with flexibility in running their programs, and minimize the bureaucratic aspects of the budgeting process. An example of a program funded by a block grant might be a safety awareness program that provides smoke detectors, fire extinguishers, and fire safety education to older adults.

Block grants are being used more and more frequently in the fire and emergency services because the fire service has done an excellent job of being accountable and responsible for the funds. Block grants also bolster community involvement because the funds obtained through the grant have a direct benefit for the community.

NOTE: **Figure 13.12** gives examples of how different funding sources function.

Block Grant — Annual government grant to help local authorities provide general services for the public good, with few restrictions.

Budget Request Justification

Justifying a budget request requires thoroughly documented research and supporting evidence to prove the request is valid. Often the documentation used in the justification is the same research that was used to prepare the budget initially. Sources for this justification include the following:

- **Organization's financial history** — Primary source of data to support the budget request, based on the actual cost of providing the services in previous budgetary cycles. This history includes, but is not limited to, the cost of fuel, maintenance, utilities, parts, training, and operating supplies. It can be used

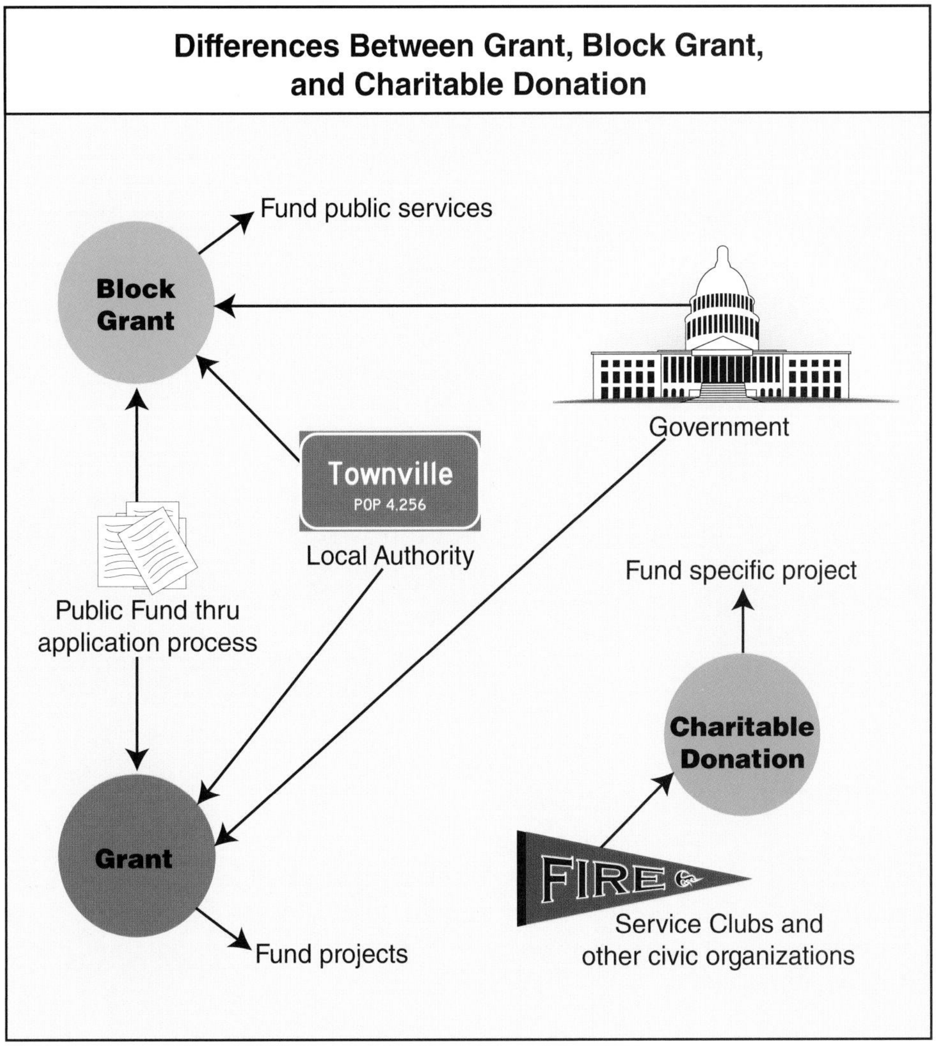

Differences Between Grant, Block Grant, and Charitable Donation

Figure 13.12 It is important to know the regulations for securing and using grants and donations.

to justify the operating budget or a capital request such as the replacement of an apparatus.

- **Actual equipment, material, or service costs** — Average product or item costs according to vendors' catalogs or price lists. This can also be determined by examining the jurisdiction's existing contracts for materials and services.

- **Third party evaluations** — Information available through the state/territorial/ provincial insurance commissions or fire service accrediting agencies.

- **Training mandates** — This is particularly important when higher levels of government place training requirements on local services and then fail to provide adequate funding.

- **Contractual requirements** — Labor/management contracts and contracts for services that an organization is obligated to provide, such as mutual or automatic aid response.

- **Injury reports and fire losses** — Incidents that resulted in firefighter injuries or fatalities may be indicators of areas where training within the organization needs to be reviewed.

- **New programs or services** — Companies that produce training materials or courses may introduce new programs or services with which the organization wants to become involved.

- **Training refinements** — Deficiencies in the current training regime may make additional funding necessary to refine existing curricula or courses.

Purchasing Process

To successfully perform its assigned mission, a fire and emergency service organization must acquire training resources such as course materials, equipment, and apparatus. Purchasing may be the responsibility of a supply, apparatus, or logistics chief; a county or city clerk; or a member of the jurisdiction's central purchasing department. A Level II Instructor may also be responsible for purchasing materials or equipment specific to the organization's training needs. Regardless of their jurisdiction's size, all supervisors should understand and follow approved purchasing procedures.

Supervisors must ensure that the organization receives the exact materials that were budgeted for and ordered, and keep purchasing expenses within the approved budget. In doing so, they must only spend funds on the items for which the money was allotted. For example, money budgeted to be spent on manuals should not be spent on training equipment.

The sections that follow outline aspects of the purchasing process. Some of the information included in these sections may be completed during the budgeting process or afterward.

Determining Funding Sources

The first step in the purchasing process is to determine sources of funding. The most common sources were discussed earlier in this chapter, in the section on budgets. But another option that may be permitted by local purchasing laws is a lease or lease/purchase arrangement. Primary funding sources that could affect instructor purchases include the following:

- **Operating funds** — Designated in the annual training budget; includes personnel and small-resource costs.

- **Capital funds** — Designated in an annual budget for purchasing capital items, which are items that cost more than an allowable fixed value. These items are specifically requested during budget preparation, and if approved they are purchased through a bidding process.

- **Grants** — Awarded by governmental agencies and NGOs, often to fund a specific program. Grants do not have to be paid back, but the jurisdiction receiving the grant must be accountable for how the funds are spent.

- **Leases or lease/purchases** — Another method of obtaining capital items, although they are not funding sources as such. Purchasing ordinances and jurisdictional laws determine their use. In some cases it may be illegal to encumber funds in the subsequent budget cycle, thereby preventing a lease. A supervisor must research this form of acquisition before including it in bid specifications. A cost/benefit analysis must be made to compare the direct purchase of equipment with the lease/purchase process cost. Definitions:

  — A lease can be used when equipment is needed only for a short duration or for extended evaluations.

  — A lease/purchase arrangement allows the purchase cost to be spread over several years.

Determining Purchasing Needs

Determining purchasing needs should have been completed during the budget process. If equipment integral to the continuation of training unexpectedly breaks, then adjustments may have to be made in the budget to purchase replacement equipment.

Needs determined during the budgeting process may be left intentionally vague. When the time comes to purchase the items in the budget, the following actions should be performed:

- **Review the standards and regulations that mandate the purchase of specific types of training equipment** — Review the legal mandates created by the AHJ for the operation of fire and emergency services training organizations.

- **Review the current resources** — Assess how well current equipment and materials meet the organization's training requirements, and determine whether instructors have quick access to them in adequate quantities.

- **Determine the amount of funds available** — Determine whether the training organization has the necessary funds for a selected purchase. It may be necessary to locate additional funds, transfer funds from unused accounts, or cancel the associated training.

Contacting Vendors

Supervisors should contact available vendors for the resources they need to purchase **(Figure 13.13, p.344)**. In some cases, supervisors may be limited in the number of vendors from whom they can make purchases. Jurisdictions may have a particular publisher from whom they purchase manuals as a matter of policy. Even in these cases, the sole manufacturer should be contacted. They may be offering special pricing or reduced rates because of contractual agreements with the jurisdiction.

Figure 13.13 Vendors specialize in resources that can be used for effective training.

If multiple manufacturers are available, the supervisor in charge of purchasing should contact them to ascertain which manufacturer offers the most suitable product at the best price. Resources may also be available through a state training agency, university, community college, or other third party either for a small fee, on loan, or as a donation.

Before purchasing from unfamiliar vendors, supervisors should conduct basic research. They can start by reviewing the business histories of both the vendors and the manufacturers they represent. They should also request a list of the most recent purchasers of the same equipment, then consult those purchasers to ask about their experience with the vendor.

Purchase Orders

To actually release funds for purchases, the supervisor first completes a purchase order, which usually includes the following information:

- Resources being purchased
- Cost of resources being purchased
- Entity from which resources are being purchased
- Any authorization or account numbers needed for processing
- Appropriate signatures to approve the request

Supervisors must become familiar with their jurisdiction's procedures for processing purchase orders, and with the accounting personnel who oversee this process. Larger departments may have a chief financial officer. In smaller departments, such as volunteer departments, the city or county clerk's office may handle all purchase orders.

Supervisors should strictly follow the jurisdiction's procedures at all times. If they do not, higher authorities may question their use of funds because there is no documentation of how the funds were distributed for purchases. In addition, following procedures helps to ensure that purchases are completed on time and that resources are acquired when they are needed.

Keeping Training Records

Level II Instructors may be involved in developing and retaining their organization's training records or in developing record keeping systems. Each jurisdiction will have certain information that the jurisdiction wishes to keep as part of a training records system. Supervisors should always abide by the AHJ's policies when retaining or discarding information. The sections that follow describe important aspects of record-keeping.

Training Information

The type and format of training records may vary widely, depending upon the specific needs of the organization. NFPA® 1401, *Recommended Practice for Fire Service Training Reports and Records*, provides examples of different training forms as well as other helpful information on their design and procedures for their effective management. Important information to be gathered for any training records system usually includes, but is not limited to, the following:

- Course name

- Dates and hours of each training session

- Names of instructors for each training session

- Student attendance rosters

- Topics taught at each session

- Lesson plans, workbooks and texts, tests, videotapes, and other course, curriculum, and program event documentation and processes

- Evaluation/testing scores of students (when applicable) as well as practical skills sheets used as evaluation criteria

- Course evaluations provided by students

- Required training and certifications that the student has completed

- Scheduled or required training that was missed

- Performance deficiencies and aptitudes noted during evaluations

- Recommended remedial training to correct deficiencies identified by testing

- Reports of skill deficiencies during routine or emergency operations

- Any other information deemed appropriate by the organization, including privileged information such as student identification numbers and locations of training sessions

Review: Types of Training Records

The following are different types of training records:

- **Attendance records** — Evidence that a student has completed a specified number of hours of training in a specific topic, such as respiratory protection or hazardous materials incident response.

- **Certification Records** — Which certifications have been completed by which students.

- **Incident/Injury Record** — Documentation of student injuries during training.

- **Test Records** — Documentation of a student's test results and testing history; these must remain secure after becoming part of a student's personal training records and/or personnel files.

- **Training Schedules** — History of drills and classes that were offered and facilities that were used.

Supervisors may also have contact with medical records, personnel records, and maintenance records or be required by the AHJ to fill out these records. If this falls under the supervisor's responsibility, he or she should follow all policies and procedures for completing and maintaining these records.

Training records are maintained at the company, district/battalion, and administrative levels of the fire and emergency services organization. Each level supplies the level above with an accumulation of information until the records become part of the organization's information management section. Instructors and supervisors typically collect information for some or all of the following types of training:

- Daily training delivered by the designated instructor, such as entry-level or recruit training. Details:

  — These records confirm the hours of training received by each student.

  — In the U.S., these records are mandated by Occupational Safety and Health Administration (OSHA) and must be made available upon request to the U.S. Department of Labor at either the federal or state level.

- Company-level training delivered by a company officer or a member of the company, such as basic skills refresher training in ropes and knots.

- Organizational training delivered to all members of an organization, such as time-management or cultural-sensitivity training.

- Individual self-study, such as preparation required to develop a new training course.

- Individual training, such as courses in public information or media events courses for the public information officer.

- Special training provided by a source outside the organization, such as courses attended at the National Fire Academy or the state/provincial fire academy.

- Degrees, certificates, or levels of training attained by members of the organization.

In order to properly maintain training records, supervisors need to take into account other record types they will need to retain. They should also know what information may be included in a training record system and how records will be managed within the system.

Record Management Systems

Level II Instructors are responsible for collecting records from instructors, then storing them in a secure location. The benefits of securing accurate training records include the following:

- Retains documents so that authorized parties may review them when necessary

- Helps administrators determine which training areas have been overemphasized or underemphasized

- Documents the fact that required training has been completed, or that required mandates are being met

- Provides information to help administrators plan and schedule future training programs

- Provides a degree of protection against lawsuits

Most types of records discussed in this manual, even test scores, can be stored in a digital format in a computer database. Computer databases vary as to their organization, the information they contain, and the digital security management that they use. Supervisors should become familiar with the databases used in their organizations. In addition, they should pay special attention to the security measures used to protect the database and follow the proper procedures to maintain database security.

Record Auditing Procedures

Record auditing is the process by which a document in a record keeping system can be traced back to the individual who created it. To make this process easier, include the following information on any record or report:

- Name of the individual who completed the record or report
- Other individuals who contributed information
- Dates and times that the records were completed

When records and reports are stored in computer databases, naming conventions should be established for computer files and folders, and the folders should be organized in a standardized way. There may be database software that will organize the files and make them easily searchable.

The records keeping system should be evaluated regularly. Doing so will help to ensure that records are easily found and retrieved should there ever be a need.

Legal Requirements for Training Records

An accurate record keeping system can provide an organization with necessary documentation for legal proceedings, management reviews, and accreditation programs, such as those conducted or administered by the following organizations:

- Insurance Services Office (ISO)
- International Fire Service Accreditation Congress (IFSAC)
- National Board on Fire Service Professional Qualifications (ProBoard)
- International Association of Fire Chiefs and International City/County Managers Association (IAFC/ICMA)
- State boards/bureaus of EMS and firefighter certification and accreditation
- American Council on Education

State/provincial and federal governments have specific laws that affect what information must be gathered and how it must be stored. These laws determine how long records must be retained, how privacy must be safeguarded, and which records must be available to the public. However, there are exemptions to these requirements that supervisors should remember.

Retention Length of Records and Reports

The length of time that records must be retained by the organization depends on state/provincial and local laws and the specific type of record. For instance, in some states employment application forms must be retained for a specified number of years, while exposure report forms and documentation must be retained for the same or longer number of years following the retirement or termination of the employee. Instructors should consult the jurisdiction's human resources or legal departments for retention guidelines on all types of records **(Figure 13.14, p.348)**.

Privacy of Records and Reports

Records that must be confidential include personnel files, individual training records, and medical files. Other personal information that must be safeguarded to ensure privacy includes Social Security numbers and test scores. Specific information regarding privacy requirements are as follows:

Figure 13.14 Each jurisdiction has different policies on how long reports and records should be retained.

- **Social Security number** — Many organizations no longer use Social Security numbers for records identification. The practice of using other identification methods reduces the potential for improper use or identity theft.

- **Personnel files** — Training records may be considered part of a private employment file, a fact that requires an organization-wide system to limit access to them. Even when local laws do not require this practice, organizations should develop and adopt policies that limit access to training records to only those personnel with a legal need to know.

- **Test scores** — Scores are considered privileged information. They are available only to authorized personnel who have a specific need to know. Examples:

  — In the U.S., the Family Educational Rights and Privacy Act (FERPA) prohibits the release of this type of information, with varying state and local restrictions. As a result, the old practice of posting test scores and other personal information on bulletin boards is no longer allowed.

  — In Canada, the Office of The Privacy Commissioner of Canada manages privacy laws. Additionally, all provinces have enacted privacy legislation of their own, such as Ontario's Municipal Freedom of Information and Protection of Privacy Act (MFIPPA). Canadian instructors must be aware of their duties and responsibilities under the applicable legislation within their jurisdictions.

Public Access to Records and Reports

While individual personnel records are confidential, many other organizational records are not. Official meeting minutes and any other notes that are taken as part of a meeting are public record. Incident or fire investigation reports can be viewed by the parties involved, or the parties who own an involved property, except in cases where statutory law specifically states otherwise. Records of responses to emergency medical incidents present restricted access issues due to confidentiality requirements. Organizations should take care when recording any of these kinds of information, because the information may later be made public. Instructors should follow the policies of the AHJ to determine which records and reports are publically accessible.

NOTE: If instructors are approached for information that might fall under privacy restrictions, they should consult their supervisor or agency counsel before releasing the information.

Open Records Act Exemptions

Many states exempt some information from the provisions of the Open Records Act, but these exemptions are limited and have been interpreted very narrowly by the courts. Federal law presumes that all records are open and places the burden on the jurisdiction to demonstrate that any requested materials are exempt. When a public record contains both exempt and nonexempt material, the exempt portion must be removed and the remaining nonexempt material disclosed. U.S. federal employees must be aware of the application of the Freedom of Information Act on U.S. government agencies. Examples of exemptions include the following:

- Medical and other records involving personal privacy

- Records relating to pending investigations

- Records required by the federal government to be kept confidential such as training, promotional, and educational records

- Trade secrets and certain information of a proprietary nature

- Research data that has *not* been published, patented, or otherwise publicly disseminated

- Confidential evaluations submitted to a public agency in connection with the hiring of a public employee

Conducting Basic Research

Policies and procedures should be based on sound research that has been gathered for one of two purposes:

1. To obtain knowledge about an open-ended question, such as: *How effective is the current training curriculum?*

2. To obtain data that supports or contradicts a proposal, such as: *Increasing the training budget will reduce on-the-job injuries.*

Supervisors use research to develop lesson plans and training courses, perform administrative duties such as purchasing equipment, develop budgets and programs, evaluate personnel, and support training content **(Figure 13.15)**. The five basic steps of research are:

Step 1: Identify the topic that is to be researched.

Step 2: List all possible topics that are similar to the main topic.

Step 3: List the various types of data that may support the topic, such as internal reports, regional or national reports, legislation, NFPA® standards, product reviews, or cost estimates.

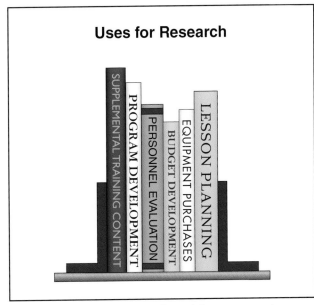

Figure 13.15 Research benefits training programs in many ways.

Step 4: List possible sources for each type of information.

Step 5: Read the gathered research and note any relevant information on the topic.

The sections that follow describe information and skills that instructors can use to perform basic research.

Data Collection

Types of data that may be useful on any number of topics may include the following:

- **Expert opinions** — Statements by credible experts or someone who has analyzed or experienced a similar situation. The supervisor's personal knowledge is an acceptable starting point when looking for this type of information.

- **Trends** — Patterns that can be traced over time and used to forecast the future; trends may be developed from raw data such as hazardous materials incident rates. Raw data must be of the same type for each entry on the timeline.

- **Models** — Frameworks of accepted practices that an organization can adapt to its own needs, such as a model building or fire code.

- **Similar situations** — Interviews with other professionals on how they handled particular situations or courses; sources for this type of research include industry journals, newspaper articles, or peers in professional organizations.

- **Statistics** — Raw data, such as a unit's response times or average staffing for units.

- **Examples** — Representations of processes, situations, items, or models that a researcher can use to illustrate concepts. A good example can be used to create an informal standard or goal that an organization is attempting to attain. An organization can determine how well it has done in reaching or surpassing the standard by using the example situation as a benchmark.

- **Analyses** — Third-party testing organizations evaluate equipment, procedures, or trends, then publish an analytical report of their findings. By reading these reports, researchers have access to objective reviews without having to perform the tests themselves.

- **Recommended/suggested practices** — Suggestions on how to do something, usually based on scientific research or trial-and-error experiences. The Hazen-Williams Water Flow Tests are an example of this type of information because they provide a basis for determining nozzle pressures on hoselines.

- **Industry standards** — Methods for accomplishing some task or function that has formalized standardization by a recognized testing or professional organization. For example, the NFPA® provides the industry standards for fire and life safety. Other types of standards are developed by engineering and scientific testing organizations such as the American Society of Mechanical Engineers (ASME) or the member organizations accredited by American National Standards Institute (ANSI).

- **Legal requirements** — Laws, codes, ordinances, and decrees that are legally binding requirements created at most levels of government to statutes that ensure the safety and welfare of a society. In the U.S., *the Code of Federal Regulations (CFR)* applies to many areas of the fire and emergency services while the *Americans with Disabilities Act (ADA)* mandates that public facilities be accessible to people with physical impairments.

- **Sources of supplemental funds** — Most fire and emergency service organizations need to have information on types of grants and loans, where to find them, how to apply for them, and how to administer them.

Information Sources

In general, data may be located from the following sources:

- Internet
- Government agencies
- Libraries **(Figure 13.16)**
- Educational institutions
- Professional organizations
- Testing and standards organizations
- Vendors/manufacturers
- Nonprofit organizations

The greatest challenge in locating reliable data is determining the credibility of the source. It is a mistake to believe everything one reads because most information (regardless of the source) is biased in some way. For example:

- Information provided by a government agency may be written in such a way as to justify that agency's actions, such as increasing taxes or proposing a noise abatement ordinance.

- Information obtained from vendors tends to show the positive results of using their products rather than providing an unbiased view, such as one provided by third-party testing agencies.

- While more and more organizations are putting credible information online, instructors are encouraged to scrutinize Internet sources more closely than others. Information that is posted online may not have been reviewed before publication.

Figure 13.16 Libraries are a well-known source for information in print or digital format.

It is important to follow accepted guidelines for determining the credibility of research material. Instructors should always attempt to find the primary source for information, for example the first time a study was reported rather than a later article that reproduces only parts of the study. The following terms are used to describe levels of research source material that a supervisor may find:

- **Primary literature** — Source material written by someone with direct knowledge of the event or topic. The material is original and considered to be the most credible type of literature to use.

- **Secondary literature** — Source material that is based on primary literature but was written or compiled by someone without direct knowledge of the event or topic. This type of literature is also acceptable as long as the primary source material was accurately recorded and evaluated.

- **Tertiary literature** — Literature that has been twice removed from the original source. This literature is usually not a good reference source and may contain errors of translation, interpretation, or context. Tertiary literature is often found on the Internet, such as an article that has been linked to multiple sites.

Researchers should always assess the quality of any source, especially one from the Internet. To do so, they must be sure the source possesses the following characteristics:

- **Credibility/Authority** — Author's credentials, quality controls used in collecting the data, and reputation of the source for providing reliable information

- **Accuracy** — How factual, recent, and comprehensive the information is

- **Reasonableness** — How objective and free from bias the information is

- **Support** — Quality of the supporting evidence and research methodology used to develop the data

- **Review** — Independent verification of the information before it is published

The Internet is an increasingly common place to find primary source material, because it contains so much readily available information. However, much of this information may be inaccurate or out of date. Instructors should consider the following aspects of data found on the Internet before assuming it is credible:

- **Authority** — Verify the authority of information found on Internet sites by considering the following:

  — Determine who is producing the document or site by examining the headers, footers, and the site address.

  — Recognize that the domains *.edu*, *.org*, *.gov*, and *.mil* are generally more reliable than *.com* domains.

  — Read the *About This Page* or *About This Company/Organization* link for more information on the sponsoring organization.

  — Look for clues to the author of a document such as links to that person's home page.

  — Look for a date stamp to see when the information was created or last updated.

  — E-mail the creator of a page (when an address is provided), and ask about the author's experience, education, or credentials.

  — Look for evidence that the source for the website would be an authority on the topic.

— Consider the credibility of an organization that refers or links to another source.

— Consider an author's biases, especially when consulting *.com* sites.

- **Functionality and User Interface** — Professionally created websites are typically more reliable than those that appear to be poorly constructed or difficult to use. Dead links, pages that will not load, and home pages that are difficult to navigate may also indicate that the site is updated infrequently, which should be a warning sign that the information may be out-of-date or inaccurate.

- **"Relinked" Information** — Many Internet sites exist to gather information from other sources and report that information to their users. Such sites are not original sources of information. Information may have been changed, quoted inaccurately, taken out of context, or presented only in part. Researchers should follow links from these sites to the original information.

There are many specific agencies or organizations that can provide research information, and many of them have an Internet presence that may be the first place to look. **Appendix C** includes a brief list of agencies, organizations, and other entities that may be good sources of research.

Supervisors who use researched material in a report or proposal must make reference to the original authors in order to give them proper credit. Where applicable, supervisors should also be sure to use the appropriate citation format if one is required.

Reference Material Citations

A supervisor may be required to adhere to a certain citation style, depending on how the material is used. Citations are used in research papers, books, articles, and electronic media to indicate the source of quotes, statistics, and other information that is not original to the writer. Citations can also be used in lesson plans to help instructors answer student questions or refer students to the source material. There are many accepted citation styles. The supervisor should be familiar with the style used by his or her organization and use it consistently.

Two popular citation styles frequently used in the fire and emergency services include the American Psychiatric Association (APA) and Chicago styles. Instructors should consult their organization's style guide or select the style that seems most appropriate. Whichever style instructors choose to use, they should use it consistently. For a book with an editor but no author, a reference page citation is as follows:

1. **APA Style** — Goodson, C. and Murnane, L. (Eds.). (2008). *Essentials of fire fighting and fire department operations 5th ed.* Stillwater, OK: Fire Protection Publications.

2. **Chicago Style** — Carl Goodson and Lynne Murnane, eds. *Essentials of Fire Fighting and Fire Department Operations 5th Ed.* Stillwater, OK: Fire Protection Publications, 2008.

For a book with a single author, a reference page citation is as follows:

1. **APA style** — Covey, S. R. (1990). *Principle-centered leadership.* New York: Fireside.

2. **Chicago style** — Covey, Stephen R. *Principle-Centered Leadership.* New York: Fireside, 1990.

Chapter Summary

Level II Instructors must be able to formulate budget needs, make purchases, maintain their organization's training records, and conduct basic research. To handle these duties effectively, supervisors must follow jurisdictional procedures for budgeting and purchasing. They must make sure that all records remain private and are accurate, comprehensive, private, and easily located. They should be familiar with appropriate sources of research information and be able to cite them using their organization's recommended citation style.

Review Questions

1. What techniques are used when supervising other instructors?

2. What tasks are necessary for scheduling instructional delivery and resources?

3. How are budget needs determined?

4. What components are involved in the purchasing process?

5. How are training records managed by a Level II Instructor?

6. What information and skills are necessary to perform basic research?

Instructor and Class Evaluations

Chapter Contents

Key Terms

Job Performance Requirements

NFPA® 1041 References

5.2.6

5.5.3

Instructor and Class Evaluations

Learning Objectives

1. Describe the process for evaluating instructors. [NFPA®1041, 5.2.6]

2. Discuss the considerations for developing class evaluation instruments. [NFPA® 1041, 5.5.3]

3. Explain the benefits of evaluation findings. [NFPA®1041, 5.2.6]

Chapter 14
Instructor and Class Evaluations

Case History

A firefighter in a municipal department completed his certification and was promoted to Level I Instructor. He began teaching using materials provided from the department. He struggled in the early training that he provided and began to become discouraged with his new duties.

His supervisor, an experienced Level II Instructor, noticed that students were not satisfied with his performance in their evaluations. He seemed uncomfortable in front of them and this nervousness translated to the students' feeling that this instructor was unprepared. The supervisor decided to observe the instructor herself. She witnessed the same behavior, but she also noticed that when this instructor stopped concentrating so intently on his notes, he had an excellent rapport with students.

The supervisor scheduled a time to speak with the instructor and pointed out his greatest strength as a rapport with students. She scheduled opportunities for him to observe his peers to get a better understanding of how to remain poised in front of students. Finally, she discovered that the first few courses the instructor had taught were on topics that he did not have a great deal of experience with. She was able to adjust his training schedule to pair him with material he knew better.

The supervisor observed the instructor again at the end of his next course. Many of his nervous habits were gone because he was more familiar with his material. In addition, the instructor had incorporated more discussion time into his lessons in order to capitalize on his rapport with students.

One of the responsibilities of the Level II Instructor identified in NFPA® 1041 is to evaluate Level I Instructors and learning environments. These evaluations measure effectiveness and efficiency based on criteria established or adopted by the AHJ. This chapter explains how both supervisory and student evaluations can be used to provide feedback about instructors and the classes that they teach.

Supervisory Instructor Evaluations

The evaluation of Level I Instructors is based on the observations of both supervisors and students. Student evaluations tell instructors about the effectiveness of an individual course and their performance as instructors. These evaluations also help to inform the supervisor's formal evaluation of an instructor, which addresses classroom conduct and teaching ability.

Many fire and emergency services organizations have a systematic personnel evaluation program that establishes guidelines and requirements for all evaluations. Although an immediate supervisor's formal evaluation is usually a requirement of these programs, the formal evaluation schedule should not deter supervisors from providing ongoing, informal feedback on an instructor's performance.

Level II Instructors serving in a supervisory role may periodically evaluate the instructors who work for them. These supervisors must be familiar with their organization's evaluation policies, including its requirements for privacy, documentation, and the monitoring of the results of the evaluation. In general, the instructor should know the following elements of a personnel evaluation program:

- Forms
- Guidelines
- Processes
- Findings

Observation as Evaluation

Evaluation is not a static, one-time event; it is an ongoing process throughout curriculum development and instruction. The supervisor and/or evaluator can gather multiple types of data, most of which is based on observing instructors as they teach. The instructor being evaluated should be seen to be attentive to the following factors:

- Student interest in the subject
- Level of student participation
- Student reaction to exercises and activities
- Student questions and comments

With feedback received from supervisory observation, instructors can change or modify instructional methods in response to supervisor feedback. Observations may also indicate changes that need to be made to a course or course materials.

Supervisory Evaluation Forms

A supervisory evaluation form should address criteria for the skills and behaviors an instructor should possess, and may include the following points:

- Classroom management considerations
- Effective interaction with students
- Proper use of verbal and nonverbal communication techniques
- Proper use of audiovisual training aids or other equipment
- Communication of all learning objectives to students enrolled in the course
- Appropriate use of questions
- Use of appropriate instructional methods

Performance Evaluation Processes

The Level II Instructor has two means for evaluating Level I Instructors: informal and formal. Informal evaluations occur often and are based on the observation of the instructors in their work environments **(Figure 14.1)**.

The formal evaluation may occur on a regular schedule (such as annually) or as needed. It uses the results of the informal observations as well as students' instructor evaluations to generate comments and suggestions. Formal evaluations are always held in private. While the format of evaluations will differ among jurisdictions, guidelines are as follows:

Figure 14.1 Informal evaluations occur in a typical work environment.

- **Train supervisors properly** — Train instructors or supervisors who are required to perform evaluations on the evaluation process used by the jurisdiction.

- **Apply in a timely manner** — Conduct evaluations at appropriate intervals, which is especially important for performance evaluations that are linked to a specific incidence of unsatisfactory performance.

- **State criteria clearly** — State goals and objectives clearly and concisely. Maintain written job-performance criteria for review at each successive evaluation.

- **Ensure standards are not discriminatory** — Apply the same job-performance standards regardless of gender, race, ethnicity, age, or other classifications.

- **Maintain consistency** — Apply job-performance standards equally throughout the training division or agency, based on the duties and responsibilities assigned to the position.

- **Maintain thorough records** — Maintain thorough and complete records of each evaluation in the employee's personnel file. Although these records are confidential and may not be made public, give a copy of the evaluation to the instructor being evaluated.

- **Ensure objectivity** — Overcome personal bias, and base the evaluation on established criteria. Objectivity is essential in all of the organization's personnel evaluations.

During a formal or informal critique, a supervisor should first give positive feedback before addressing areas in which the evaluated instructor should improve. Supervisors should give constructive suggestions that show the instructors how to improve specific aspects of their teaching performance. Comments should refer to observed or credibly reported behaviors.

Informal evaluations have the advantage of being immediate. For example, an instructor-supervisor may wish to review course outcomes and student evaluations with instructors after training courses. This debriefing allows the supervisor to immediately address performance weaknesses and to identify potential problems with course materials.

Instructors who are performing effectively should be praised in front of their students and peers. But if instructors are performing below expectations, comments and suggestions for improvement should be offered in private. A written record should also be kept of informal evaluations, to be used for reference during formal evaluations.

Instructor evaluations can be divided into the following three stages:

- **Before the Evaluation** — Steps:

    1. Communicate the date, time, and location of the evaluation to the instructor being evaluated.

    2. Review the evaluation materials, including student evaluation surveys, previous formal evaluations, and previously documented personal observations.

    3. Discuss the evaluation process with the instructor being evaluated.

    4. Be thoroughly familiar with organizational policies or criteria.

- **Observation** — Steps:

    1. Have the organizational policies or criteria available to review.

    2. Take notes while observing in order to be able to give specific feedback to the instructor **(Figure 14.2)**.

    3. Use the evaluation form that the organization provides to reduce the potential for subjectivity and ensure consistency between evaluations.

    4. Remember the following points while observing:

        — Evaluate instructors based on their classroom presentations.

        — Do not prejudge instructors based on individual bias or rumors.

        — Assign evaluation points to teaching skills and topic knowledge as a way of objectively judging the instructor's teaching ability.

        — Look for instructional qualities in all presentation, demonstration, and performance areas of teaching.

- **Performance Review** — Steps:

    1. Discuss the evaluation in private.

    2. Reinforce that the purpose of the evaluation is to recognize instructor weaknesses and offer the means to improve.

    3. Compliment instructors' strengths as well as identifying their weaknesses.

    4. Ask for the instructor's opinion on his or her own performance.

    5. Make note of the instructor's comments to compare with the notes made during the formal evaluation.

    6. Explain what the instructor did well and what areas may need improvement.

After the formal evaluation, the supervisor must hold the instructor accountable for making any necessary improvements. Without accountability, the instructor has no motivation to change. The supervisor should conduct further observations to determine whether the instructor has adequately addressed specific deficiencies identified during the evaluation. If not, the supervisor must hold additional formal meetings with the instructor to determine whether supplementary training would be beneficial. If even this step does not raise the instructor's performance to the required level, the instructor may have to be assigned to nonteaching duties, with a more qualified instructor teaching the remainder of the course.

Inexperienced or underperforming instructors may benefit from observing or working with a more experienced instructor, who acts as a mentor and models appropriate teaching methods. Working with other instructors gives inexperienced

Figure 14.2 By taking notes, the observer can expand the usefulness of feedback.

Figure 14.3 Mentors should model appropriate actions and behaviors.

instructors opportunities to observe models of the desired instructional methods and teaching behaviors. Mentors must be carefully selected to ensure that they model appropriate methods to their inexperienced colleagues **(Figure 14.3)**.

Class Evaluations

In addition to evaluating Level I Instructors, Level II Instructors may also create and distribute class evaluations to students, so that they can provide feedback about courses they have taken. There are two different types, in which students evaluate either the instructor or the course itself. Both are described in the sections that follow.

Student Evaluations of Instructors

Student evaluations are the most immediate form of feedback an instructor receives after a course. Evaluation forms are typically surveys with questions relating to the students' learning experience in the class and their impressions of the instructor. Level II Instructors may be asked to create these forms and require that students complete them after every course. These evaluations are also considered during formal evaluations.

Student evaluations of instructor performance are highly subjective and may vary greatly. The following factors may influence student responses on evaluations:

- Student's background knowledge of the subject
- Student's reason for attending the class (voluntary or mandatory)
- Personality of either the instructor or the student
- Preconceived ideas held by the student
- Frustration or pressure the student feels at the time the form is completed

Evaluation forms should include questions on the following instructor characteristics:

- Preparation
- Presentation skills
- Knowledge of the subject
- Interest and enthusiasm for the subject

- Ability to answer students' questions
- Interaction with students
- Concern for students
- Strengths, both interpersonal and instructional
- Weaknesses, both interpersonal and instructional
- Time-management skills
- Whether or not students would choose to take another class with this instructor

Research shows that student evaluations are most accurate when they are completed during class and collected immediately. Instructors must make sure to allot sufficient class time for students to complete their evaluations. If students are asked to complete surveys at home on their own time, many will not complete them, yielding incomplete data for the supervisor to assess instructor performance.

Completed student surveys should be gathered and forwarded to the instructor's supervisor. Responses are then compiled and reviewed to help determine the effectiveness of the instructor. When weaknesses are consistently mentioned, the supervisor should schedule a review with the instructor. Instructors who receive positive remarks should be informed of the remarks and commended.

Student anonymity is crucial during the evaluation process, especially during in-house training with an instructor from the same department or agency. The training division should have a policy that requires the instructor to leave the room while evaluations are being completed, but only after appointing a volunteer to collect the completed evaluations and seal them in an envelope **(Figure 14.4)**.

Organizations that have this type of policy should also provide a thorough summary report to the instructor. Students should not be permitted to sign the evaluation forms.

Student Class Evaluations

Like their evaluations of instructors, students' evaluations of a class are subjective and can vary widely. Evaluation surveys should ask them about the benefits they feel they received from a class, focusing on perceptions of their own learning experience and the learning environment. A thorough evaluation survey should ask students about their classroom experience, addressing the following essential areas of the instructional process:

- **Reaction** — Were students satisfied with the course? What reason do they give for their opinion?
- **Knowledge** — What new knowledge did students acquire and demonstrate?
- **Skills** — What new skills did students acquire and demonstrate?
- **Attitudes** — How has the training perceivably changed their opinions, values, and beliefs?
- **Environment** — Did the learning environment offer them a distraction free, safe place to learn?
- **Safety** — Were appropriate safety precautions followed throughout the class?
- **Materials** — Were the training aids and equipment provided sufficient to help students meet learning objectives?

- **Results** — How effectively do students feel that the course objectives were met during training? Did the course meet their expectations? Was the course directly related to their jobs and duties?

Questions on most instructor/course evaluation surveys ask students to respond on a continuum that ranges from very satisfied to very dissatisfied. Assigning numerical values to these responses – for example, from 1 (poor) to 5 (best) – allows supervisors to statistically average the results from one or more classes **(Figure 14.5, p.366)**.

Surveys should always leave space for open-ended answers or comments. Doing so allows students to express more complete thoughts that may not be represented by a numerical value or specific question. Students should not be required to sign the survey form, but an optional signature line may be provided for students who volunteer to be contacted by the supervisor, in order to provide additional information.

Figure 14.4 It is a common practice to have the instructor leave the room while students complete instructor evaluations. A student should be designated to collect the evaluations.

Class evaluations, like student evaluations of instructors, gather the most accurate data when they are completed during class and collected immediately, usually toward the end of a course. These evaluations can prove invaluable for future assessments of overall training programs.

NOTE: Class evaluations are often combined with student evaluations of instructors and do not have a separate form or designation.

Findings from Evaluations

Evaluations are intended to identify an instructor's strengths and weaknesses. After making that determination, the supervisor should craft an appropriate response to *those* strengths and weaknesses. The instructor should always be included in the decision-making process used to apply strengths constructively or correct weakness.

Instructor Strengths

Strengths should be cultivated and used to the benefit of the individual instructor, as well as the division, organization, and community. Through coaching and mentoring, a supervisor can assist the instructor in determining the best use of strengths. This assistance may involve further training opportunities, career-path decisions, advanced degrees, or potential promotions. Additional authority and responsibilities can reward the instructor and further utilize strong attributes. From a supervisory standpoint, helping an instructor build upon strengths is one of the best ways to build the instructor's confidence. Playing to an individual's strengths helps to ensure high quality instruction over the long term.

Instructor Weaknesses

The supervisor has numerous tools available to address instructors' weaknesses. Counseling, coaching, and mentoring can all be useful when trying to help an instructor improve teaching performance.

The supervisor should work with the instructor to determine the steps necessary to overcome a weakness. This action gives the instructor greater ownership

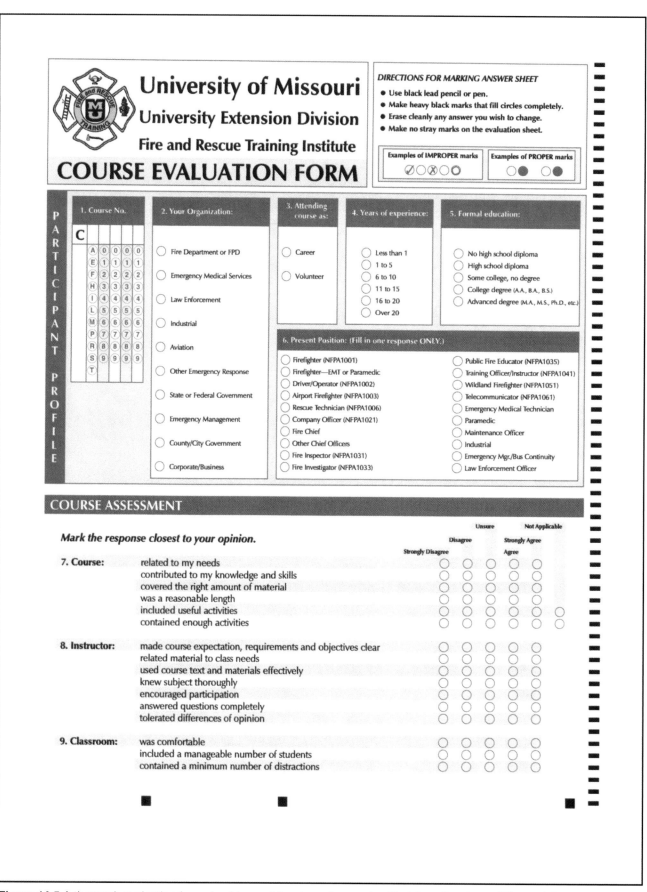

Figure 14.5 A thorough evaluation form should permit input on all aspects of training. *Courtesy of Fire and Rescue Training Institute University of Missouri.*

COURSE ASSESSMENT (continued)

Mark the response closest to your opinion.

		Strongly Disagree	Disagree	Unsure	Agree	Strongly Agree	Not Applicable
10. Outside Activities:	included a manageable number of students	○	○	○	○	○	
	adequate/enough equipment available	○	○	○	○	○	
	activities performed were realistic	○	○	○	○	○	
	activities performed were relevant to the course objectives	○	○	○	○	○	
	adequate opportunity given to perform the activities	○	○	○	○	○	
	no outside activities	○	○	○	○	○	○
11. Visual materials were:	related to the course	○	○	○	○	○	
	good quality	○	○	○	○	○	
	in appropriate number	○	○	○	○	○	
	easy to see	○	○	○	○	○	
12. Printed materials were:	well organized	○	○	○	○	○	
	complete	○	○	○	○	○	
	readable (printed well)	○	○	○	○	○	

SUGGESTIONS

13. How could the course content or structure be improved?

14. How could the instructor improve the class delivery?

15. How could the classroom be improved?

16. How could outside activities be improved?

17. How could the audiovisual materials be improved to increase learning?

18. How could the printed materials be improved to increase learning?

Please feel free to use additional blank paper, if additional comments are needed.

CHECK FRONT PAGE TO MAKE SURE YOU HAVE COMPLETED ALL QUESTIONS.

and a stake in the corrective process and final outcome. To effectively correct a weakness, an instructor must be able to take responsibility for both the weakness and the method for correcting it.

When these tools prove ineffective, further steps must be taken, such as re-training, professional counseling, or disciplinary action. Assistance from outside the division (such as the organization's human resources department) may be required for these responses.

Chapter Summary

Level II Instructors typically supervise Level I Instructors in the training division. This responsibility includes evaluating the job-performance of each instructor and evaluating the courses and lessons that instructors teach. To do so effectively, the instructor-supervisor must be trained in the following areas:

- Using evaluation techniques
- Administering the organization's personnel evaluation program
- Developing evaluation forms and surveys
- Using information from student evaluations of instructors and courses

The instructor-supervisor may also be required to create these evaluation forms. They must fully understand and practice these skills so that the evaluation process produces accurate information that can be used to improve instructor performance and the overall quality of training courses.

Review Questions

1. What guidelines should be followed during the formal evaluation process?

2. What should be considered when developing instructor and class evaluation forms that students will complete?

3. How do you address strengths and weaknesses that are revealed during instructor evaluations?

Section C. Instructor III

Course and Curriculum Development

Chapter Contents

chapter 15

Key Terms

Job Performance Requirements

NFPA® 1041 References

6.2.5	6.3.4	6.3.7
6.3.2	6.3.5	6.5.3
6.3.3	6.3.6	6.5.5

The Level III Instructor is responsible for managing the training program, designing and modifying courses and curricula, and creating course goals. Requisite knowledge includes instructional design and technical writing skills. These responsibilities are an expansion on the Level II Instructor's responsibility to create and modify lesson plans.

Four-Step Development Model

Course — Series of lessons that lead to the completion of a discipline or certification.

Curriculum — Series of courses in which students are introduced to skills and knowledge required for a specific discipline.

Program — Collection of curricula and the resources necessary to deliver the instruction for those curricula.

In order to create a **course** or **curriculum** that can be used as part of an overall training **program**, an instructor should use a planning model to guide his or her decisions **(Figure 15.1)**. For the purpose of this chapter, a four-step model is outlined that should be an effective method for most instructors and most courses. This four-step development model includes the following steps **(Figure 15.2)**:

Step 1: **Identify training needs** — Perform a needs analysis to determine the course or curriculum required to meet the organization's needs and jurisdiction's mandates. Use this step to also determine the need for alterations to existing courses or curricula when deficiencies are found in the *evaluate* step.

Step 2: **Design a course or curriculum** — Design a course or curriculum that will meet the established requirements.

Step 3: **Implement the course or curriculum** — Perform a pilot presentation of the course or curriculum. Add the course or curriculum to the training schedule when it meets the identified needs.

Step 4: **Evaluate the course or curriculum** — Determine the effectiveness of the course or curriculum in meeting the requirements. Conduct evaluations following the initial pilot test and following each presentation of the course.

Courses may be revised, replaced, or removed from the curriculum when the *identify* and *evaluation* steps indicate that they no longer provide the desired outcomes. At the same time, entire curricula may also be altered, replaced, or abandoned when program evaluations indicate such an action is necessary. The remaining sections in this chapter elaborate on these steps and also offer suggestions for revising a course or curriculum after completing the steps.

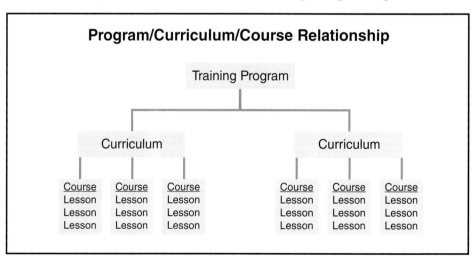

Figure 15.1 A planning model will illustrate how each component of a curriculum fits within the overall training program.

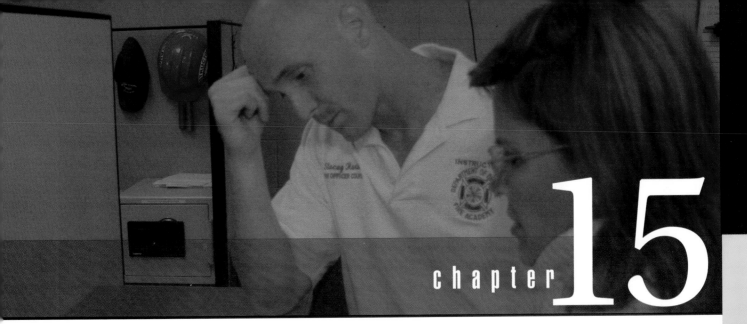

Key Terms

Job Performance Requirements

NFPA® 1041 References

6.2.5	6.3.4	6.3.7
6.3.2	6.3.5	6.5.3
6.3.3	6.3.6	6.5.5

Course and Curriculum Development

Learning Objectives

1. Describe the four-step development model. [NFPA® 1041, 6.3.2, 6.3.3]

2. Explain the processes used to identify training needs. [NFPA® 1041, 6.3.2, 6.3.3]

3. Describe the parts of course or curriculum design. [NFPA® 1041, 6.3.3, 6.3.5, 6.3.6, 6.3.7]

4. Discuss the steps included when implementing a course or curriculum. [NFPA® 1041, 6.3.4]

5. Identify data used to evaluate a course or curriculum. [NFPA® 1041, 6.2.5, 6.5.3]

6. Explain the processes used to evaluate and revise test instruments. [NFPA® 1041, 6.5.5]

7. Identify the actions an instructor should take when planning revisions. [NFPA® 1041, 6.3.4]

Chapter 15
Course and Curriculum Development

Section C: Instructor III

This chapter and the chapters that follow discuss the JPRs that affect Level III Instructors in NFPA® 1041, *Standard for Fire Service Instructor Professional Qualifications*. The previous chapters of this book, which present information for Levels I and II, are prerequisite knowledge for these remaining chapters. Where appropriate, short review sections will be included in the upcoming chapters, but with a shift in emphasis toward JPRs for Level III. Any student or instructor who does not feel confident in his or her knowledge of the information in the previous chapters of this book is encouraged to review any portions of the text that may help him or her to learn this new material.

Case History

After completing Level III Instructor certification, a fire instructor was promoted to the level of training division chief in his department. The fire chief asked the new training chief to prepare a report that identified the adequacy of the new recruit school. The fire chief particularly wanted to know how the new course met the state's testing requirements. He was concerned because of a recent increase in graduates from the recruit course who could not pass the state's certification exam. The pass rate had fallen from 90% to 70%, and more students were requiring remediation before beginning their regular duties.

The new training chief evaluated the curriculum for the recruit school and discovered that it had not been updated to the most recent state standards. The state had adopted newly revised national standards, and the department had not updated its curriculum to coincide. The new training chief wrote a budget request to purchase new curriculum materials and support materials that reflected the latest national standard. He also required instructors under his supervision to attend training session so that their instructional methods could better align with the new curriculum. They were taught the new objectives, developed new lesson plans, and constructed new test items.

During the next recruit school, passing rates rebounded. Identifying the new curriculum and implementing it made all the difference.

The Level III Instructor is responsible for managing the training program, designing and modifying courses and curricula, and creating course goals. Requisite knowledge includes instructional design and technical writing skills. These responsibilities are an expansion on the Level II Instructor's responsibility to create and modify lesson plans.

Four-Step Development Model

In order to create a **course** or **curriculum** that can be used as part of an overall training **program**, an instructor should use a planning model to guide his or her decisions **(Figure 15.1)**. For the purpose of this chapter, a four-step model is outlined that should be an effective method for most instructors and most courses. This four-step development model includes the following steps **(Figure 15.2)**:

Step 1: **Identify training needs** — Perform a needs analysis to determine the course or curriculum required to meet the organization's needs and jurisdiction's mandates. Use this step to also determine the need for alterations to existing courses or curricula when deficiencies are found in the *evaluate* step.

Step 2: **Design a course or curriculum** — Design a course or curriculum that will meet the established requirements.

Step 3: **Implement the course or curriculum** — Perform a pilot presentation of the course or curriculum. Add the course or curriculum to the training schedule when it meets the identified needs.

Step 4: **Evaluate the course or curriculum** — Determine the effectiveness of the course or curriculum in meeting the requirements. Conduct evaluations following the initial pilot test and following each presentation of the course.

Courses may be revised, replaced, or removed from the curriculum when the *identify* and *evaluation* steps indicate that they no longer provide the desired outcomes. At the same time, entire curricula may also be altered, replaced, or abandoned when program evaluations indicate such an action is necessary. The remaining sections in this chapter elaborate on these steps and also offer suggestions for revising a course or curriculum after completing the steps.

Course — Series of lessons that lead to the completion of a discipline or certification.

Curriculum — Series of courses in which students are introduced to skills and knowledge required for a specific discipline.

Program — Collection of curricula and the resources necessary to deliver the instruction for those curricula.

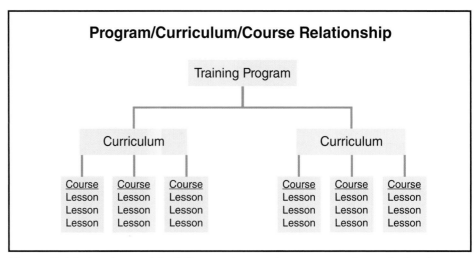

Figure 15.1 A planning model will illustrate how each component of a curriculum fits within the overall training program.

Identifying Training Needs

The identification step begins with the realization that a change in the organization's operating environment has occurred, requiring a change in the organization's service delivery. The realization that changes need to be made to either courses, curricula, or programs may come in the following forms:

- State/provincial or federal mandate that may require the fire department to provide technical rescue services based on a perceived need

- Request from a stakeholder group such as a governing body

- Evaluation such as a program evaluation

- Event such as the loss of services provided by another agency; for example, the loss of an independent or private EMS provider may cause the fire department to add EMS

- Changes in nationally recognized standards

When it is apparent that a change is required or that different or additional services are required, the organization must perform a needs analysis. A needs analysis should determine how the current service level and capability differ from new requirements. It may also indicate how much and what type of training is required to ensure that the organization can provide the new level of service. This analysis is a function of the administration of the organization and may include representatives from all divisions of the organization. The processes that are available to the instructor for identifying needs include the following:

- Needs analysis
- Job performance requirements
- Task analysis
- Cost/benefit analysis

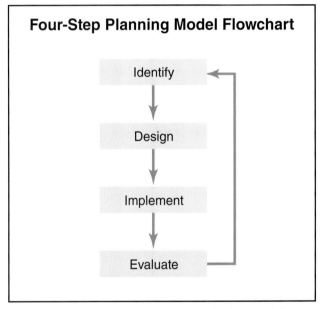

Figure 15.2 Each part of the four-step planning model builds on the previous step.

In addition, the instructor should understand how work should be assigned within the organization to ensure the efficient creation of quality courses and curriculum.

Needs Analysis

With thoughtful questioning, carefully designed surveys, and in-depth research, a needs analysis accomplishes several functions such as the following:

- Defines current levels of knowledge, skills, and attitudes of emergency service personnel
- Determines whether a need exists and indicates whether the need would receive the most benefit from training, equipment to perform a task, administrative policies or commitment, or a change in procedures
- Identifies specific individuals, work groups, or organizations that need training, equipment, or procedure change
- Identifies a method to achieve desired levels of knowledge, skills, or attitudes

To determine needs in the areas of knowledge, skills, or attitudes, the instructor analyzes the following items:

- Operational reports
- Injury records
- Accident reports
- Results of promotional exams
- Personnel, operation, and training records
- NFPA® standards

Various methods are used to determine individual training needs or readiness for a training course or curriculum such as the following:

- **Pretest** — Type of test used by organizations to determine the current level of training or skill of potential students. Pretests help instructors identify those topics within a course that need more emphasis during instruction **(Figure 15.3)**. Pretests are also useful in identifying that students have met the prerequisites for a course.

- **Agency training history** — Reviewing the training history may indicate whether prerequisite training has been previously offered.

- **Prerequisite training or skill level requirement** — Minimum level of skill required (prerequisite) for prospective students before they enter certain training courses. Some departments use regularly scheduled skill evaluations as records of the skill level of their firefighters and EMS responders.

- **Training records** — The following elements contained in training records may be used to determine whether a student has the necessary knowledge or skills to be admitted to a course:

  — Completion of specific courses

  — Training certifications

  — Professional development activity

  — Verification of skills or required knowledge on a pretest

Regardless of the technique used to determine training needs, instructors need to know the current knowledge or skill level of the organization's current members before proceeding with course or curriculum development. This guideline prevents the level or complexity of the instruction from being inappropriate for some or even all of the course or curriculum. Based on the national mandate and the organization's needs analysis, an instructor should use the analysis process to determine the training requirements that will be the basis for the required curriculum.

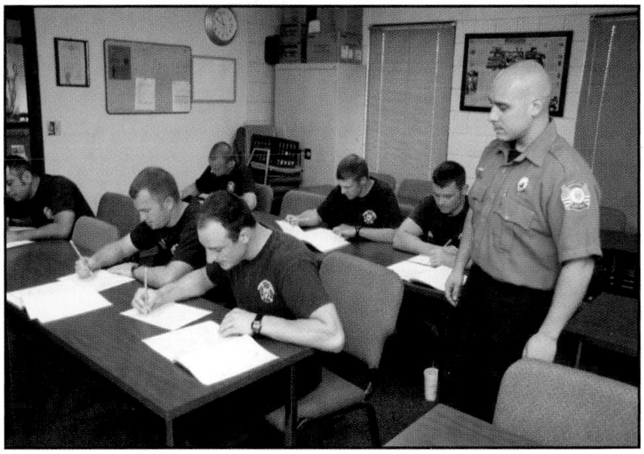

Records and reports are the raw information for making decisions about training needs. To justify the creation of courses, instructors should be able to organize this information into a proposal for the course. For example, the instructor could calculate a percentage of how many personnel have completed EMS training. Or, the instructor may create a statistical analysis of firefighter injuries in the jurisdiction based upon individual injury reports over the previous year. Collating data and showing patterns are essential skills for completing a needs analysis.

Figure 15.3 Pretests help instructors gauge the abilities of students in the class.

Job Performance Requirements

When evaluating existing training materials, instructors should establish the skills/knowledge that are prerequisite for students to take a course, and the skills/knowledge that students must master over the duration of a course. These parameters must be established in order to effectively and efficiently develop and present a course or curriculum.

Starting and ending points are often determined by the skills that personnel must learn and perform on their jobs. Program planners often start their needs analysis by identifying and reviewing national standards and determining minimum job performance requirements (JPRs) or performances required for a specific job based on those standards. In addition, instructors need to understand how JPRs apply in their jurisdictions. Additional JPRs that are jurisdiction specific may need to be developed in order to meet the jurisdiction's training needs.

JPRs are grouped according to job duties (functional areas of responsibility within a job). After determining JPRs, planners evaluate resources and select learning objectives that will be used in designing and implementing the revision of existing courses and curricula or developing new programs.

Professional qualifications standards can be used for the following purposes:

- Designing and evaluating training
- Certifying personnel
- Measuring and critiquing on-the-job performances
- Defining hiring practices
- Setting organizational policies, procedures, and goals

Professional qualifications standards are often written in the JPR format and organized by areas of responsibility (duties). The list of JPRs for each duty defines what an individual should be able to do in order to successfully perform that duty. The standard containing each duty and its JPRs defines and describes the job, giving instructors and planners an end point around which to design and teach a training curriculum.

Task Analysis

Task Analysis — Systematic analysis of duties for a specific job or jobs, which identifies and describes all component tasks of that job; enables program developers to design appropriate training for personnel and trainees who must learn certain tasks to perform a job.

In order to create a course or curriculum, an instructor must understand the tasks that are going to be taught as part of the training. Conducting a **task analysis** is the best way for the instructor to understand what skills need to be included and taught in the course **(Figure 15.4)**.

A task analysis is a detailed review of each physical task or job that is performed as part of a certain skill or set of job functions. Each task is divided into steps that contribute to the correct completion of the task. In order to perform a task analysis, the instructor must first collect information on the specific tasks that compose the job. Instructors can use either formal or informal methods to collect information as follows:

- Formal methods:
  — Carefully designed and executed surveys
  — Opinion polls
  — Checklists
  — Observations
  — Psychological profiles
  — Research analyses
  — Tests
- Informal methods:
  — Conversations
  — Casual observations of activities and habits
  — Other unobtrusive measures

The information is then used to determine the steps that compose the task. The following four organizational models can determine the order in which steps must be accomplished **(Figure 15.5, p.380)**:

- **Sequential** — Arranging tasks in order of operation
- **Cause and effect** — Completing one action or determining the existence of a condition before deciding on the next appropriate action or step
- **Model-based** — Model used for professional tasks when the steps for performing the tasks are vague or difficult to define
- **Cognitive** — Critical decision-based model that focuses on the psychological processes that underlie the physical task

The model that is used most often is the sequential task analysis. In this model, the steps are arranged in sequence from first to last. The model may be used for a simple task (depicted in a linear fashion) or a complex task that may contain a combination of simple tasks, some performed simultaneously.

Steps that are considered key points are used to create the teaching outline for the task. Some steps may require the student to make a decision before performing the step. Decisions may be based on safety concerns or cause and effect considerations. For instance, before raising a ground ladder, the student must determine whether overhead obstructions or electrical power lines are present.

Task Analysis Worksheet

Occupation: _____   Job: _____

Block: _____   Task: _____

Performance Steps: Individual steps that are required to complete the task listed above.	Key Points: Individual steps stated in outline form, including cognitive and behavioral points.
1.	I. A. 1. 2. B. 1. 2.
2.	II. A. 1. 2. B. 1. 2.
3.	III. A. 1. 2. B. 1. 2.

Figure 15.4 The task analysis details each portion or step in learning a required skill.

Cost/Benefit Analysis

As part of the needs analysis, the instructor should also perform a **cost/benefit analysis**. The cost of creating a curriculum or providing the training internally should be estimated and compared to the cost of purchasing an existing curriculum or contracting with an external agency to provide the training.

Cost/Benefit Analysis — Systematic methodology to compare costs and benefits to make cost-effective funding decisions on projects.

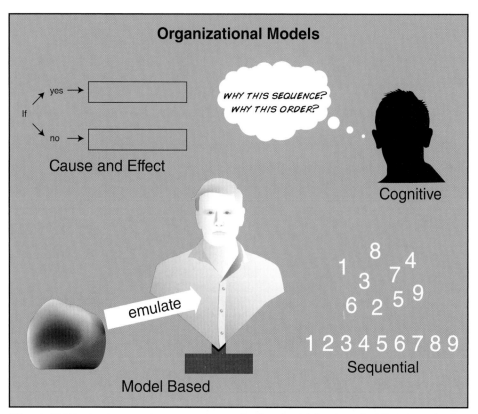

Figure 15.5 Instructors can use several organizational models when deciding the order in which students should complete steps.

Each hour of actual training time is generally the result of many more hours of development. Development hours also translate to funds expended for salaries and resources. Many organizations may have neither the personnel hours nor the funds to develop their own courses and curriculum. It may be more cost-effective to purchase an existing curriculum or use training available from state/provincial or national agencies or other sources. For instance, instead of developing a new pumper driver/operator course, curriculum from IFSTA could be used.

Designing a Course or Curriculum

Once the type and quantity of required training have been identified, an instructor designs a course or curriculum that will meet those requirements. The sections that follow describe both course and curriculum design respectively.

Course Design

To design a course, an instructor must perform the following tasks:

- Identify a course goal.
- Develop learning objectives.
- Group similar learning objectives.
- Develop lesson plans.
- Sequence lessons into a course.
- Create appropriate student, course, and instructor evaluation instruments.

Identify a Course Goal

The instructor must determine the course goal (often referred to as a course objective): a statement of the desired outcome of the course. However, a course goal does not state the performance level of the student, only what the course will enable the student to do. The lesson goals and learning objectives collectively contribute to achieving the course goal. An example of a course goal might be, *The High-Angle Rescue Course will provide students with the knowledge and skills to operate at the rope technician level* (**Figure 15.6**).

A course goal does not contain student performances, conditions, or standards that students must meet. The performances, conditions, or standards are found in the learning objectives.

Develop Learning Objectives

Based upon information gathered during task analysis, learning objectives are developed. These objectives are developed with the course goal in mind. Each objective should in some way move the student closer to achieving the course goal. Information about developing objectives can be found in Chapter 4, Instructional Materials and Equipment and Chapter 10, Lesson Plan Development.

Learning objectives must clearly support the course goals (the destination or end point) of the training course or curriculum. Instructors must evaluate and select objectives for completeness and consistency with the level of instruction and learning domain. Instructors further evaluate objectives during the course to ensure that they achieve the change in student performance required in the needs analysis.

Figure 15.6 An example of a course objective might be that students learn the skills to perform rope rescues.

Group Similar Learning Objectives

Similar objectives are grouped together and paired with the steps in the task analysis. This procedure ensures that objectives match the skills and are in the proper sequence to accomplish the task and therefore the job. Grouping learning objectives also helps ensure that lesson plans can be developed around topic areas to meet the course goals. Finally, when creating a course to teach specific job performance requirements (JPRs), the JPRs may offer a model for grouping the objectives. Following the JPRs in this fashion also allows the instructor to correlate the learning objectives to the appropriate JPRs before the course begins.

Develop Lesson Plans

When the preceding steps are finished, the outline for a lesson plan is basically complete. The required knowledge or skills are listed in the outline and represent the information that must be presented to the students. At this point, the instructor would use the skills learned in Chapter 10, Lesson Plan Development, to create lessons for each group of learning objectives.

Sequence Lessons into a Course

Once the lessons are created for the required learning objectives, they must be sequentially grouped to create a course. The lessons must be placed in order so that the most basic knowledge is taught first. Subsequent lessons build upon the basic knowledge until the student is able to perform the final course outcome or objective **(Figure 15.7)**. A student should not advance to a higher level if the current level of learning has not been mastered.

Create a Course Outline

Once lessons have been sequenced, a course outline is constructed as a guide for the instructor who will be teaching the course. Adding student assignments, dates of quizzes and tests, and days with special instructions can transform the outline into a syllabus for students. Course outlines begin with stating the course goal and the certifications that it meets (if necessary). It should indicate the course materials to be used, the order of lessons, and what evaluation instruments will be used. Time frames should also be established in the outline, for example, how many lessons are meant to be taught over a certain amount of time.

Create Appropriate Evaluation Instruments

Evaluations are commonly used at the administrative level to determine the effectiveness of courses and instructors, as well as on the accomplishments of the students who participate in these courses. Evaluations identify course strengths and weaknesses in areas such as the following:

- Time allotted
- Equipment used or needed
- Instructor and student expectations
- Instructional methods used
- Learning environments used
- Evaluation methods used

For instructors, evaluations provide an assessment of their own performance, teaching methods, and skill. For students, evaluations provide feedback on their knowledge and skill level and assess needs for further study or practice.

Example Lesson List				
Chapter	Chapter Title	Suggested Time	Text Reference	Activities/Skills
1	Introduction to Hazardous Materials	2 hours	6-59	
2	Hazardous Materials Identification	4 hours	60-163	Learning Activities 2-1, 2-2, 2-3
3	Awareness-Level Actions at Hazardous Materials Incidents	2 hours	164-187	Skill Sheet 3-1

Figure 15.7 Lessons should build from the simple to the complex.

From evaluations of student performance, instructors and training managers receive feedback on test validity and reliability as well as on the effectiveness of the instructor and course. Low test scores do not always indicate that the student did not learn. In those respects, evaluations may provide information for examining and analyzing reasons for failure and determining areas to adjust and improve. Low scores could also indicate one of the following situations has occurred:

- Instructor did not teach to the objectives.
- Course was not suited to the level of the student.
- Evaluation instrument (test) was not valid.

Curriculum Design

Curriculum design is oriented toward determining which courses should be grouped together to meet a larger goal. To design a curriculum, an instructor must perform the following tasks:

- Identify the curriculum goal.
- Identify courses for the curriculum.
- Sequence courses into a curriculum.

Identify a Curriculum Goal

Curriculum goals are similar to course goals except that they apply to a number of courses collectively. An example of a curriculum goal might be, *The Technical Rescue Curriculum will provide students with the necessary knowledge and skills to meet NFPA® certification requirements.* Just as with course goals, a curriculum goal does not contain student performances, conditions, or standards that students must meet. The performances, conditions, or standards are found in the learning objectives related to the various courses in the curriculum.

Identify Courses for the Curriculum

A curriculum is comprised of a number of courses. When developing a new curriculum, existing courses should be analyzed to determine which might be included in the curriculum. Any areas that are not covered after adding existing courses may indicate a need to create new courses to meet the curriculum goal.

Sequence Courses into a Curriculum

Courses are placed into a sequence that is logical and progressive **(Figure 15.8)**. The sequence of courses may be more flexible than the sequence of lessons. In addition, courses may be completed over a period of time with only a few prerequisites. However, courses must be completed satisfactorily before the following events occur:

- Curriculum is considered complete.
- Students' efforts are validated.
- Certificates are awarded.

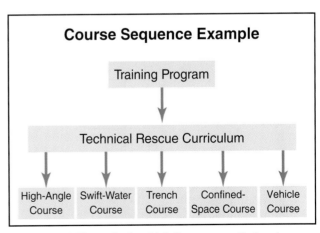

Figure 15.8 The order in which the courses that make up a curriculum are studied may or may not be flexible.

Fire Service Terminology and Technical Writing

Knowledge of fire terminology and technical writing are listed as prerequisite knowledge for Level III Instructors in NFPA® 1041. By the time instructors are considering becoming a Level III Instructor, they are generally very familiar with fire service terminology. When in doubt about terminology, instructors should consult other references such as IFSTA's **Fire Service Orientation and Terminology**.

With regard to technical writing, the topic is very broad and outside the scope of this manual. If instructors feel that their writing needs work, they should seek out professional development opportunities to become better writers. Instructors are also encouraged to give any materials that they develop to someone else to review.

In general, there are three guidelines to remember for creating good technical writing:

- Be concise.
- Write to the intended audience of the document.
- Ensure that grammar and spelling are correct.

Implementing the Course or Curriculum

Throughout the process of instructional design, program developers must be aware of the reality of implementing the training course or curriculum. When instructors have completed the initial design steps through the final writing of lesson plans and development of evaluation instruments, their next logical step is to implement the curriculum.

Implementation requires the Level III Instructor to perform or delegate the following functions:

- Acquire funding and facilities.
- Determine instructor and student time requirements.
- Find or train qualified instructors.
- Determine and create or obtain appropriate training aids or materials.

The Level III Instructor must confirm, for example, that the course or curriculum can be presented in the existing facility. The location, design, and equipment of a facility directly affects the kinds of activities that instructors can direct and students can perform to achieve course objectives.

Before implementation begins, instructors perform a detailed formative evaluation. Ideally, formative evaluations have been in progress throughout the design phase. These evaluations include the following items:

- Reviews by peers or supervisors
- Consultations with subject-matter experts
- Reviews by prospective instructors
- Any other steps that perform the following functions:
  - Helps to ensure the quality of the course or curriculum
  - Monitors the course or curriculum continually to ensure its focus on meeting performance objectives

Once everyone is satisfied that the formative evaluation and ensuing corrections indicate that the course is ready to move forward, instructors can take the necessary steps to implement the training course or curriculum. Implementation actions typically include the following steps:

Step 1: Obtain final course approval.

Step 2: Assemble, create, or select appropriate training aids or materials.

Step 3: Schedule facilities and equipment.

Step 4: Select qualified instructors.

Step 5: Establish appropriate training records systems or databases.

Step 6: Schedule and announce the course or curriculum.

Step 7: Select students.

Step 8: Present a pilot version of the course.

Each organization or jurisdiction may have different requirements for obtaining course or curriculum approval for implementation. Instructors may give presentations to approval authorities about how a course supports organizational learning goals and objectives. The presentation gives information on the financial and time commitments that the organization will have to invest to implement the course. Instructors should provide details on required facilities and equipment and the necessary instructor and student hours.

Once the course has been approved, it can be implemented. The first implementation of a course is known as a **pilot course**. The purpose of a pilot course is to evaluate the effectiveness of the course as follows:

Pilot Course — First implementation of a newly developed course; intended to allow instructors to evaluate a new course and make changes for improvement.

- Verify that the course content meets course and curriculum goals.

- Evaluate the appropriateness of facilities, props, materials, logistics support, and audiovisual training aids.

- Evaluate the course design and time allotment.

- Evaluate the effectiveness of the learning activities in the course.

Pilot courses should be taught by experienced instructors who are able to adapt sections of a course that are untried and may not provide efficient training **(Figure 15.9)**. These instructors should also be qualified to teach the subject matter in the course.

Figure 15.9 Pilot testing is done in small groups to ensure that the lesson will provide efficient training.

Evaluation of the pilot delivery is based on feedback received from instructors, observers, and students as well as student performance on formative evaluation instruments. The evaluation forms and surveys for a pilot course may be more detailed than what would normally be used to evaluate a course that has been taught before. Evaluation may also occur during a pilot course on a lesson-by-lesson basis with more specific feedback from students. Pilot evaluations also present opportunities to determine the effectiveness of the course evaluation process and instruments.

Alterations are made to correct any problems that are discovered in the course evaluations. After making changes to the course, the course should be pilot tested again to determine whether the changes have had a positive effect.

Evaluate the Course or Curriculum

Instructors and students can perform a summative evaluation at the end of each course to determine whether the course met the educational goals of the organization. This evaluation answers the following two questions:

1. Did students meet learning objectives and course or curriculum goals?

2. Was training conducted as designed and within the resources allocated?

Any of the following data can be analyzed as part of a summative evaluation:

- Students' scores on written or performance tests
- Students' behaviors observed in the field
- Feedback from students and instructors
- Feedback from field supervisors

A summative evaluation is performed after each delivery of the course. In part, the trends identified in student performance help evaluators judge whether the course successfully met course and curriculum goals. These evaluations also determine whether course delivery continues as is, continues with necessary adjustments, or is discontinued. In order to accurately measure the improvement in student performance, course or curriculum evaluators need to compare the post-course performance to the performance level observed in the needs analysis and pretests (if given).

In addition to evaluating students' performances and whether they meet course learning objectives and JPRs, there must be an evaluation system for course materials, testing instruments, and instructor performance. A detailed discussion on student evaluations is presented in Chapter 13, Instructor and Class Evaluations.

Evaluating Course Materials

Both instructors and students should have input into the assessment of teaching and learning materials (textbooks, study materials, audiovisual aids, props, etc). The results should answer the following two questions:

1. Did the materials support the objectives?

2. Were the materials relevant or applicable to job requirements?

Evaluating Instructor Performances

An excellent course design with appropriate training materials can be jeopardized by one or more instructors whose teaching skills are not adequate. When establishing instructor evaluation instruments, ensure that they answer the following questions:

- How well does the instructor know the subject being taught?

- How enthusiastic is the instructor for the topic and teaching?

- How well does the instructor provide the knowledge necessary to meet the lesson and course objectives?

- How well is the instructor prepared?

- How well is the instructor organized?

- How well does the instructor relate to or interact with students?

- How well does the instructor respond to and answer student questions?

During the presentation of a curriculum, an instructor should be periodically evaluated by more experienced instructors with subject-matter expertise. Student input is also an important component in instructor evaluation. Students can complete carefully designed course-feedback instruments that elicit objective responses. The results of instructor evaluations may show the need for either enhanced instructor development or only the need for appropriate instructor orientation, particularly when new courses are being introduced.

Evaluating Testing Instruments

Testing is a measurement process that determines whether learning has occurred. Giving a test is only part of the process. Scoring and analyzing the results also serve necessary functions. The primary purpose of analyzing test results is the same as the purpose of evaluation — to improve the teaching/learning process. Performing simple test results analyses provides instructors, test developers, and organizations with information on test validity and reliability.

The results of a test analysis identify test items that may need altering, rewording, or restructuring to make them more easily understood and significant to the learning objectives being tested. Instructors can perform some simple analyses to assess the effectiveness of test items. A list of corrective actions is also provided in the sections below to help an instructor determine how to alter test items that require attention.

Test Validity and Reliability

When test results are not valid or reliable, they have no meaning. As defined previously, validity is the degree to which a test measures what it was designed to measure. Reliability is the consistency of test scores from one measurement to another. Reliability is a condition of validity.

Validity has a specific meaning when interpreting criterion-referenced tests. For these tests, validity refers to the measurement of mastery or nonmastery by a student as compared against the established learning objectives.

Similarly, **reliability** has a specific meaning when interpreting criterion-referenced tests. For these tests, reliability indicates the consistency of results in classifying mastery or nonmastery of an individual.

The length of a test has some relevance to reliability and validity. Longer tests are, in general, more reliable than short tests but not necessarily more valid. However, it is also true that long tests may lack reliability if the test is overly long. When assessing reliability and validity, test length should also be evaluated.

Validity — Extent to which a test or other assessment technique measures the learner qualities (knowledge or skills) that it is meant to measure.

Reliability — A condition of validity; the extent to which a test or test item consistently and accurately produces the same results or scores when given to a set of learners on different occasions, marked by different assessors, or marked by the same assessors on different occasions.

Test-Result Analysis

Most test-result analysis is currently performed using computer software. The software can analyze the mean (average) scores for any given exam. The software will also indicate the questions that were most frequently missed and how many students missed them. Using these numerical values, a test's overall difficulty can be established. Tests that most students failed may need to be revised to ensure that more students pass the exam. A high failure rate may indicate that the test is not accurately reflecting the learning objectives that were taught during the class. Similarly, tests that have a very high passing rate may indicate that the test reveals its answers too easily and is not indicating a recall of learning objectives on the part of the student.

Test Item Analysis

A test item analysis allows instructors to use systematic methods to assess the quality of an item on a test. Three relatively simple measures of quality can be computed when using a multiple-choice test-item format: difficulty index, discrimination index, and distractor analysis. Analyses of other test formats such as short-answer and essay rely on proper test item construction.

Most of the time, instructors are interested in measuring a student's minimal competency in an area, and thus they rely on criterion-referenced tests. Ideally, an item's difficulty should be similar to the test's criterion level. Difficulty is a simple proportion of how many students in a class or training group selected the correct answer. If the percentage of students who answered the item correctly is close to the criterion (passing) level for the test, then the item is likely of the appropriate difficulty level for the test **(Figure 15.10)**.

Part of assessing the difficulty of a test item is evaluating the item's distractors. This evaluation applies specifically to multiple-choice questions. Distractors are wrong answers that should be written to make them enticing options for a student to choose. Distractor analysis is the simple process of examining responses for each test item to determine the distribution of responses across the range of possibilities. For example, the correct answer is not likely to be any specific choice out of four options. Item quality refers to the effectiveness of the distractors. Distractors that are not selected by any test taker need revision.

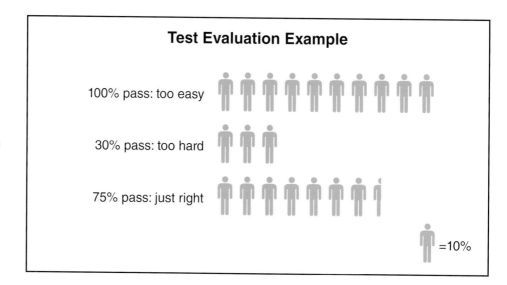

Figure 15.10 A test question that proves to be too easy or too difficult should be reevaluated.

Some procedures that instructors can use to revise a test are as follows:

- **Remove poor test items and recalculate the score** — Take this action after carefully evaluating the test item and determining that its content or structure was misleading to students.

- **Review the test analysis, adjust the test items, and give the test again** — Take this action when distractors or test items would benefit from rewording.

- **Teach the lesson again and retest** — Take this action when it appears that certain critical information was not taught or was not clear to students during the program.

Other options include a review of the instruction, circumstances of the instruction, and testing situations. Any of these factors may have confused, misled, or distracted the students. Adjust the instruction, teach the lesson again, and administer the test as necessary when critical changes need to be made. When two or more identical classes are held at the same time, another corrective analysis technique is to compare test results of all classes, then determine the appropriate steps to take.

What This Means to You

You are evaluating student scores on an exam. The average grade on the exam according to your scoring software is 60%, 10% lower than the criterion passing level for the test, which is 70%. You are concerned that the test may be too difficult. You begin examining the individual test items to find out how many students got each right or wrong and which answers were selected.

On question number 10, only 5 out of the 20 students who took the test selected the correct answer, response C. The question only had 25% correct, well below the criterion for the test. Upon further examination, those who got the question wrong all selected the same distractor instead of the correct answer. You discover that there are other questions like this one on the test. You have to make a determination as to whether the distractors are too close to the correct answer to offer the student a reasonable choice or whether the stems are leading students toward the chosen distractors.

In this situation, you would make the recommendation that the test is unreliable and requires revision. The revisions could be performed yourself or assigned to someone else in your agency. If the test was provided to you from a third-party publisher, you might consider examining the other materials you have received from them and/or consider using a different publisher in the future.

Course or Curriculum Revision

The evaluation of the training course or curriculum may determine the need for revision of the course or curriculum. The instructor or training manager should regularly assess the need for curriculum revision to improve student learning or provide students with new learning opportunities. Revisions may become necessary because of changes in operational standards, department protocols, new technologies, or the standards of appropriate accrediting bodies.

When planning revisions, the instructor should take the following actions:

- Determine whether the revision is mission appropriate for the department/ organization, training division, or agency. Does the proposed revision help and support the organization to meet its mission statement or goal? If not, then the revision should not be made or the course or curriculum should be altered so that it does meet the mission statement or goal.

- Involve other branches or divisions of the department/organization that may be affected by the proposed changes.
- Involve the entire training division or agency membership in the development process.
- Evaluate the existing resources and potential needs regarding staffing, funding, time, technology, equipment, props, and facilities.
- Communicate clearly to the organization the reason for the proposed revision as well as the anticipated results of the change.
- Create clear, concise revision proposals that meet the criteria for any new course or curriculum.
- Apply the four-step planning model to the revision of the course or curriculum.

Periodic evaluations of all courses and curricula should be scheduled to determine whether they still meet the original needs of the organization because the current course outcomes may not resemble those of the original course design.

Chapter Summary

Analyzing and planning instruction can include tasks ranging from planning a single course to developing a training program, curriculum, or course for the entire organization. The Level III Instructor must understand the analysis process in order to be able to determine the types of training required to meet the organization's needs.

It is also important for the training manager to have an understanding in the application of planning models, including the four-step method. This planning model can be applied to instructional development, course development, and program development. Each of these components is essential to the knowledge base required for any instructor who is responsible for managing training.

Review Questions

1. What are the four steps of the development model?
2. What analyses are used to identify training needs?
3. What tasks are followed to design a course? A curriculum?
4. How does an instructor implement the course or curriculum?
5. Where does an instructor get data used to evaluate a course or curriculum?
6. How does an instructor evaluate testing instruments?
7. What actions should an instructor take when planning revisions?

Training Program Evaluation

Chapter Contents

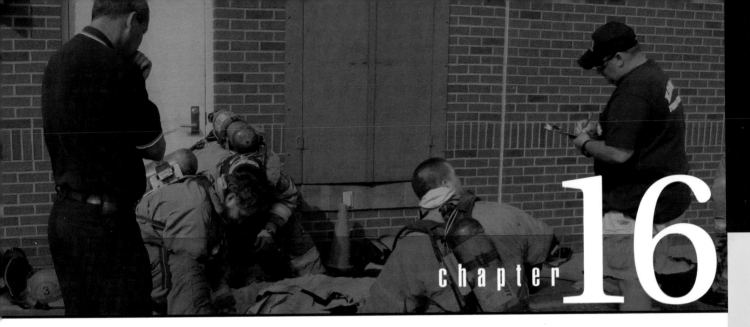

Key Terms

Job Performance Requirements

NFPA® 1041 References

6.2.7

6.5.2

6.5.3

6.5.4

Learning Objectives

1. Discuss the types and categories of evaluations used in fire and emergency service programs. [NFPA®1041, 6.5.2]

2. Discuss the ways that instructors gather behavioral data as part of an evaluation plan. [NFPA®1041, 6.5.3, 6.5.4]

3. Describe the steps to be taken after reviewing evaluations. [NFPA®1041, 6.2.7, 6.5.2]

Chapter 16
Training Program Evaluation

Case History

A certain fire chief had served on the advisory board for a college's fire training program for the past five years. The chief had stated to the advisory board that recruit training at the college was more tailored to passing the state's board exam and not to end-user needs. His training division had to provide additional instruction to new recruits in order for them to function safely and effectively within their departments. Others on the advisory committee reinforced his concern and threatened to no longer use the college as their training resource for basic fire academy.

The fire service training program director took note of the concerns and implemented a plan to evaluate the program's effectiveness. The evaluation discovered many shortcomings in the program ranging from personnel issues to lack of adequate training space within the college. Furthermore, the training budget, accrediting agency, state fire commission, and fire community all discovered ways in which they contributed to the program's problems.

The identified weaknesses were corrected, and the college made a commitment to take local needs assessments into account when planning courses and curriculum. A method of taking employer surveys was implemented that helped evaluate the satisfaction of end-users.

The program evaluation led to steady improvement at the college. Enrollment in the fire-training program increased every year following, which led to an increase in funding. The College Board was able to approve construction of a state-of-the-art training facility and add more instructors.

Fire and emergency services organizations provide a wide variety of both internal and external programs. Internal programs include training, professional development, health and wellness promotion, and equipment/facility maintenance. External programs are the result of community expectations and are derived from the mission statement of the organization. External programs include (but are not limited to) emergency medical assistance, fire suppression, public education, inspections, plans review, and code enforcement. Level III Instructors are responsible for evaluating their organizations' training programs.

Evaluation Methodology

Agencies can use several types of evaluations to answer questions and gather information on topics unique to their agencies. When tailored to meet specific agency criteria, evaluations can help agencies determine whether or not they are meeting their organizational goals.

Three generally accepted types of evaluations used for programs are as follows:

- **Goal-based evaluations** — Determine how well a program is meeting its current goals or objectives.

- **Process-based evaluations** — Determine how a program works in practice and highlight its strengths and weaknesses; process evaluation focuses on a lesson, course, or curriculum taught during the fulfillment of a program. In organizations that provide training, process-based evaluations may refer to the formal plan for developing or revising curriculum.

- **Outcome-based evaluations** — Provide actual, measurable benefits that are created as a result of the program's existence; for example, the number of classes delivered and the number of students taught.

The following actions should be included in a typical process of evaluation:

- Set criteria by identifying the problems or issues that must be addressed.

- Determine what data is currently available for evaluation.

- Determine what new data will have to be collected for evaluation.

- Identify the evaluation model that will be most effective.

- Determine the amount of time necessary to complete the evaluation.

- Identify the personnel who will be responsible for making the evaluation.

- Conduct the evaluation.

- Analyze the results of the evaluation and develop conclusions based on the results.

- Establish multiple sets of reasonable actions to take based on the results.

- Prepare a specialized final report for each audience that will be affected by the outcome of the evaluations.

- Develop revision strategies and priorities.

An evaluation plan should be a formal element in the planning process. Selecting and performing the appropriate evaluation type will generate the most useful information about each specific stage of program development, delivery, or revision.

Qualitative evaluation is a subjective form of evaluation, while **quantitative evaluation** is objective. These two categories of evaluation can be further described as follows:

1. **Qualitative evaluation** — Often based on nonnumeric analysis, although data may have numeric values assigned; determines whether the program meets the values established for the program. This type of data is difficult to tabulate into precise categories, and it is usually gathered through the following methods:

   — Open-ended questions

   — Interviews of students **(Figure 16.1)**

Qualitative Evaluation —
Evaluation based on non-numerical analysis and intended to assess the quality of something.

Quantitative Evaluation —
Evaluation based on numeric or statistical analysis and intended to discover quantifiable data.

— Course and curriculum evaluations

— Evaluation surveys completed by students

— Instructor and supervisor observations

2. **Quantitative evaluation** — Based on a numeric or statistical analysis; the program is evaluated against specific numeric criteria. Information gathered locally may be judged against statistics gathered on a local or national level. Quantitative evaluation works best when information is gathered from a large number of respondents. Details:

— Data is gathered from questionnaires that contain yes/no questions, checklists, or preference scales **(Figure 16.2)**.

— The content limit placed on the respondent's answers may discourage fresh concepts from being developed.

— Responses to the surveys are typically limited.

A typical example of qualitative versus quantitative evaluation may be represented by the construction of course evaluation forms. A form on which students respond to open-ended questions in an essay or short answer format yields qualitative results. A form that requires students to rate certain aspects of the course on a 1 to 5 scale yields quantitative results.

Evaluation Plans

The basic framework for all types of evaluations should be maintained in a written evaluation plan that contains the step-by-step process for the various types of evaluations used by the jurisdiction. The plan ensures that agency policies and procedures are followed, which in turn ensures that the process is conducted in the same manner each time it is implemented. The plan must contain enough information for anyone to understand and follow it. Records must be kept on all formal evaluations.

When an appropriate evaluation plan is applied to a program, the plan can be used as the basis for the evaluation report and serve as the outline for organizing the collected results. A complete evaluation plan includes a review of behavioral objectives and test results in order to allow an informed decision about whether the results are a true measure of the objectives. This review process enables Level III Instructors to meet the primary purpose of evaluation, which is to improve the teaching and learning process. Many evaluation techniques may be used to assess learning levels and to determine how instruction can be modified to enhance learning.

One model specific to evaluating training in an organization is Kirkpatrick's Four-Level Training Evaluation Model, as follows:

Figure 16.1 Qualitative evaluation includes information gathered directly from students.

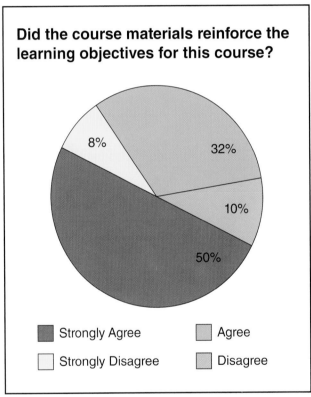

Did the course materials reinforce the learning objectives for this course?

- 32%
- 10%
- 50%
- 8%

◼ Strongly Agree ◼ Agree

☐ Strongly Disagree ◼ Disagree

Figure 16.2 Data from questionnaires can be graphed to give a clearer picture of course evaluations.

- **Reaction of students** — What they thought and felt about the training; corresponds to student evaluations of courses and instructors

- **Learning** — Resulting increase in knowledge or capability; corresponds to cognitive tests (written and oral) given to students

- **Behavior** — Extent of improvement in student capabilities and application of learned skills; corresponds to psychomotor skills tests for students and instructor evaluations for instructors

- **Results** — Effects on the business or environment resulting from the trainee's performance; corresponds to training program evaluations

The sections that follow describe additional ways in which Level III Instructors can gather behavioral data about their organizations' programs as a whole.

NFA Evaluation Plan

The evaluation process used by the National Fire Academy (NFA) is based on the systems approach and includes the following elements **(Figure 16.3)**:

- **Input** — Resources such as personnel, equipment, and finances that are devoted to the specific activity being measured; resources are stated in quantities such as the following:

  — Amount of money allotted for training

  — Number of instructors

  — Number of courses taught

  — Number of hours per class

- **Process** (*may also be referred to as* **transformation** *or* **thru-put**) — Change that occurs to resources; any activity such as training, purchasing, or hiring

- **Output** — Quantity of services that are the result of input and process; quantity may be stated in the following terms:

  — Number of students enrolled

  — Hours of training provided

  — Number of certification requirements met

- **Output efficiency** — Input divided by the output; for example, the amount of money allotted divided by the number of hours of training delivered results in a cost per instructional hour of training

- **Outcome** — Results of the process

- **Intermediate outcome** — Factors that are expected to directly change an outcome; may include an increased number of enrollments or hours of training

Retrospective Evaluations

Retrospective evaluation occurs when the intent of the evaluation is to assess the achievements or outcomes of the program. Details about these evaluations are as follows:

- Encompasses the overall effectiveness of the program

- Identifies the need for new programs

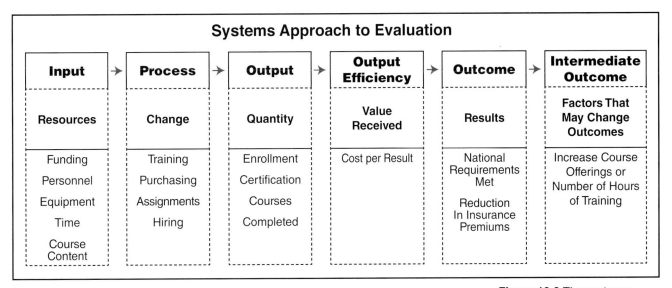

Systems Approach to Evaluation

Input		Process		Output		Output Efficiency		Outcome		Intermediate Outcome
Resources		Change		Quantity		Value Received		Results		Factors That May Change Outcomes
Funding		Training		Enrollment		Cost per Result		National Requirements Met		Increase Course Offerings or Number of Hours of Training
Personnel		Purchasing		Certification						
Equipment		Assignments		Courses				Reduction In Insurance Premiums		
Time		Hiring		Completed						
Course Content										

Figure 16.3 The systems approach to evaluation analyzes set training elements to determine outcomes.

- Provides a comparison with the past outcomes
- Documents the achievements of the program
- Documents students' habits
- Relies on evidence

Observation of Instructors

Just as testing occurs throughout instruction, course evaluation occurs before, during, and after instruction. Instructors can gather evidence, most of which is observational, during individual classes over the duration of a course.

With feedback received during instruction, instructors can change or modify instructional methods to meet the needs of the class. In some cases, it will be clear that a course needs to be changed on a permanent basis. The judgment of instructors is essential when making decisions about a program under development.

Supervisor Surveys

The training course or lesson evaluation process also includes surveys completed by supervisory personnel such as company officers, supervisors, and division managers within the organization. These individuals witness how students trained in the agency perform on the job after training. They are aware of any changes in the skills, behaviors, and attitudes that these individuals display following completion of a course. Supervisors provide invaluable information about the successes and results of training courses.

Survey forms can be distributed or made available to the appropriate supervisory personnel some time after the completion of the course or lesson. These surveys can also be repeated at certain intervals such as three months after a course and again six months after a course. Survey items should be constructed to assess how a student has applied the learned knowledge, skills, or behavioral habits while on duty.

Student Learning Surveys

Some organizations use similar course or lesson evaluation forms for students to determine how they are using the information or skills learned in the course. These forms may be distributed and completed at the same time that the

Figure 16.4 Conducting written evaluations will enable instructors to gauge the effectiveness of the course.

supervisor survey is completed. By having both the student and the supervisor work together on completing their surveys, a more complete and honest critique of the material presented to the student can be obtained.

Evaluating a training course includes determining the satisfaction of the students with the course **(Figure 16.4)**. Students who participate in effective training sessions are more likely to appreciate the time spent on the course. Likewise, students are the first to recognize an ineffective training session.

Organizational Evaluations

An organizational evaluation is intended to compare an organization's mission statement with its output; specifically, if the training division or agency is meeting its responsibilities, acting with the proper authority, and providing the best service possible. The mission statement of a training division may be based upon an established standard (such as an NFPA® standard) or may have been developed by a local board or authority.

Overall performance of the organization, which includes the internal divisions or branches of the department, is judged against the criteria that were established for the organization. Organizational evaluations may be conducted internally, by an outside agency, or by a third-party. Internal evaluation is a quality-control measure that is part of the planning process. Outside agencies that may evaluate the organization include the local jurisdiction, state/territory/province, or national government. These organizations provide a process that allows jurisdictions or organizations to be evaluated on the quality of fire and emergency services that are available. The third-party evaluation may be conducted by organizations such as the following:

● Insurance Services Office (ISO)

● Commission on Accreditation of Ambulance Services (CAAS)

● State boards of EMS or state agencies for public health

● Commission on Fire Accreditation International (CFAI)

The U.S. Dept of Defense (DOD) and the Canadian Forces Fire Academy (CFFA) along with state and provincial fire training systems that provide certification in the United States can be accredited by the International Fire Service Accreditation Congress (IFSAC) and/or the National Board on Fire Service Professional Qualifications (ProBoard). With certain exceptions, these agencies do not typically evaluate or accredit individual departments.

The results of organizational performance evaluations, either internal or external, help the leadership of the department or organization improve services and adjust to potential changes in the expected services. Evaluations are viewed as management tools that result in positive changes.

Performance Measurement

Training divisions within fire departments may also develop performance measurements in order to evaluate success of the training division. These performance measurements can be used to justify existing budgets, plan for future expectations, and support the efficiency of the training division. These performance measures can be tracked on a quarterly basis or on a regular schedule determined by the AHJ. Examples of items that could be part of a training division's performance measurement include **(Figure 16.5)**:

- Percentage of firefighters certified to various levels of the NFPA® Professional Qualifications standards

- Percentage of individuals who attend special team training such as technical rescue

- Percentage of students who successfully complete recruit academies

- Number of training injuries per year

- Customer approval ratings (CARs) taken from course evaluations

- Output numbers to include number of courses, students, and instructional hours

- Cost per instructional hour of training

Course and Instructional Design Evaluations

Instructional design is composed of the analysis of training needs, the systematic design of learning activities, and the assessment of the learning process. As training requirements change or when activities are no longer effective, the instructional process changes.

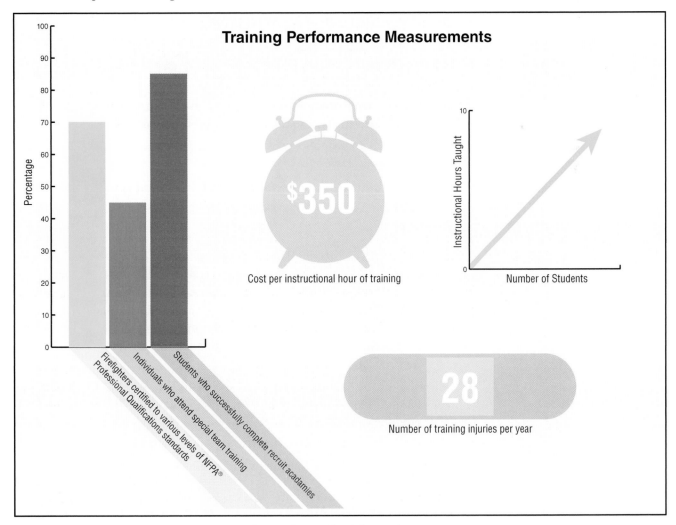

Figure 16.5 A number of items should be used to track overall training performance.

Instructors must always be alert to ways of improving or updating instruction or even eliminating instruction that is no longer needed. Instructional content, methods, and techniques must remain flexible in order to serve their intended purpose.

Test scores are only one form of evidence to support or refute the success of the learning process. For example, students' behavior in training environments may indicate a higher awareness of safety and skill-related knowledge than their test scores indicate.

In any case, it is important that the evaluation process is useful to its users, thus data collection must be accurate. Evaluation instruments, as mentioned previously, should always be easy and practical to administer, and results should be easy to report. Planning the approach to evaluation is also important. To get the most from a course evaluation, the instructor must plan the approach by thinking through and answering the following questions:

- How did training affect students' attitudes and behavior? What did they learn? How was the organization affected by the results? How are these factors quantified?

- How can identified concerns be addressed?

- Will information gathering be administered using tests, questionnaires, or surveys?

- What are the objectives of the training program? Are the evaluation criteria based on these objectives?

- How do criteria indicate improvement between expected and actual performance when measured against the results of the needs analysis?

- What data sources are already available to help measure results (productivity reports, daily log sheets, and training and personnel records)?

- What alternative methods for gathering data are available (interviews and on-site observations)?

- What are the best and most cost-effective methods for measuring the results of the training? Are there less costly, more efficient ways of administering the evaluation?

Evaluation Results and Recommendations

The evaluation process helps Level III Instructors determine what could be changed to ensure that learning occurs in the easiest and most efficient way possible for students. Evaluations help guide the adjustment of the final program. With the help of these evaluations and course reactions, developers can ensure a successful program.

Unless the results collected from tests and course feedback are used to make some decisions about future instruction, any time, money, and effort expended on the evaluation process are wasted. After reviewing the evaluations, Level III Instructors should take the following three steps:

Step 1: Determine areas for improvement based on student outcomes — Example questions:

— Were course objectives appropriate?

— Did the course outline and materials match the learning objectives?

— Did the instructional methods and aids facilitate learning?

— Did the instructor's presentation style impede learning?

— Was the learning environment conducive to learning?

— Were testing instruments and test administration valid and reliable?

— Were there personal or logistical problems that inhibited learning?

— What student learning weaknesses were revealed?

Step 2: Identify actions to correct deficiencies — Example actions:

— Revise course objectives.

— Modify the course outline and materials to match objectives.

— Change instructional methods/aids to facilitate learning.

— Improve presentation style to foster learning.

— Enhance the learning environment to promote learning.

— Alter evaluation techniques to produce valid and reliable instruments.

— Provide support for students and offer referral services.

— Provide extra learning opportunities such as learning activity packets, individual or pair assignments, group study, or one-on-one tutoring.

Step 3: Document and report results as appropriate — Example actions:

— Keep daily records of training activities.

— Maintain individual training records.

— Retain class test results and results of analyses.

NOTE: Provide written progress reports to management that outline findings in Steps 1 and 2.

Evaluations can also be used in the review of material and overall evaluation of the training program. Some agencies refer to this as their **Customer Approval Rating (CAR)** or Customer Satisfaction Rating (CSR). It is easy to manage this process when the information is provided in a computer database. Small departments can manage this process manually.

The examples in **Table 16.1, p.404** show the use of the overall CAR. From this data an organization can look at areas of the course that may need improving, such as instructor competency. Each category has been assigned a value. Some categories, such as the outdoor factor in the Case Law course, may not apply.

Typically, when evaluations of entire programs are performed, the purpose is to make recommendations to agency administrators to justify a change in policy or recommend new courses. Level III Instructors should be prepared to present their findings using statistical analysis and summarization of the findings to present a cohesive argument for proposed changes. Their recommendations should be based on gathered evidence. Evidence that may not show the results that instructors were expecting should be evaluated based on its relevance. Any relevant information should be accounted for as part of the recommendation, even evidence that may be in contradiction to the instructor's argument. Including such evidence helps to minimize bias in the recommendation. Finally, any recommendation should reflect agency goals. If new courses, policies, and procedures are needed, reinforcing how changes will support existing agency goals will help new recommendations be accepted.

Customer Approval Rating (CAR) — Organizational rating that adds a quantifiable ranking to qualitative evaluations. *Also known as* Customer Satisfaction Rating (CSR).

Table 16.1
Course Performance Ratings Examples

Farm Accident Rescue		Farm Machinery Rescue: Technician	
Total Courses: 1		Total Courses: 1	
CAR	3.53	CAR	3.36
Instructor	3.59	Instructor	3.67
Classroom	3.40	Classroom	2.90
Outdoor	3.50	Outdoor	3.07
Visuals	3.63	Visuals	3.63
Print	3.60	Print	3.53
Completing the NFIRS* Report and Writing Incident Reports		Fire and Emergency Case Law	
Total Courses: 1		Total Courses: 1	
CAR	2.60	CAR	3.40
Instructor	2.70	Instructor	3.41
Classroom	2.47	Classroom	3.70
Outdoor	2.22	Outdoor	NA
Visuals	2.75	Visuals	3.18
Print	2.73	Print	3.57

*NFIRS = National Fire Incident Reporting System

Source: *Courtesy of Fire and Rescue Training Institute, University of Missouri.*

Chapter Summary

Evaluation is an essential component of any program because it allows administrators the option of correcting instructional weaknesses before they impact learning. Level III Instructors should understand the methodology behind evaluations, as well as how to establish an evaluation plan. They should also understand what the best sources of information are for each portion of the plan. Finally, they should know how to utilize the results generated from the data they have gathered during evaluations.

Review Questions

1. What evaluations are used in fire and emergency service programs?

2. In what ways do instructors gather behavioral data about their organizations?

3. How are evaluation results used by an Instructor III?

Training Program Administration

Chapter Contents

Key Terms

Job Performance Requirements

NFPA® 1041 References

6.2.2	6.2.6
6.2.3	6.3.2
6.2.4	6.3.5
6.2.5	

Learning Objectives

1. Discuss the functions that a record-keeping system should perform. [NFPA®1041, 6.2.2]

2. Explain disclosure of information. [NFPA®1041, 6.2.2]

3. Explain the necessity for developing forms for a training record system. [NFPA®1041, 6.2.2]

4. Describe an Instructor Level III's role in conducting an agency level needs analysis. [NFPA®1041, 6.3.2]

5. Discuss the process of developing organizational training policies, procedures, and guidelines. [NFPA®1041, 6.2.3]

6. Explain the influence that standards have on training policies. [NFPA®1041, 6.3.5]

7. Explain the equipment purchasing process. [NFPA®1041, 6.2.6]

8. Identify the Instructor Level III's human resource responsibilities. [NFPA®1041, 6.2.4]

9. Discuss the process of personnel evaluations. [NFPA®1041, 6.2.5]

Chapter 17
Training Program Administration

Case History

A serious training incident involving anhydrous ammonia resulted in the death of one firefighter and the disability of another firefighter. When the accident was investigated, the training program administrator was required to disclose the training records of the two firefighters, information from the course they were attending, and safety policies used during evolutions at training agency.

During the investigation, firefighters in the course and their departments submitted that the training they had taken from the agency did not include specific information about handling anhydrous ammonia. However, when cross examined, the course syllabus and training roster that the agency disclosed disproved this accusation. The syllabus stated that the afternoon session on the day before the accident included information regarding special situations involving anhydrous ammonia. The training roster showed that the two firefighters did not return to class after the lunch hour the day before the accident.

At a training agency, any accident or line of duty death will result in the individuals' training records being reviewed. Proper documentation by the training agency will assist in the accident investigation and can help prevent negligence by the department training program.

Level III Instructors have the highest level of administrative duties in a training agency or division. They are responsible for maintaining the entire training record-keeping system for the entire agency or division, and they also are the starting point for all training policies and procedures. Level III Instructors create the various forms the agency uses and are responsible for expensive training-related purchases. This chapter describes the administrative duties that Level III Instructors perform.

NOTE: In smaller departments, Level I or II Instructors may be responsible for some of these same duties.

Record-Keeping Systems

Record-keeping encompasses a wide range of information organizing skills and results in the proper documentation of the policies and transactions of the organization. The information stored in records can be used for many purposes including the development or alteration of policies, procedures, and guidelines. Record-keeping also includes the use of the following:

- Statistical analysis
- Strategic handling of data pulled directly from tests
- Other evaluations to establish trends and relationships

This information can be used to formulate training policies, mandate safe practices, or change procedures. The organization must create and preserve adequate and proper documentation of its activities in a record-keeping system that supports operational needs, protects individual rights, and promotes accountability.

Record-keeping systems may be manual or automated. A manual system involves the physical collection, organization, storage, preservation, and disposal of hard copy records and materials. These records may include reports, forms, maps, graphs, illustrations, audio/video recordings, and photographs.

An automated system uses the electronic storage of data in computer databases. These systems are typically referred to as information systems. These systems allow instructors direct access to the files for uploading or updating records. Information systems should require password-protected computer security to limit access to only authorized personnel. Firewalls and Internet security must be established to prevent outside attack of servers that instructors can access remotely. Level III Instructors should work closely with their information technology departments to establish these security measures.

Either type of system must be able to perform the following functions:

- Organize records
- Index records
- Allow only authorized staff members to access the records
- Ensure that records are easily found when requested

Record-keeping systems consist of more than the software applications or filing systems designed to manage the records. The system is also composed of the following resources:

- **People** — Personnel who are trained in the operation of the system.
- **Policies** — Codified statements that define the system, the data to be gathered, and how data are stored, accessed, analyzed, and disposed of.
- **Procedures** — Methods used to meet the requirements of the policies.
- **Tools** — Record-keeping instruments designed to manage and control the records over time; these instruments include disposal schedules and access and security classification systems.
- **Technology** — Software, hardware, physical storage, and disposal equipment.
- **Training and Education** — Ongoing personnel training and refresher courses required to manage the system.
- **Maintenance** — System support that ensures that the system continues to operate correctly and efficiently and is protected in the event the system experiences a malfunction.

Level III Instructors have the task of ensuring that these components work together and that the system functions according to agency policies. In addition, Level III Instructors should consult applicable standards for record-keeping in the fire and emergency services as a model for their record-keeping policies. NFPA® 1401, *Recommended Practice for Fire Service Training Reports and Records,* provides some examples of training forms as well as information on the design and procedures for effective record-keeping. The format of records may also depend on the type of training for which information is being gathered **(Figure 17.1)**.

Department of Fire Programs

Standard Roll Call Form

COURSE ____________________

LOCATION ____________________

SCHOOL NUMBER ____________________

STUDENT NAME (Print Clearly)	STUDENT ID	Date of Birth	FDID#	Hours and Subject Codes				CAREER	VOLUNTEER

Figure 17.1 A typical roll-call form needs to provide spaces for relevant student and classroom information.

Disclosure of Information

As described in Chapter 13, Supervisory and Administrative Duties, Level II Instructors must be able to identify what records are considered public and what records are protected as private. Level III Instructors will often be asked to apply this knowledge to facilitate a disclosure of information. **Disclosure** is a legal term referring to the act of giving out information either voluntarily or to meet legal requirements or agency policy requirements. A disclosure is often a formal process, such as when training records are requested by a court order.

Some records can be released without any authorization. For example, if planning documents that instructors used to create a course are requested as part of an investigation, these documents should be freely available. Similarly, instructional materials can be requested without compromising privacy.

Disclosures begin to get complicated when the records requested have privacy requirements attached to them. For example, under the **Family Educational Rights and Privacy Act (FERPA)** test records cannot be disclosed without the written consent of the student. If a chief or commanding officer wanted to request the test records of a subordinate, he or she could not do so without informing the student. Similar requirements exist for other personnel records and any medical records kept in the record-keeping system.

Disclosures that take place as a result of a court order may circumvent some rules of privacy. Level III Instructors should maintain familiarity with the local and state/provincial laws that apply to the subpoenaing of documents for use in legal cases.

Development of Forms

Standardized forms ensure that information mandated by law and stored in the record-keeping system is consistent and complete. Forms are developed based on the types of information outlined in the organization's policies and legal requirements.

When the Level III Instructor begins to create a form to aid in gathering a particular type of data, the relevant policies and legal requirements surrounding each type of data should be researched. At the same time, the instructor

Disclosure — Legal term referring to the act of giving out information either voluntarily or to meet legal requirements or agency policy requirements.

Family Educational Rights and Privacy Act (FERPA) — Legislation that provides that an individual's school records are confidential and that information contained in those records may not be released without the individual's prior written consent.

should investigate whether forms that gather the same information already exist or are provided by other levels of government.

The widespread use of computers makes the creation of forms very easy. Forms such as course attendance sheets may be simple documents that are printed and filled in by hand. Information from completed forms may be compiled into databases **(Figure 17.2)**.

Regardless of other formatting and style features, forms should have fields that are consistent with other training forms used by the organization. For instance, Field 1 may always contain the date; Field 2 may always contain the instructor's name; Field 3 may always contain the student's name, and so on. The more consistent the assignment of data to specific fields, the easier the form will be to use and the easier the information will be to locate, analyze, and store.

Agency Level Needs Analysis

Level III Instructors apply needs analyses to policies at all levels of their agencies. Level III Instructors identify and address needs projected for the future rather than reacting to immediate situations. For example, Level III Instructors examine the personnel training and educational needs of their organizations and make decisions about selecting staff or adjusting the instructional duties of existing personnel. Needs analysis may include identifying other agencies that can provide training facilities, mutual aid, and equipment when funding does not exist to acquire these resources.

Agency-wide needs and task analysis are generally not the responsibility of one individual, nor is it performed without research and data analysis. The sections that follow discuss these issues as they relate to task and needs analysis.

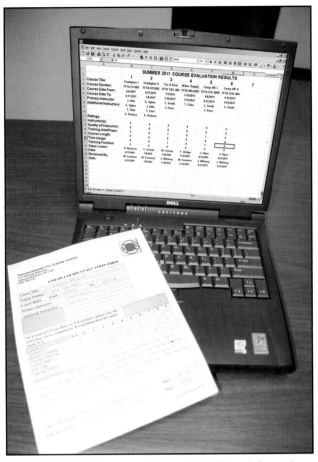

Figure 17.2 Written information can be entered into electronic databases.

Review: Prerequisites for Task and Needs Analysis

Prerequisite information for performing task and needs analysis has been discussed earlier in this manual. Students or instructors can review this information in the following chapters:

- **Development of JPRs** — Chapter 10, Lesson Plan Development
- **Lesson planning** — Chapter 10, Lesson Plan Development
- **Instructional methods** — Chapter 6, Classroom Instruction; Chapter 7, Skills-Based Training Beyond the Classroom
- **Characteristics of adult learners** — Chapter 2, Principles of Learning; Chapter 6, Classroom Instruction
- **Instructional media** — Chapter 4, Instructional Materials and Equipment
- **Development of evaluation instruments** — Chapter 12, Test Item Construction; Chapter 14, Instructor and Class Evaluations
- **Conducting research** — Chapter 13, Supervisory and Administrative Duties
- **Task analysis** — Chapter 15, Course and Curriculum Development

Committee Meetings

Involving employees in the analysis process is one strategy that Level III Instructors use to include instructors in the decision-making process. Involving employees also creates an opportunity for the Level III Instructor to delegate research tasks. Delegating tasks and involving employees in decision-making are often accomplished during a meeting.

Level III Instructors should schedule meetings at an appropriate interval to allow those attending the meetings the time needed to perform their duties. Meetings should have an agenda so that attendees know what to expect and can plan to spend the time efficiently.

Whenever possible, meetings should be limited to a relatively small number of people, especially when input is going to be requested from those in attendance **(Figure 17.3)**. The individuals invited to the meeting should be those who are most relevant to the project or analysis. The attendees can then communicate any needed information to others not in attendance.

Finally, Level III Instructors may attend committee meetings to report findings to higher ranking members of their jurisdictions. Any presentations they make should be concise and informed by evidence from research.

Data Organization and Interpretation

Data gathered from meetings and research must be organized and interpreted. There are many ways of doing this, and Level III Instructors will discover what methods work best for them. The most important outcome of interpretation is that the information tells a story, supports a proposal, and/or answers an analysis question. For example, research stating that training injuries were lower than the previous year is good news. The Level III Instructor can justify continuing those policies in the future if that information can be correlated with changes in training policies or courses from the previous year.

Figure 17.3 Keep committee membership to a manageable level.

Development of Training Policies, Procedures, and Guidelines

Written policies, procedures, and guidelines are essential for the effective and efficient operation of any fire and emergency services organization. Place into writing the expectations of the organization based on the organizational values and strategic and operational plans.

The documents must contain information that is current and appropriate. Therefore, the organization should have a process to perform the following functions:

- Identify a need for new policy, procedure, or guideline .
- Develop draft document.
- Submit draft for review.
- Adopt policy, procedure, or guideline.
- Publish document.
- Implement document's contents.
- Evaluate effectiveness.

In addition, the organization should be familiar with existing standards and the process for adopting them into law. The sections that follow describe the functions involved in creating new policies, procedures, and guidelines and also provide definitions of important terminology for completing the process.

Figure 17.4 The presence of rapid intervention crews during training evolutions is an example of a policy instituted for student safety.

Policies

A **policy** is a guiding principle that organizations develop, adopt, and use as a basis or foundation for decision-making **(Figure 17.4)**. Policies help organizations address specific issues or problems. Training policies serve to guide an organization's training function on a day-to-day basis and are often accompanied by procedures for fulfilling the requirements of the policies. For policies to be effective, they must have the following characteristics:

- Written using language that is simple, concise, and respectful
- Adopted through a process that provides reasoned feedback
- Explicitly supported by the organization's administration and training manager

In some cases, policies are developed at the local level. In other cases, organizational training policies are based upon state, provincial, or federal laws or standards. For example, the *U.S. Code of Federal Regulations (CFR)* identifies specific requirements for the training of personnel who respond to hazardous materials incidents.

These federal regulations often serve as the basis for locally adopted training requirements. Sometimes, these regulations, such as Respiratory Protection Training, *CFR* 1910.134, require the development of local policies and procedures. A resource for developing local policies include standards such as NFPA® 1201, *Standard for Providing Emergency Services to the Public*, and NFPA® 1500, *Standard on Fire Department Occupational Safety and Health Program*.

Policy — Organizational principle that is developed and adopted as a basis for decision-making.

Procedures and Guidelines

Level III Instructors are responsible for ensuring that instructors comply with training policies. To facilitate this compliance, training managers develop **procedures** and **guidelines** that outline the approved methods involved in fulfilling obligations as well as what autonomy instructors have to make decisions. Procedures and guidelines are management tools and may either accompany policies or exist independently from them. Consider the following two definitions and explanations:

1. **Procedure** — Identifies the steps that must be taken to fulfill the intent of a policy and is written to support a policy. For example, a policy may state that all live fire-training evolutions must be conducted in compliance with NFPA® 1403, *Standard on Live Fire Training Evolutions*. The procedures accompanying this policy consist of steps the instructor takes to ensure that the policy is achieved, including such actions as the following:

   — Establish the Incident Command System (ICS) based on the National Incident Management System (NIMS) model.

   — Inspect the training structure **(Figure 17.5)**.

   — Provide a Safety Officer for evolutions.

   — Require use of appropriate protective equipment.

   — Use qualified instructors who are knowledgeable of fire behavior.

   Well-defined procedures yield the advantage of consistency in implementing a policy. Procedures are indispensable in programs where adherence to policy may have a direct impact on training such as the following:

   — Implementing safety precautions during training

   — Hiring or evaluating personnel

   — Acquiring structures

Figure 17.5 Inspecting training structures and props is an important procedure that should be part of the safety policies in training organizations.

2. **Guideline** — Identifies a general philosophy; guidelines may be part of a policy or exist independently which simultaneously provide direction and autonomy for achieving the overall goal of the guideline or policy. Examples:

   — An organization may have a policy for conducting training in inclement or extreme weather conditions.

   — Included in the policy are guidelines that provide information that guides decision-making such as when it is appropriate to either cancel or reschedule training.

   — The information in the guidelines gives instructors the autonomy they need to consider all factors involved before making a decision.

Identifying a Need for a New Policy, Procedure, or Guideline

The steps for determining the need for a new policy, procedure, or guideline are as follows **(Figure 17.6)**:

Step 1: Identify the problem — Determine whether the problem or new development requires the force of a new policy, procedure, or guideline to be resolved appropriately. Some situations may be best addressed using a narrow focus and will not require formal organization-level change.

Step 2: Collect the data to evaluate the need — Data may come from personnel interviews, product literature, or activity reports. Determine whether data is quantitative or qualitative.

Step 3: Select the evaluation model — Determine whether an evaluation model is goal-based, process-based, or outcome-based.

Step 4: Establish a timetable for making the needs evaluation — Determine the amount of time that will be required to evaluate the problem. The complexity of the problem and amount of information that must be evaluated factor into this estimation.

Step 5: Conduct the evaluation — Follow the recommended steps for the model that is most appropriate for the situation.

Step 6: Select the best response to the need — Determine the best policy, procedure, or guideline to solve the problem. Remember that this determination may include no policy, procedure, or guideline at all.

Step 7: Select alternative responses — Select a second-best choice to accommodate a situation in which a contingency plan is necessary because of external influences. Personal safety should not be compromised for any personnel in any long-term decision.

Step 8: Establish a revision process or schedule — Create a revision process as part of the policy, procedure, or guideline. Revision may be a general process for all policies, procedures, or guidelines, or one that is specific to each policy, procedure, or guideline.

Step 9: Recommend the policy, procedure, or guideline that best meets the need — Determine whether the recommended policy, procedure, or guideline needs to be formally adopted by the jurisdiction because policies, procedures, or guidelines may have the effect of law. Formal approval requires that the policy, procedure, or guideline be supported by documentation.

Developing a Draft Document

After a need is identified, an individual or committee develops a draft of the document according to the following guidelines:

• Determine whether a policy, procedure, or guideline is the most appropriate for the issue or incident or all three are needed.

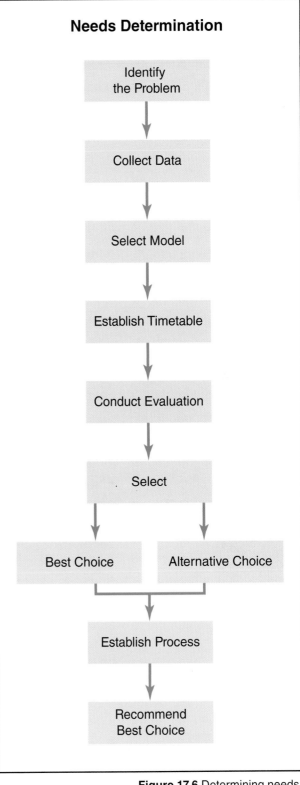

Figure 17.6 Determining needs for new policies can be made less complicated by following a step-by-step process.

- Always select the least restrictive type of document.
- Use similar existing policies, procedures, or guidelines as references when possible.
- Follow agency or national models for format, terminology, and organization.
- Include the date the document becomes effective if adopted.
- List the person or unit responsible for managing the new policy, procedure, or guideline and any other policy, procedure, or guideline to which it is related. Additional requirements for each type of document:
  — Policy must also state to whom or what it applies and the specific rules of application.
  — Procedure must contain the steps to follow and the policy to which it applies.
  — Guideline must include to whom or what it applies and the guideline statement.
- Conduct research on the legality of the new policy, procedure, or guideline because the documented issue or incident may have potential legal implications. The process follows:
  — Determine whether the issue or incident is addressed in existing organizational policies.
  — Review NFPA® standards that address the issue or incident.
  — Seek similar issue or incident resolutions from other organizations.
- Submit the draft document to the organization's legal counsel for review. It is the training manager's responsibility to ensure that any document is legally and administratively valid before concluding the draft development step in the adoption process.

Submitting a Draft for Review

The draft document should be submitted for organizational review and comment. Review and comment opportunities are especially important for those documents that are controversial or affect multiple groups in an organization. For example, a proposed policy on attendance at training sessions certainly affects students more than instructors or administrators.

When the obligations necessitate a policy, procedure, or guideline to enforce an action, then it is appropriate to adopt one, even when it is not popular with members of the organization. Use the following review-process steps:

Step 1: Provide personnel an opportunity to respond with feedback and input on any document that affects them. The draft document does not have to be reviewed by all personnel, but it should be reviewed by those responsible for managing the fire and emergency services responders and other personnel who will be affected.

Step 2: Provide a comment period for the draft document and review all comments.

Step 3: Evaluate comments and amend the draft document as necessary.

Adopting a Policy, Procedure, or Guideline

The policy, procedure, or guideline is ready for adoption once feedback has been evaluated, and the document has been amended (if necessary). The appropriate manager or administrator endorses the document. For example, a policy affecting the training program is given to the training manager for endorsement. When a broader policy affects the entire organization, the endorsement must come from the organization's chief executive officer. An endorsement signals to organizational personnel that the policy, procedure, or guideline has official sanction.

Publishing a Document

Once the document has all the necessary signatures, the policy, procedure, or guideline is ready for publication. Anyone potentially affected by the policy, procedure, or guideline must be informed of the change or addition of duties. Memos often inform personnel, but when the document is implementing a substantial change or addressing a critical issue, the best method for communicating the new policy, procedure, or guideline is a face-to-face meeting with personnel and supervisors **(Figure 17.7)**. A face-to-face meeting provides the following opportunities for personnel to:

Figure 17.7 Meetings to discuss new policies are important, especially when changes are significant or complicated.

- Ask questions.

- Gain clarification.

- Ensure understanding.

Regardless of the method used, everyone with an interest in the policy, procedure, or guideline should be informed before it takes effect. Without this communication, instructors and affected personnel may not be able to comply with the relevant changes.

Implementing a Document's Contents

Experience has shown that improper implementation of policies, procedures, and guidelines is the primary cause for the failure of personnel to accept and adhere to the contents of those documents. The main intent of most of these documents is to create a change in behavior. To ensure that personnel learn, adopt, and practice these changes, they must be educated about the new policy, procedure, or guideline.

Acceptance of change requires that personnel know the reason for the change, understand the benefits of the change, and accept that the change is an improvement over the previous situation or process. Other requirements of the implementation step include providing the necessary equipment, support, and training required by the new policy, procedure, or guideline.

Implementation of any policy, procedure, or guideline must be consistent, fair, and documented. Credibility of new requirements as well as the administration that supports them can be destroyed when personnel perceive that implementation and enforcement are inconsistent.

Evaluating Effectiveness

When the policy, procedure, or guideline is implemented, it must be monitored for effectiveness. Chief officers, managers, and supervisors can observe the new requirement in use and determine its effectiveness based on the established criteria. If observations indicate that the new requirement does not provide the necessary change, the policy, procedure, or guideline process of development should be evaluated.

Interviews with concerned personnel may indicate that additional education, support, or changes would help individuals accept the new requirements. Monitoring of the policy, procedure, or guideline should continue. A periodic review should be performed to determine whether the document requires revision, replacement, or abandonment based on changes in the operating environment.

Standards that Influence Training

Standards are key elements in any training program. Organizations adopt standards to provide the basis for performance or operational requirements. The most common standards used by fire and emergency services organizations in North America are those from the NFPA®. These standards address many issues including professional qualifications, firefighter health and safety programs, and organizational structure. Training managers often make decisions based on standards. Some of the more commonly used NFPA® standards that affect training are included in **Appendix K**.

Other standards used in the fire and emergency services include governmental standards and regulations. For example, many of the policies and requirements for hazardous materials programs are found in federal laws. Also, most states and provinces have specific requirements for emergency medical services (EMS) training and certification. An organization's training program must comply with the standards that apply to the subjects taught.

Most standards reflect state/provincial or national norms for fire and emergency services. For example, professionals from appropriate fire and emergency services organizations develop NFPA® standards through a consensus process. NFPA® members have the opportunity then to either ratify or reject the proposed standards. This process allows standards to change over time to reflect the needs and current practices of the fire and emergency services.

Many standards can affect an organization's training program; therefore, it is advisable for training managers to learn about standards that affect their particular organizations. For example, when an organization participates in a state or provincial fire and life safety education certification program, the training manager should review NFPA® 1035, *Standard for Professional Qualifications for Fire and Life Safety Educator* (**Figure 17.8**).

When there is an NFPA® or other standard used for identifying either organizational training requirements or operations, the organization should formally adopt it. Adopting a standard gives it formal authority in the organization and allows the training manager to enforce the requirements set forth in the standard.

Of course, adoption also allows the training manager to hold organizational personnel accountable for meeting the requirements in the standard. The adoption process for a standard is the same as that used for adopting new policies, procedures, or guidelines.

Equipment Purchasing Policies

Level III Instructors may be responsible for making the large equipment purchases, known as *capital purchases*, for training established in capital budgets. As previously described in Chapter 13, capital purchases are used specifically for very expensive, one-time-purchase resources — for example, a new apparatus or a portable training structure. Because of their expense, the purchase of capital resources are scrutinized closely. Funding for these purchases may be provided with a specific use mandated, for example, a bond issue in a community to fund a training facility or a grant for purchasing a simulator. The money must be spent as designated and must be well documented.

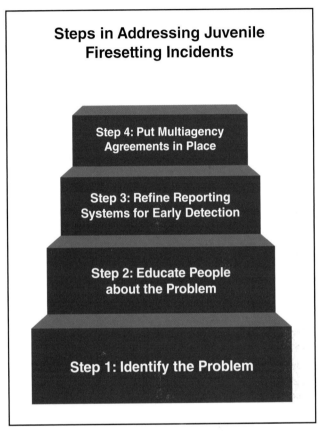

Steps in Addressing Juvenile Firesetting Incidents

Step 4: Put Multiagency Agreements in Place

Step 3: Refine Reporting Systems for Early Detection

Step 2: Educate People about the Problem

Step 1: Identify the Problem

Figure 17.8 When presenting information to the public, training managers should review information important to the public such as the steps in addressing juvenile firesetting incidents.

When making capital purchases, there is a bid process conducted to ensure that the organization is performing all due diligence to purchase a quality resource at an appropriate and reasonable price. The bid process begins with performing research about the capital resource in question and includes the following actions:

- **Survey other jurisdictions** — Contact other jurisdictions who use similar resources.

- **Review standards and regulations** — Any capital resource must be in compliance with current standards and regulations applicable to the purchase.

- **Review industry trends** — Any capital purchase should match current industry trends to ensure that those responders training with the resource will encounter similar resources in the field.

- **Compare various products** — The bid process involves examining multiple products to make an informed decision. Comparing various products before the bid process gives the instructor options for which item at which price range would best suit the needs of the training organization.

- **Determine equipment compatibility** — Any capital purchase must be useable. Equipment that is incompatible with current training equipment becomes a waste of money.

When the jurisdiction permits or requires it, a **request for proposal (RFP)** should be developed especially for capital purchases. After doing so, the bidding process can be conducted. The sections that follow describe these two steps.

NOTE: Some departments may have a bidding process for purchases that are in the operational budget as well as for purchases in the capital budget. If this is the case, then instructors should familiarize themselves with the procedures for these bidding processes.

Developing a Request for Proposal (RFP)

An RFP defines the needs of the organization and allows manufacturers or their authorized distributors to decide whether they can meet purchasing specifications. An RFP must have the following components:

- Specific schedule outline

- Bid dates and delivery dates

- Provisions for supplying equipment for scheduled evaluations

- Training dates for the benefit of maintenance technicians and instructors

An RFP also allows the jurisdiction to limit or specify which companies can bid based on the response to the RFP and participation in prebid meetings. The RFP process reduces the number of bidders to companies that are capable of meeting the purchasing specifications. Companies are eliminated from consideration in the following situations:

- Failure to meet delivery deadlines

- Unable to provide the required performance bonds

- Lack of established financial support to complete the contract

- Documented history of contract violations

Before writing the RFP, an instructor should consult both legal counsel and the AHJ's purchasing laws to determine what kinds of controls can legally be placed on bids or bidders. The selection of bidders must not be subjective or arbitrary. A sample RFP is found in **Appendix L**.

RFPs may also include language about evaluating equipment to be purchased before the bid process can continue. Evaluating a piece of equipment usually involves inspecting the item through direct contact. The RFP or other organizational document should include a checklist of criteria to which the particular piece of equipment should conform. For example, respiratory protection evaluation criteria may include (but are not limited to) the following factors:

- Maneuverability

- Flexibility

- Effect on vision

- Ease of donning

- Ease of doffing
- Effect on workload
- Comfort
- Durability
- Ease of operation
- Compatibility with operational procedures

In addition to evaluating equipment, instructors should also review any product data made available to them. Some factors to consider are as follows:

- **Features** — List the various features and accessories available with the equipment.

- **Durability** — Answer the following questions: How sturdy is the equipment? Are plastic parts easily broken? Will the equipment stand up to rough treatment?

- **Lifecycle cost** — Include the initial purchase price (which may have to be estimated based on the list price) and the cost of annual maintenance, parts, and support paid in increments over the life expectancy of the equipment to determine lifecycle cost.

- **Maintenance requirements** — Determine maintenance requirements by considering the manufacturer's suggested maintenance schedule, the level of technician certification and training, and whether maintenance can be done in-house or by a contract vendor approved by the manufacturer **(Figure 17.9)**.

- **Infrastructure** — Answer the following questions: What is the existing infrastructure that supports the department's current equipment? What changes or investments are required to redesign the equipment maintenance facility, modify existing systems, and retrofit apparatus mounting hardware?

Figure 17.9 Maintenance on training equipment may be simple enough to complete in-house; however, a qualified individual should perform the maintenance.

Creating Purchasing Specifications

The practice of creating purchasing specifications follows the RFP process. The purchasing department prepares the wording of the legal requirements (sometimes referred to as "boilerplate" due to the repeated use of standard language) which define the legal obligations that are necessary to meet the specifications. These features are required in all purchasing specifications. The instructor does not develop these particular sections of the specifications but should be aware of them and their effect on potential bidders. These requirements may include the following:

- Vendor attendance at pre-bid meetings
- Warranties
- Liability or performance bonds
- Specified delivery times
- Payment schedules
- Financial statements

The development of the product-specific specifications is the responsibility of the instructor (**Figure 17.10**). The language must be clear and concise. Each detail of the design requirement must be included and nothing should be assumed. Most manufacturers provide sample specifications forms as a guide. Some of the topics that should be included in purchasing specifications are as follows:

- NIOSH/Mine Safety and Health Administration (MSHA) current standard requirements or ANSI certification for the intended use when applicable
- NFPA® compliance when applicable
- Number of units to be purchased
- Design requirements
- Delivery date
- Warranty
- Accessories
- Training for maintenance technicians
- Training for operational personnel
- Start-up parts inventory
- Acceptance testing
- Technical support
- Penalties for late or no delivery

The Level III Instructor must be fully aware of purchasing ordinances or laws in the event that specifications are too restrictive and legally prohibited. For example, when a specific feature that meets valid operational requirements is only available from a single manufacturer, an option for bidding for an equal alternative or a method to take exception to the specifications must be included. Similarly, a **restrictive bid (sole-sourced)** is one that includes many specifications that only one manufacturer can meet. Therefore, this type of bid may be prohibited by the purchasing ordinances or laws of the AHJ. When a specific item of equipment is determined to meet the organization's needs to the exclusion of all others, thereby preventing an open-bid process, a variance or exemption from the approved purchasing process may be required from the jurisdiction's purchasing and legal departments.

Once approved by the jurisdiction's finance or purchasing officer, the purchasing department issues the purchasing requests to qualified bidders and sets a date for the opening of the bids. The bids may only be returned to and handled by the purchasing department. Once received, qualified bids are given to the instructor who is responsible for evaluation. When all of the data are collected and reviewed, the Level III Instructor selects or recommends the equipment that best meets the established needs of the training division.

Bid Evaluation and Awarding of the Contract

The instructor may or may not be involved in the evaluation and awarding of bids. If an instructor is part of the process, the instructor who is involved in the evaluation and awarding of bids should help evaluate and score the qualified bids based on the original purchasing specifications. A matrix or spreadsheet can be created with the specific requirements listed down the side and individual bidders listed across the top. Values can be assigned to each requirement and inserted into the

Restrictive Bid — Bid that includes many specifications that only one manufacturer can meet; *also known as* Sole-Sourced Bid.

ITEM #	QTY	OPTION & CODE #	DETAILED DESCRIPTION	UNIT PRICE	AMOUNT
			State Fire Service Training Academy Specification Worksheet		
1	1	J14	100009341 – 2011 Chevrolet Silverado 3500HD 2WD Reg Cab, 137.5" WB, 59.8" CA WT (CC31003), DUAL REAR WHEEL	$20,329.00	$20,329.00
2	1	L20	GVW 13200 DRW	$0.00	$0.00
3	1	L24	TRANSMISSION, ALLISON 1000 6-SPEED AUTOMATIC, electronically controlled w/overdrive, electronic engine grade braking and tow/haul mode. Includes (KNP) external transmission oil cooler		
4	1	L25	AUXILLARY transmission oil cooler	$0.00	$0.00
5	1	L28	SOLID PAINT, FIRE ENGINE RED IN COLOR	$0.00	$0.00
6	1	L29	MIRRORS, OUTSIDE MANUAL, BLACK, manual-folding	$0.00	$0.00
7	1	L31	POWER DOOR LOCK WITH REMOTE KEYLESS ENTRY	$0.00	$0.00
8	1	L32	POWER WINDOWS	$0.00	$0.00
9	1	L35	AUDIO SYSTEM, AM/FM/CD STEREO	$0.00	$0.00
10	1	L36	TILT STEERING WHEEL	$0.00	$0.00
11	1	L38	SEATS, FRONT 40/20/40 SPLIT-BENCH, 3-passenger, driver and front passenger manual reclining with outboard head restraints and center fold-down armrest w/storage.	$0.00	$0.00
12	1	P69	ENGINE, DURAMAX 6.6L V8 TURBO DIESEL V8, B20-DIESEL COMPATIBLE, (335 hp [249.8 kW]@ 3100 rpm, 685 lb-ft of torque [924.8 N-m]@ 1600 rpm), (Requires [MW7] Allison 1000 6-speed automatic transmission and [ZW9] pickup box. Includes [K40] exhaust brake, [TUV] heavy-duty dual, 730 cold-cranking-amp battery and [K05] engine block heater.)	$7,135.00	$7,135.00
13	1	P72	REAR AXLE, 3.73 RATIO W/LIMITED SLIP REAR AXLE	$0.00	$0.00
14	1	P86	DAYTIME RUNNING LIGHTS	$0.00	$0.00
15	1	P95	ELECTRIC BRAKE CONTROLLER	$177.00	$177.00
16	1	P96	ADD FRONT TOW HOOKS	$0.00	$0.00
17	1	P98	CRUISE CONTROL	$228.00	$228.00
18	1	J108	HEAVY DUTY FLOOR MATS	$76.00	$76.00
			TOTAL	**$27,945.00**	**$27,945.00**

Figure 17.10 Features required from purchased equipment should be explained in detail so they can be checked against a manufacturer's documentation.

corresponding box, depending on whether the bidder exceeded, met, or failed to meet the specification. Scoring must be equitable and well documented. In most jurisdictions in the U.S., this information and process may be subject to the U.S. Freedom of Information Act (or applicable state statutes and local ordinances) and outside review.

Following evaluation, a recommendation is made about which bidder should be awarded a purchase contract. The legal department writes a contract, and the AHJ awards the bid to the winning supplier. The contract binds both the supplier to meet the specifications and the jurisdiction to pay for the goods or services.

Administration of the contract is the responsibility of the purchasing department. This department acts on behalf of the emergency services organization that receives the goods or services. The emergency services organization is then responsible for the following actions regarding the purchased equipment, materials, or apparatus:

- Accept
- Test
- Inventory
- Store
- Maintain
- Place into service (**Figure 17.11**)

Figure 17.11 Placing items into service may include a public demonstration of their function.

What This Means to You

The budgeting and purchasing processes can be complicated. Following your organizations' policies and procedures is crucial to your success and reputation as an instructor. You may not be an expert in the financing of your organization, but you are expected to use funds wisely and make purchases that are thoroughly documented. You should work closely with the individuals in your organization who are experts in the budgeting and purchasing process. Relying on their expertise will help to ensure that funds are spent as they were intended.

Human Resources Management

The Level III Instructor may relinquish some responsibility for teaching and assume more responsibility for supervising instructors and other staff members. As a result, Level III Instructors may have certain human resource responsibilities including selecting instructional staff, helping ensure that instructors maintain appropriate qualifications, and advertising positions.

Instructional Staff Selection

Selecting competent instructional staff is a key management function of Level III Instructors. In addition, determining whether instructor roles are short-term or long-term aids in the selection process. When the instructor is only going to teach one course or topic, then the role may be considered *short-term*. When the instructor is expected to perform the function for an extended period such as five years, then the role is long-term and the selection criteria will be different.

Next, the Level III Instructor should determine the instructors' roles in the organization and the qualifications they need to teach the training programs. Establishing their positions in the organizational structure gives importance to the instructor role. Instructors, whether long- or short-term, are essential to program planning.

Instructor Qualifications

Level III Instructors function as intermediaries between administration and the personnel being trained. Instructors actively apply knowledge and skills on the job at various ranks or positions in the organization. Their experiences are critical components of their qualifications.

Few instructors are qualified to teach all the topics required in a modern fire and emergency services curriculum. Rather, instructors tend to specialize in certain areas and become proficient in teaching knowledge and skills specific to their areas of experience and expertise. The Level III Instructor should base instructor selection upon the topics to be taught and the designated instructor roles in the organization and training program.

In addition to topic expertise, instructors must have credibility with the personnel being trained. Personnel perceive that instructors have credibility when they display technical proficiency and evidence of formal training and education and demonstrate instructional experience. Other factors affecting credibility include rank, reputation, and respect among members of the organization.

When determining instructor qualifications, establishing credibility in technical proficiency and professional experience in the subject to be taught are important factors. Instructors who have neither skill nor credibility in the desired teaching areas will not be effective.

Instructors must be effective communicators. Topic expertise and credibility are only effective when instructors are able to transmit knowledge and demonstrate skills in methods that program participants can understand and apply.

NOTE: See Chapter 1, The Instructor as a Professional, for additional information.

Along with the technical qualifications, an instructor must also be qualified and certified. Qualifications can be based on legally adopted or nationally recognized certification standards. For example, fire instructors should meet the Instructor I requirements of NFPA® 1041. When there are no personnel who meet these requirements, Level III Instructors need to provide instructor-training programs in order to qualify and develop in-house instructors. Training, program resources, and information are generally available from local, state, or provincial training organizations.

Position Advertising

After instructor roles and qualifications are determined, the Level III Instructor must advertise or market the position to prospective candidates both inside and outside the organization. All eligible personnel within the organization must be made aware of openings.

An organization may have policies or other requirements (such as required rank or service time) that limit the number of applicants, but these requirements must also be advertised so that interested personnel may choose an appropriate course of action. When the position involves a change in working conditions (increase in pay, change in hours of work, or other benefits), personnel policies or union/management agreements may require that the process follow a specific set of steps.

Personnel Evaluations

The personnel evaluation process begins with an initial meeting between the Level III Instructor and the new instructor or staff member. At this point, the training division's expectations for the job performance of the employee are established. Performance standards are outlined and agreed upon by both parties.

Some fire and emergency services organizations have a probationary period for new instructors or staff members. The job performance requirements that were established initially provide the basis for performance evaluations during this probationary period. The Level III Instructor or supervisor must continually monitor the job performance of new instructors or staff members and provide appropriate feedback.

Feedback may include additional information about what is expected or praise for meeting or exceeding expectations. This probationary period is most effective when the supervisor provides enough information and access to appropriate resources for improvement. In addition, the new instructor should be encouraged to ask questions to clarify any misunderstandings.

Fire and emergency services personnel should also be familiar with the concept of a 360-degree feedback evaluation. It is similar to the type of size-up that occurs at an emergency incident when the Incident Commander (IC) requests situation reports from all sides of the incident. The need for tactical changes becomes apparent quickly, and the IC then responds accordingly.

When the concept is applied to the human resources program, the process and the results are similar. The information used in the performance evaluation is gathered from multiple people who have direct professional contact with the person who is being evaluated. The information that is gathered is based on the performance they observe.

Responses must remain confidential to protect the people who are providing the information. Confidentiality also encourages respondents to speak freely and offer constructive criticism.

Feedback should also support a plan for the improvement of any behaviors that are perceived to be below standard. Evaluations and the interpretation of results should be administered and performed by a professional trained in this technique.

NOTE: Level III Instructors may not be responsible for formal, performance-based evaluations if they are not the official head of their division or do not have direct reports assigned to them.

Chapter Summary

Level III Instructors are the highest level administrators in their training agencies or divisions. As such, they have administrative duties that affect their entire organizations. Level III Instructors manage the record-keeping systems for their organizations as well as make policy and purchasing decisions. They are responsible for gathering data as a part of organization wide needs analysis. This research may include delegating research tasks to instructors. Finally, Level III Instructors are responsible for hiring qualified personnel in their organizations and evaluating employees on a regular basis.

Review Questions

1. What are the functions of a record-keeping system?

2. What is disclosure of information?

3. Why would an instructor need to develop forms for a training record system?

4. How does an Instructor III conduct an agency level needs analysis?

5. What influences the development of organizational training policies, procedures, and guidelines?

6. Why do standards influence training?

7. What steps must be taken to make capital equipment purchases?

8. What are the human resource responsibilities of a Level III Instructor?

9. How does a Level III Instructor process personnel evaluations?

Appendices

Contents

Appendix A
Chapter and Page Correlation to NFPA® 1041 Requirements

NFPA® 1041 Competencies	Chapter References	Page References
4.2.2	4	71-102
4.2.4	9	249-251
4.2.5	3, 4, 6, 9	56-59, 81, 125-131, 246-249
4.3.2	4, 5, 6, 7	71-84, 107-121, 133-178, 193-220
4.3.3	3, 4, 5, 7	52-56, 73, 107-114, 200-216
4.4.2	3, 4, 5, 6, 7	59-66, 84-99, 107-121, 133-170, 178-188, 200-216
4.4.3	2, 3, 4, 6, 7	34-44, 52-59, 71-80, 125-170, 193-220
4.4.4	3	59-64
4.4.5	2, 6	38-41, 44-46, 177-188
4.4.6	4, 6	84-101, 137-139, 165, 166
4.4.7	4, 6	89-96, 137-139, 165, 166
4.5.2	1, 6, 8	20-23, 155-159, 226-232
4.5.3	8	233-240
4.5.4	6, 8	125-139, 179-181, 239, 240
4.5.5	6, 8	125-139, 179-181, 239, 240
5.2.2	13	326-336
5.2.3	13	336-344
5.2.4	13	336-344

NFPA® 1041 Competencies	Chapter References	Page References
5.2.5	13	344-349
5.2.6	13, 14	326-330, 359-362, 365-368
5.3.2	10, 13	256-274, 331-333, 349-353
5.3.3	10, 13	256-274, 331-333, 349-353
5.4.2	10	275
5.4.3	11	281-292
5.5.2	12	298-320
5.5.3	14	363-365
6.2.2	17	409-413
6.2.3	17	415-420
6.2.4	17	426-428
6.2.5	15, 17	386, 387, 428
6.2.6	17	421-426
6.2.7	16	402-404
6.3.2	15, 17	374-384, 414
6.3.3	15	375-384
6.3.4	15	375, 384-386, 389, 390
6.3.5	15, 17	381, 420, 421
6.3.6	15	381
6.3.7	15	375, 377, 380-384
6.5.2	16	396-404
6.5.3	15, 16	384-387, 396-404
6.5.4	16	396-404
6.5.5	15	387-389

Appendix B
Americans with Disabilities Act (ADA)

The Americans with Disabilities Act prohibits discrimination against a qualified individual with a disability in application, hiring, advancement, discharge, compensation, job training, and other terms, conditions, and privileges of employment. The act also prohibits certain questions of job applicants, including those of medical history, workers' compensation or health insurance claims, absenteeism due to illness, mental illness, and past treatment for alcoholism. Employers must provide reasonable accommodations for disabled workers, and training organizations must provide them for disabled students. Definitions included in the act are as follows:

- *Disabled person* — One who has a physical or mental impairment that limits one or more life activities, has a record of such impairment, and is regarded as having the impairment.

- *Qualified individual with disability* — Person with a disability who, with or without reasonable accommodations, can perform the essential functions of the position.

- *Reasonable accommodations* — Facilities (such as restrooms, telephones, parking spaces, and drinking fountains) remodeled and made readily accessible to and usable by individuals with disabilities. Includes the following:

  — Acquiring or modifying equipment or devices

  — Adjusting or modifying examinations or training materials or policies appropriately

  — Providing qualified readers or interpreters

  — Adjusting work schedules

  — Providing other reasonable accommodations for disabled individuals

Appendix C
Sources for Research and Resources

The entities below are a listing of possible sources for instructor research and information. The list should not be considered a comprehensive list. In addition, an Internet search will reveal the web presence of many of these sources.

- U.S. and Canadian National Government Agencies:
    - National Fire Incident Reporting System (NFIRS)
    - Division of Adult Education and Literacy
    - National Institute for Occupational Safety and Health (NIOSH)
    - Centers for Disease Control and Prevention (CDC)
    - World Health Organization (WHO)
    - U.S. Federal Emergency Management Agency (FEMA)
    - U.S. Fire Administration (USFA)
    - U.S. Department of Homeland Security (DHS)
    - Public Safety and Emergency Preparedness Canada (PSEPC)
    - National Institute of Standards and Technology (NIST)
    - State/Provincial Government Agencies
- Libraries:
    - Public Libraries
    - Collegiate Libraries
    - U.S. National Fire Academy Learning Resource Center
    - Fire Protection Publications Library at Oklahoma State University
    - Fire Service Programs Library at Oklahoma State
    - Worchester Polytechnic Institute
    - American Library Association
- Periodicals and Publications:
    - Educational Leadership, from Association for Supervision and Curriculum Development (ASCD)
    - International Fire Service Journal of Leadership and Management (IFSJLM)
    - Speaking of Fire, from Oklahoma State University, Fire Protection Publications
    - Training Magazine, from Lakewood Publications, Inc.
    - Vocational Education Journal, from American Vocational Association, Inc.
    - Training and Development, from American Society for Training and Development, Inc.
    - Instruct-o-Gram and The Voice, from International Society for Fire Service Instructors (ISFSI)
    - Domain, from National Associations of EMS Educators (NAMESE)
    - Safety-Gram, from Fire Department Safety Officers Association (FDSOA)
- Professional Organizations:
    - American Society for Training and Development, Inc. (ASTD)

- International Society of Five Service Instructors (ISFSI)
- International Association of Fire Chiefs (IAFC)
- Canadian Association of Fire Chiefs (CAFC)
- International Association of Fire Fighters (IAFF)
- Canadian Volunteer Fire Fighters Association (CVFFA)
- National Association of EMS Educators (NAEMSE)
- National Volunteer Fire Council (NVFC)
- International Association of Black Professional Fire Fighters (IABPFF)
- Women in the Fire Service (WFS)
- African American Women in the Fire Service (AAWFS)
- Black Women in the Fire Service (BWFS)
- Women Chief Fire Officers (WCFO)
- National Association of Hispanic Fire Fighters (NAHFF)
- North American Fire Training Directors (NAFTD)
- Fire Department Safety Officers Association (FDSOA)
- American Society of Safety Engineers (ASSA)
- Canadian Society of Safety Engineers (CSSE)
- International Association of Arson Investigators (IAAI)
- National Association of Emergency Medical Technicians (NAEMT)
- Training Resources and Data Exchange (TRADE)
- Volunteer Fire Insurance Service (VFIS)
- Emergency Services Education and Consulting Group (ESECG)
- International Fire Service Training Association (IFSTA)
- Congressional Fire Services Institute (CFSI)
- Home Fire Sprinkler Coalition
- International City/County Management Association (ICMA)
- Learning Disabilities Association of America (LDA)
- Association of Education and Communication Technology

- Testing and Standards Organizations:
  - National Fire Protection Association® (NFPA®)
  - Underwriters Laboratories Inc. (UL)
  - Underwriters' Laboratories of Canada (ULC)
  - FM Global (formerly Factory Mutual)
  - New York Firefighter and Code Enforcement Standards and Education Committee
  - American National Standards Institute (ANSI)
- Vendors/Manufacturers:
  - Fire and Emergency Manufacturer's and Services Association (FEMSA)
  - Fire Apparatus Manufacturers Association (FAMA)
  - National Emergency Equipment Dealers Association (NEEDA)

— Ambulance Manufacturers Division of the National Truck Equipment Association (NTEA)

- Nonprofit Organizations:
  - Home Safety Council (HSC)
  - Association of State and Territorial Health Officials (ASTHO)
  - National Safe Kids Campaign®
  - Other public safety councils at federal, state/provincial, and local levels

Appendix D
Sample Model Release Form

_____ has requested that I grant, release, and discharge certain rights arising
YOUR ORGANIZATION

from my participation, or the participation of an infant or minor child for whom I execute custody, in a video or

audio recording or presentation or photographs to be used in/for _____
NAME OF PRODUCT

_____and any associated products.

This grant, release, and discharge of said rights is made freely and without expectation of recompense of any kind,

in full cognizance of the risks inherent in the operational techniques employed in the production, including, but

not limited to, the focusing of lights upon me or the infant or minor child; and in contemplation of the reliance

by_____ upon the rights herein granted and released.
YOUR ORGANIZATION

I hereby grant and release to _____ the following rights:
YOUR ORGANIZATION

a. To use my name, or that of said infant or minor child, in any manner; photographs, likenesses, acts, poses, plays,

and appearances made in connection with the said production to record, reproduce, amplify, simulate, filter or

otherwise distort my voice or the child's voice and all instrumental, musical, and other sound effects produced by

me or by the child; and to reproduce, duplicate, publish, exhibit, use or transmit the same or any parts thereof, by

any means, in any manner and for any purpose whatsoever; and to do the same perpetually.

b. To "double" or "dub" my voice, acts, poses, plays, and appearances, or those of the infant or minor child, and all

instrumental, musical and/or other sound effects produced by me or said infant or minor child to such extent as

may be desired by_____.
YOUR ORGANIZATION

c. I further waive any right that I may have to inspect and/or approve the finished product or the promotional copy

or other matter that may be used in connection therewith or the use to which it may be applied.

This voluntary grant and release will not be made the basis of a future claim of any kind against

_____. I release and discharge _____ from
YOUR ORGANIZATION   YOUR ORGANIZATION

any cause of action arising from my participation or the participation of the infant or minor child in the production.

This grant, release, and discharge shall inure to the benefit of_____, and its of-
YOUR ORGANIZATION

ficers, agents, servants, and employees when acting in their official capacities; and to persons, firms, or corporations

contracting, _____ and their heirs, executors, administrators, successors, or assigns;
YOUR ORGANIZATION

and to any other persons lawfully reproducing, distributing, exhibiting, or otherwise using the said production or

any portion thereof.

The person or persons granting and releasing the rights set forth above are as follows:

_____
TALENT

_____
TYPED OR PRINTED NAME   SIGNATURE   DATE

PARENT OR LEGAL GUARDIAN (Complete if talent is under 18 years of age)

_____
TYPED OR PRINTED NAME   SIGNATURE   DATE

WITNESS

_____
TYPED OR PRINTED NAME   SIGNATURE   DATE

Appendix E
OSHA State-Plan States and Non-State-Plan States

State-Plan States	Non-State-Plan States
Alaska	Alabama
Arizona	Arkansas
California	Colorado
Connecticut (state and local government employees only)	Delaware
Hawaii	District of Columbia
Indiana	Florida
Iowa	Georgia
Kentucky	Guam
Maryland	Idaho
Michigan	Illinois
Minnesota	Kansas
Nevada	Louisiana
New Mexico	Maine
New York (state and local government employees only)	Massachusetts
North Carolina	Mississippi
Oregon	Missouri
Puerto Rico	Montana
South Carolina	Nebraska
Tennessee	New Hampshire
Utah	New Jersey
Vermont	North Dakota
Virginia	Ohio
Virgin Islands	Oklahoma
Washington	Pennsylvania
Wyoming	Rhode Island
	South Dakota
	Texas
	West Virginia
	Wisconsin

Appendix F
Incident Command System Forms

The following NIMS-ICS forms are available from numerous Internet sites in PDF format. Although there are approximately 26 forms available to assist in the establishment of an incident command, this appendix contains only 8 forms that may be the most useful to instructors. The forms are public domain and may be copied or accessed from other sources on the Internet. The forms contained here are:

ICS-201	Incident Briefing
ICS-202	Incident Objectives
ICS-203	Organization Assignment List
ICS-204	Assignment List
ICS-205	Incident Radio Communications Plan
ICS-206	Medical Plan
ICS-215	Operational Planning Worksheet
ICS-215A	Incident Action Safety Plan Analysis

ICS Form 201

INCIDENT BRIEFING	1. Incident Name	2. Date Prepared	3. Time Prepared

4. Map Sketch

5. Prepared by (Name and Position)

ICS 201
Page 1 of 4

6. Summary of Current Actions

ICS 201	Page 2

7. Current Organization

| ICS 201 | Page 3 |

8. Resources Summary				
Resources Ordered	Resource Identification	ETA	On Scene	Location/Assignment

ICS 201	Page 4

ICS Form 202

INCIDENT OBJECTIVES	1. INCIDENT NAME	2. DATE	3. TIME

4. OPERATIONAL PERIOD (DATE/TIME)

5. GENERAL CONTROL OBJECTIVES FOR THE INCIDENT (INCLUDE ALTERNATIVES)

6. WEATHER FORECAST FOR OPERATIONAL PERIOD

7. GENERAL SAFETY MESSAGE

8. Attachments (☑ if attached)

☐ Organization List (ICS 203)   ☐ Medical Plan (ICS 206)   ☐ Weather Forecast

☐ Assignment List (ICS 204)   ☐ Incident Map   ☐ _____

☐ Communications Plan (ICS 205)   ☐ Traffic Plan   ☐ _____

9. PREPARED BY (PLANNING SECTION CHIEF)	10. APPROVED BY (INCIDENT COMMANDER)

Organization Assignment List, ICS Form 203

ORGANIZATION ASSIGMENT LIST	1. INCIDENT NAME	2. DATE PREPARED	3. TIME PREPARED

| POSITION | NAME | 4. OPERATIONAL PERIOD (DATE/TIME) | |

5. INCIDENT COMMAND AND STAFF

Position	
INCIDENT COMMANDER	
DEPUTY	
SAFETY OFFICER	
INFORMATION OFFICER	
LIAISON OFFICER	

6. AGENCY REPRESENTATIVES

AGENCY	NAME

7. PLANNING SECTION

Position	
CHIEF	
DEPUTY	
RESOURCES UNIT	
SITUATION UNIT	
DOCUMENTATION UNIT	
DEMOBILIZATION UNIT	
TECHNICAL SPECIALISTS	

8. LOGISTICS SECTION

Position	
CHIEF	
DEPUTY	

a. SUPPORT BRANCH

Position	
DIRECTOR	
SUPPLY UNIT	
FACILITIES UNIT	
GROUND SUPPORT UNIT	

b. SERVICE BRANCH

Position	
DIRECTOR	
COMMUNICATIONS UNIT	
MEDICAL UNIT	
FOOD UNIT	

9. OPERATIONS SECTION

CHIEF	
DEPUTY	

a. BRANCH I- DIVISION/GROUPS

BRANCH DIRECTOR	
DEPUTY	
DIVISION/GROUP	
DIVISION/ GROUP	
DIVISION/ GROUP	
DIVISION/GROUP	
DIVISION /GROUP	

b. BRANCH II- DIVISIONS/GROUPS

Position	
BRANCH DIRECTOR	
DEPUTY	
DIVISION/GROUP	
DIVISION/GROUP	
DIVISION/GROUP	
DIVISION/GROUP	

c. BRANCH III- DIVISIONS/GROUPS

Position	
BRANCH DIRECTOR	
DEPUTY	
DIVISION/GROUP	
DIVISION/GROUP	
DIVISION/GROUP	

d. AIR OPERATIONS BRANCH

AIR OPERATIONS BR. DIR.	
AIR TACTICAL GROUP SUP.	
AIR SUPPORT GROUP SUP.	
HELICOPTER COORDINATOR	
AIR TANKER/FIXED WING CRD.	

10. FINANCE/ADMINISTRATION SECTION

CHIEF	
DEPUTY	
TIME UNIT	
PROCUREMENT UNIT	
COMPENSATION/CLAIMS UNIT	
COST UNIT	

PREPARED BY (RESOURCES UNIT)

Sample Assignment List, ICS Form 204

1. BRANCH	2. DIVISION/GROUP	**ASSIGNMENT LIST**

3. INCIDENT NAME	4. OPERATIONAL PERIOD DATE _____ TIME _____

5. OPERATIONAL PERSONNEL

OPERATIONS CHIEF _____ DIVISION/GROUP SUPERVISOR _____

BRANCH DIRECTOR _____ AIR TACTICAL GROUP SUPERVISOR _____

6. RESOURCES ASSIGNED TO THIS PERIOD

STRIKE TEAM/TASK FORCE/ RESOURCE DESIGNATOR	EMT	LEADER	NUMBER PERSONS	TRANS. NEEDED	PICKUP PT./TIME	DROP OFF PT./TIME

7. CONTROL OPERATIONS

8. SPECIAL INSTRUCTIONS

9. DIVISION/GROUP COMMUNICATIONS SUMMARY

FUNCTION		FREQ.	SYSTEM	CHAN.	FUNCTION		FREQ.	SYSTEM	CHAN.
COMMAND	LOCAL				SUPPORT	LOCAL			
	REPEAT					REPEAT			
DIV./GROUP TACTICAL					GROUND TO AIR				

PREPARED BY (RESOURCE UNIT LEADER)	APPROVED BY (PLANNING SECT. CH.)	DATE	TIME

Sample Incident Communications Plan, ICS Form 205

INCIDENT RADIO COMMUNICATIONS PLAN			1. Incident Name	2. Date/Time Prepared	3. Operational Period Date/Time
4. Basic Radio Channel Utilization					
System/Cache	Channel	Function	Frequency/Tone	Assignment	Remarks
5. Prepared by (Communications Unit)					

Medical Plan, ICS Form 206

MEDICAL PLAN	1. Incident Name	2. Date Prepared	3. Time Prepared	4. Operational Period

5. Incident Medical Aid Station

Medical Aid Stations	Location	Paramedics Yes	No

6. Transportation

A. Ambulance Services

Name	Address	Phone	Paramedics Yes	No

B. Incident Ambulances

Name	Location	Paramedics Yes	No

7. Hospitals

Name	Address	Travel Time Air	Ground	Phone	Helipad Yes	No	Burn Center Yes	No

8. Medical Emergency Procedures

Prepared by (Medical Unit Leader)	10. Reviewed by (Safety Officer)

ICS Form 215

OPERATIONAL PLANNING WORKSHEET

1. Incident Name

2. Date Prepared / Time Prepared

3. Operational Period (Date/Time)

4. Division/Group or Other Location	5. Work Assignments		Resource by Type (Show Strike Team as ST)																			6. Reporting Location	7. Requested Arrival Time
			1	2	3	4	1	2	3	4	1	2	3	4	1	2	3	4	1	2	3	4		
		Req																						
		Have																						
		Need																						
		Req																						
		Have																						
		Need																						
		Req																						
		Have																						
		Need																						
9. Total Resources - Single		Req																						
		Have																						
		Need																						
Total Resources - Strike Teams		Req																						
		Have																						
		Need																						

Prepared by (Name and Position)

Incident Action Plan Safety & Risk Analysis Form, ICS 215A

INCIDENT ACTION PLAN SAFETY ANALYSIS	1. Incident Name	2. Date	3. Time

Division or Group	Potential Hazards								Mitigations (e.g., PPE, buddy system, escape routes)
	Type of Hazard:	Type of Hazard:	Type of Hazard:	Type of Hazard:	Type of Hazard:	Type of Hazard:	Type of Hazard:	Type of Hazard:	

Prepared by (Name and Position)

WORKPLACE SOLUTIONS

From the National Institute for Occupational Safety and Health

Preventing Deaths and Injuries to Fire Fighters during Live-Fire Training in Acquired Structures

Summary

Fire fighters are subjected to many hazards when participating in live-fire training. Training facilities with approved burn buildings should be used for live-fire training whenever possible. However, when acquired structures are used for live-fire training, NIOSH strongly recommends that fire departments follow the national consensus guidelines in NFPA 1403, standard on live-fire training evolutions [NFPA 2002a] to reduce the risk of injury and death. These guidelines are summarized in the recommendations in this document.

Description of Exposure

Live-fire training exercises are a crucial element in the structural fire fighting curriculum. Live-fire training is often conducted in burn buildings designed and approved for such training. Unlike burn buildings, acquired structures are obtained from a private property owner and are not designed or intended for live-fire applications. Several factors associated with live-fire training in acquired structures create safety concerns for fire departments: insufficient or unstable structural components (i.e. floors, railings, stairs, chimneys, and ceilings), limited access to entry and exit paths, hidden combustible materials, debris, and inadequate ventilation [NFPA 2002a].

During 1983–2002, 10 fire fighters died as a result of injuries while participating in live-fire training exercises at acquired structures [Fahy 2003]. During 2000–2002, the NIOSH Fire Fighter Fatality Investigation and Prevention Program investigated three incidents involving four fire fighters who sustained fatal traumatic injuries while participating in live-fire training in acquired structures [NIOSH 2000, 2001, 2002]. Two of these cases are described below.

Case Studies

Case 1

A volunteer fire fighter (the victim) died and two other fire fighters were injured during a live-fire training exercise in a two-story duplex. The victim and anoth-

DEPARTMENT OF HEALTH AND HUMAN SERVICES
Centers for Disease Control and Prevention
National Institute for Occupational Safety and Health

er fire fighter played the role of trapped fire fighters under a table on the second floor. The victim did not have any formal training, and the other fire fighter had been with the department for about 1 year. A burn barrel on the second floor was not producing enough smoke, so the instructor lit a second flare to ignite a foam mattress sleeper sofa next to the stairs on the first floor. The fire rapidly progressed up the stairway, trapping the fire fighters on the second floor. The trapped fire fighters were recovered from their original position and removed from the structure. The victim was unresponsive, and advanced life-saving procedures were initiated en route to the local hospital where he was pronounced dead. The cause of death was listed as asphyxia due to smoke inhalation [NIOSH 2001].

Case 2

A career lieutenant and a career fire fighter died while participating in live-fire training at an acquired vacant structure. The fire was built in a closet with five wooden pallets and bales of straw as fuel. To produce a larger fire, fire fighters added a twin-sized urethane foam mattress to the fire. The search and rescue team (the two victims) entered the structure to "rescue" a mannequin. The fire intensified, and smoke filled the burn room and the hallway. The Incident Commander (IC) ordered ventilation so a window was broken. Heavy smoke followed by intense flames were emitted. A flashover is believed to have occurred seconds after the window was vented. (Flashover is when all surfaces and objects in a space have been heated to their ignition temperatures.) The IC and fire fighters on the scene did not realize that the victims were in the burn room at the time of the flashover. Failing to contact the two victims by radio, the IC sent in the Rapid Intervention Team. Approximately 10 minutes after the flashover, the IC called for an accountability check on the radio and receiving no response from the victims, he sounded the air horns to evacuate the structure. The attack crew then found one of the victims lying on the floor next to the closet where the fire had been ignited. The second victim was found lying next to the window of the burn room. The victims were both transported by ambulances to a local hospital where they were pronounced dead. The cause of death for both was smoke inhalation and thermal injuries [NIOSH 2002].

Controls

Whenever possible, NIOSH recommends that training facilities with approved burn buildings be used for live-fire training. To minimize risks when participating in live-fire training, NIOSH recommends that fire departments comply with NFPA 1403 [NFPA 2002a], including the following precautions:

Instructors

- Ensure that the instructor in charge is aware of his or her responsibility for overall coordination of the training and compliance with NFPA 1403.

- Ensure that instructors are qualified to provide live-fire training. Verify instructor [NFPA 2002b] and officer qualifications [NFPA 2003a] through national certifying agencies such as the National Professional Qualifications Board, the International Fire Service Accreditation Congress, or through a State fire board or commission.

Site Set Up

- Ensure that the acquired structure is adequate and safe to be used for live-fire training. Use Appendix B of NFPA 1403 as a checklist for pre-burn planning, building preparation, and pre-burn/post-burn procedures.

- Develop, implement, and train fire fighters in standard operating procedures (SOPs) for live-fire training.

- Conduct a pre-burn briefing session for all participants, and establish an evacuation plan and signal.

- Ensure that a sufficient water supply is available.

- Ensure that the fuels used in the live-fire training have known burning characteristics.

- Inspect the structure for possible environmental hazards.

- Do not use flammable or combustible liquids in live-fire training.

- Do not set fires for live-fire training in any designated exit paths.

- Do not allow anyone to play the role of victim inside the structure during live-fire training.

- Establish a method of fire ground communication among the IC and fire fighters.

- Ensure that proper ventilation is in place before the onset of a controlled burn and is coordinated with interior operations.

- Ensure that backup personnel are standing by with equipment, ready to provide assistance or rescue.

- Ensure that all fire fighters participating in live-fire training have had minimum basic training.

- Ensure that each fire fighter is equipped with NFPA-compliant full protective clothing, a NIOSH approved self-contained breathing apparatus (SCBA), and a personal alert safety system (PASS).

- Establish rehabilitation operations at training exercises that pose the risk of fire fighters exceeding a safe level of physical or mental endurance [NFPA 2003b].

Site Safety

- Appoint a separate, adequately trained safety officer that has the authority to intervene in any aspect of the live-fire training.

- Ensure that all participants are accounted for when entering and exiting the building.

- Assign only one person as the ignition officer. Ensure that he or she is not a fire fighter participating in the training.

- Ensure that the ignition officer lights only one training fire at a time.

- Ensure that a charged hose line is present while igniting the fire.

- Use a thermal imaging camera during live-fire training situations to observe fire fighters and monitor heat conditions for safety.

Training Participants

- Follow Standard Operating Procedures (SOPs) established by the department.

- Use NFPA-compliant full protective clothing, an SCBA, and a PASS device, as provided by the department.

- Do not enter a hazardous environment alone. Enter only as a team of two or more.

- Be familiar with the fire department's evacuation plan and signal.

States

- Ensure that acquired structures that will be used in live-fire training are inspected to identify and eliminate hazards.

- Develop a procedure to issue permits to use inspected acquired structures for live-fire training.

- Check NFPA 1403 for voluntary guidelines on issuing permits [NFPA 2002a].

Acknowledgments

The principal contributors to this publication were Jay Tarley and Carolyn Guglielmo, NIOSH.

References

NFPA [2002a]. NFPA 1403, standard on live fire training evolutions. Quincy, MA: National Fire Protection Association.

NFPA [2002b]. NFPA 1041, standard for fire service instructor professional qualifications. Quincy, MA: National Fire Protection Association.

NFPA [2003a]. NFPA 1021, standard for fire officer professional qualifications. Quincy, MA: National Fire Protection Association.

NFPA [2003b]. NFPA 1584, recommended practice on the rehabilitation of members operating at incident scene operations and training exercises. Quincy, MA: National Fire Protection Association.

NIOSH [2000]. Volunteer assistant chief dies during a controlled-burn training evolution—Delaware. Cincinnati, OH: U.S. Department of Health and Human Services, Public Health Service, Centers for Disease Control and Prevention, National Institute for Occupational

Safety and Health, DHHS (NIOSH) Publication No. F2000–27. Fire Fighter Fatality Investigation Report F2000–27. [www.cdc.gov/niosh/face200027.html]

NIOSH [2001]. Volunteer fire fighter dies and two others are injured during live-fire training—NY. Cincinnati, OH: U.S. Department of Health and Human Services, Public Health Service, Centers for Disease Control and Prevention, National Institute for Occupational Safety and Health, DHHS (NIOSH) Publication No. F2001–38. Fire Fighter Fatality Investigation Report F2001–38. [www.cdc.gov/niosh/face200138.html]

NIOSH [2002]. Career lieutenant and fire fighter die in flashover during a live-fire training evolution—FL. Cincinnati, OH: U.S. Department of Health and Human Services, Public Health Service, Centers for Disease Control and Prevention, National Institute for Occupational Safety and Health, DHHS (NIOSH) Publication No. F2002–34. Fire Fighter Fatality Investigation Report F2002–34. [www.cdc.gov/niosh/face200234.html]

Fahy R (rfahy@NFPA.org) [2003]. NFPA Live-fire training deaths. Personal communication email message to Jay Tarley (jst9@cdc.gov), February 10, 2003.

For More Information

The information in this document is based on fatality investigations and expert review. More information about the Fire Fighter Fatality Investigation and Prevention Program is available at www.cdc.gov/niosh/firehome.html

To receive more information about occupational safety and health topics, contact NIOSH at

NIOSH
Publications Dissemination
4676 Columbia Parkway
Cincinnati, OH 45226–1998

Telephone: 1–800–35–NIOSH (1–800–356–4674)
Fax: 513–533–8573 ▪ E-mail: pubstaft@cdc.gov

or visit the NIOSH Web site at www.cdc.gov/niosh

For a monthly update on news at NIOSH, subscribe to NIOSH eNews by visiting www.cdc.gov/niosh/eNews.

Preventing Deaths and Injuries to Fire Fighters during Live-Fire Training in Acquired Structures

Mention of any company or product does not constitute endorsement by NIOSH. In addition, citations to Web sites external to NIOSH do not constitute NIOSH endorsement of the sponsoring organizations or their programs or products. Furthermore, NIOSH is not responsible for the content of these Web sites.

As part of the Centers for Disease Control and Prevention, NIOSH is the Federal agency responsible for conducting research and making recommendations to prevent work-related illnesses and injuries. All Workplace Solutions are based on research studies that show how worker exposures to hazardous agents or activities can be significantly reduced.

DHHS (NIOSH) Publication No. 2005–102

SAFER • HEALTHIER • PEOPLE™

October 2004

DEPARTMENT OF HEALTH AND HUMAN SERVICES
Centers for Disease Control and Prevention
National Institute for Occupational Safety and Health
4676 Columbia Parkway
Cincinnati, OH 45226–1998

Appendix H
Acquired Structure Checklists and Forms

Below are checklists and form letters that are examples of necessary documents that should be completed before live-fire training at an acquired structure. The "Live Fire Evaluation Sample Checklist" is reproduced with permission from NFPA® 1403, *Live Fire Training Evolutions*, © 2007 National Fire Protection Association®. This is not the complete and official position of the NFPA® on the referenced subject, which is represented only by the standard in its entirety. The other forms are used with permission from the Gainseville Fire Rescue Training Bureau.

LIVE FIRE EVALUATION SAMPLE CHECKLIST

PERMITS, DOCUMENTS, NOTIFICATIONS, INSURANCE.

___ 1. Written documentation received from owner:
  ❑ Permission to burn structure
  ❑ Proof of clear title
  ❑ Certificate of insurance cancellation
  ❑ Acknowledgement of post-burn property condition
___ 2. Local burn permit received
___ 3. Permission obtained to utilize fire hydrants
___ 4. Notification made to appropriate dispatch office of date, time, and location of burn
___ 5. Notification made to all affected police agencies:
  ❑ Received authority to block off roads
  ❑ Received assistance in traffic control
___ 6. Notification made to owners and users of adjacent property of date, time and location of burn
___ 7. Liability insurance obtained covering damage to other property
___ 8. Written evidence of prerequisite training obtained from participating students from outside agencies

PREBURN PLANNING.

___ 1. Preburn plans made, showing the following:
  ❑ Site plan drawing, including all exposures
  ❑ Floor plan detailing all rooms, hallways, and exterior openings
  ❑ Location of command post
  ❑ Position of all apparatus
  ❑ Position of all hoses, including backup lines
  ❑ Location of emergency escape routes
  ❑ Location of emergency evacuation assembly areas
  ❑ Location of ingress and egress routes for emergency vehicles
___ 2. Available water supply determined
___ 3. Required fire flow determined for the acquired structure/live fire training structure/burn prop and exposure buildings
___ 4. Required reserve flow determined (50 percent of fire flow)
___ 5. Apparatus pumps obtained that meet or exceed the required fire flow for the building and exposures
___ 6. Separate water sources established for attack

and backup hose lines
___ 7. Periodic weather reports obtained
___ 8. Parking areas designated and marked:
  ❑ Apparatus staging
  ❑ Ambulances
  ❑ Police vehicles
  ❑ Press vehicles
  ❑ Private vehicles
___ 9. Operations area established and perimeter marked
___ 10. Communications frequencies established, equipment obtained

TRAINING STRUCTURE PREPARATION.

___ 1. Training structure inspected to determine structural integrity
___ 2. All utilities disconnected (acquired structures only)
___ 3. Highly combustible interior wall and ceiling coverings removed
___ 4. All holes in walls and ceilings patched
___ 5. Materials of exceptional weight removed from above training area (or area sealed from activity)
___ 6. Ventilation openings of adequate size precut for each separate roof area
___ 7. Windows checked and operated, openings closed
___ 8. Doors checked and operated, opened or closed, as needed
___ 9. Training structure components checked and operated:
  ❑ Roof scuttles
  ❑ Automatic ventilators
  ❑ Mechanical equipment
  ❑ Lighting equipment
  ❑ Manual or automatic sprinklers
  ❑ Standpipes
___ 10. Stairways made safe with railings in place
___ 11. Chimney checked for stability
___ 12. Fuel tanks and closed vessels removed or adequately vented
___ 13. Unnecessary inside and outside debris removed
___ 14. Porches and outside steps made safe
___ 15. Cisterns, wells, cesspools, and other ground openings fenced or filled

NFPA 1403 (p. 1 of 2)

LIVE FIRE EVALUATION SAMPLE CHECKLIST †(continued)

__ 16. Hazards from toxic weeds, hives, and vermin eliminated

__ 17. Hazardous trees, brush, and surrounding vegetation removed

__ 18. Exposures such as buildings, trees and utilities removed or protected

__ 19. All extraordinary exterior and interior hazards remedied

__ 20. Fire "sets" prepared:
  ❑ Class A materials only
  ❑ No flammable or combustible liquids
  ❑ No contaminated materials

PREBURN PROCEDURES.

__ 1. All participants briefed:
  ❑ Training structure layout
  ❑ Crew and instructor assignments
  ❑ Safety rules
  ❑ Training structure evacuation procedure
  ❑ Evacuation signal (demonstrate)

__ 2. All hose lines checked:
  ❑ Sufficient size for the area of fire involvement
  ❑ Charged and test flowed
  ❑ Supervised by qualified instructors
  ❑ Adequate number of personnel

__ 3. Necessary tools and equipment positioned

__ 4. Participants checked:
  ❑ Approved full protective clothing
  ❑ Self-contained breathing apparatus (SCBA)
  ❑ Adequate SCBA air volume
  ❑ All equipment properly donned

POST-BURN PROCEDURES

__ 1. All personnel accounted for

__ 2. Remaining fire overhauled, as needed

__ 3. Training structure inspected for stability and hazards where more training is to follow (see Training Structure Preparation)

__ 4. Training critique conducted

__ 5. Records and reports prepared, as required:
  ❑ Account of activities conducted
  ❑ List of instructors and assignments
  ❑ List of other participants
  ❑ Documentation of unusual conditions or events
  ❑ Documentation of injuries incurred and treatment rendered
  ❑ Documentation of changes or deterioration of live fire training structure
  ❑ Acquired structure release
  ❑ Student training records
  ❑ Certificates of completion

__ 6. Building and property released to owner, release document signed

---

RELEASE FORM

Having agreed with the Building Official, City of _____, that a structure owned by me and located at _____ is unfit for human habitation and is beyond rehabilitation, I further agree that the structure should be demolished. In order that demolition may be accomplished, I give my consent to the City of _____, to demolish, by burning or other means, the said structure.

I further release the City of _____ from any claim for loss resulting from such demolition.

Fire Department _____
Address _____
City, State _____
Date _____
Owner/Agent _____
Owner/Agent _____
Witness _____

NFPA 1403 (p. 2 of 2)

Gainesville Fire Rescue Department
Important Notice

Our Department has a training program designed to help our firefighters maintain their skills, as well as train on new equipment and fire fighting techniques. In order to do this, we routinely burn vacant houses to simulate true working conditions. Since this is a common practice around the country, the National Fire Protection Association (NFPA) has developed a standard for Fire Department Training Burns, NFPA 1403. This standard is designed to maintain a safe training environment and is strictly adhered to by the Gainesville Fire Rescue Department.

You may see a number of fire department apparatus in your neighborhood. There is nothing to be concerned about because we are running training evolutions.

Due to the smoke generated by a burning house, we request that you keep your windows and doors closed on the following date(s):

_____

We anticipate completion by the end of the day.

We also request that you avoid parking on the street so that fire apparatus can have easy access to the building.

Sincerely,

Gainesville Fire Rescue Training Bureau

Sample Agreement Form Between
Agency/Municipality and Owner of Acquired Structure

Agreement to Destroy Structure and Release

THIS AGREEMENT entered into this _____ day of _____, 20_____, by and between the City of Gainesville, hereinafter called the "City," and _____, called "Owners."

W I T N E S S E T H:

WHEREAS, Owners are the owners of certain property located within the city of Gainesville, which property contains a structure the Owners wish to have destroyed, and

WHEREAS, the City of Gainesville Fire Rescue Department is willing to destroy the structure as part of a training exercise for its employees.

NOW, THEREFORE, in consideration of the mutual premises and agreements herein contained and other good and valuable consideration, the parties do hereby mutually agree as follows:

1.   The City of Gainesville Fire Rescue Department agrees to destroy the structure located on the property owned by the Owners, the property and structure being more particularly described as follows:

2.   The Owners agree to allow the structure to be destroyed in the course of a training exercise conducted by the city of Gainesville Fire Rescue Department.

3.   The Owners hereby warranty that they are in fact the sole owners of the structure and/or property described herein and, by affixation of the signatures hereunder, attest to the fact. The Owners further certify that there are no outstanding or unsatisfied mortgages, liens, claims or any other type of encumbrances on or against the above described property or structure.

4.   The Owners further certify that no claim for loss under any insurance policy will be made because of damage, or because of destruction of the structure, as a result of the Fire Rescue Department's training activities at said structure. The Owners further certify that as of _____, 20_____, there is no effective insurance policy covering the structure

described in paragraph one (1) under which the activities described herein by the City would constitute a claim.

5. Upon completion of said destruction, the Owners agree to remove any and all debris remaining on the property. The Owners hereby acknowledge that the City's activities in razing, demolishing, and destroying the structure described in paragraph one (1) will, except as describe in paragraph six (6), result in the structure being wrecked and reduced to ruin. What remains of the structure will be worthless rubble and debris, which could constitute a danger to persons entering the premises and should be expeditiously removed by the Owners.

6. If for any reason whatsoever the city of Gainesville Fire Rescue Department finds or determines that it cannot begin or complete the destruction of said structure, the owners, upon notification of the fire rescue Department's inability or unwillingness to destroy or complete destruction of said structure, agree to expeditiously complete the destruction and debris removal of said structure or otherwise restore the property to such condition as to meet the minimum building and/or housing codes in effect within the government having jurisdiction.

7. The Owners understand and acknowledge their continuing control over, and liability for, damages occurring on or about the property described in Paragraph one (1) above; except during the actual training exercise authorized herein. It is specifically understood that the City's liability during the training exercise does not include the settling of ash on surrounding property. The training exercise shall be conducted between _____ and _____. When the training is concluded, control over and sole liability for damages occurring on or about the premises shall automatically revert to the Owners, unless notification to the contrary is made by the City.

8. The Owners agree to indemnify and save harmless the city of Gainesville, the city of Gainesville Fire Rescue Department, its officers, agents and employees from and against any and all claims, suits, actions, damages or causes of action arising out of the destruction of the structure described herein or the fact that any representation made herein was false when made, for any personal injury, loss of life, or damage to property sustained in or about the owned property by reason of the destruction of the structure located thereon except those injuries, losses or damages solely attributable to the gross negligence of the City, its agents and employees, and for and against any orders, judgments or decrees which may be entered thereon and from and against all costs, attorney's fees, expenses and liabilities incurred in or about the defense of such claims and investigation thereof.

9.   Nothing contained in this contract shall be interpreted as a waiver of the city's sovereign immunity granted under Section 768.28, Florida Statutes.

IN WITNESS WHEREOF, we the undersigned have set our hands and seals first written above.

CITY OF GAINESVILLE, FLORIDA

By _____

City Manager

Approved as to form and legality:

By _____

City Attorney

WITNESSES: OWNERS:

_____   _____

_____   _____

SWORN TO AND SUBSCRIBED before me this _____ day of _____, 20____.

_____

Notary Public

My Commission Expires:

_____

Chapter 12

Firefighter Orientation and Safety
Information Sheet 1B-1 Accidents & Injuries

Accidents

Accidents are unplanned events that may result in bodily injury, illness, or physical or property loss. H. W. Heinrich of the Travelers Insurance Company devoted the greater portion of his life to the study of industrial accidents and their prevention. Heinrich proposed that there were five factors involved in an accident sequence:

1. Social environment
2. Human factors
3. Unsafe acts or conditions
4. Accident
5. Injury

He found that the last factor in the sequence, an injury, was always preceded by an accident. But, in order for an accident to occur, some unsafe act had to be committed or some unsafe condition had to exist. The unsafe act or condition was invariably caused by the human factor. In turn, the human factors responsible resulted from inherited characteristics or social and environmental conditioning. Heinrich called his findings the Domino Theory because like a row of end-standing dominoes, the activation of one factor precipitated the activation of the next, and the next, eventually resulting in an accident or injury.

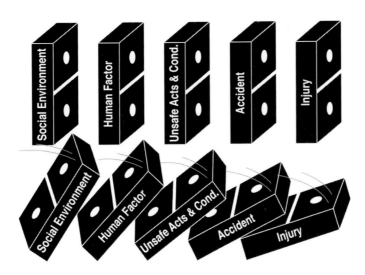

In Heinrich's Domino Theory, the emphasis on accident (and thus injury) control is in the middle of the sequence — at the unsafe act or mechanical or physical hazard. If this act or hazard is removed, the sequence is interrupted and the injury cannot occur.

Replace a Hose Gasket

Skills Sheet 1

Name_____ Date _____

Evaluator _____ Competency Rating _____

References	NFPA® 1001, *Prevention, Preparedness, and Maintenance* 5.5.4 **Essentials**, pages 405, 406 and 439
Prerequisites	None
Introduction	Before any piece of equipment is placed on the apparatus, it should be in top operating condition. Hose couplings are vital for attaching hose to other hose and nozzles. If they or their gaskets are damaged, they can hinder the mission and endanger firefighters' lives.
Equipment & Personnel	• One firefighter in protective clothing • Hoses with male, female, and sexless couplings • Replacement gaskets of appropriate types and sizes

OPERATION	KEY POINTS	ATTEMPT NO. 1 2 3
Replace a Hose Gasket		
1. Remove and discard old or damaged gasket.	In proper receptacle.	— — —
2. Pick up new gasket.	Between middle finger and thumb.	— — —
3. Fold loop upward.	With index finger.	— — —
4. Place gasket into swivel.	a. Large loop first.	
	b. Smoothing as necessary to seat.	— — —
	Time (Total)	— — —

EVALUATOR'S COMMENTS

_____

_____

Inspect Hose Couplings

Skills Sheet 2

Name_____ Date _____

Evaluator _____ Competency Rating _____

References	NFPA® 1001, *Prevention, Preparedness, and Maintenance* 5.5.4 **Essentials**, pages 405, 406 and 439
Prerequisites	None
Introduction	Before any piece of equipment is placed on the apparatus, it should be in top operating condition. Hose couplings are vital for attaching hose to other hose and nozzles. If they or their gaskets are damaged, they can hinder the mission and endanger firefighters' lives.
Equipment & Personnel	• One firefighter in protective clothing • Hoses with male, female, and sexless couplings • Replacement gaskets of appropriate types and sizes

OPERATION	KEY POINTS	ATTEMPT NO. 1 2 3

Replace a Hose Gasket

1. Inspect the male couplings. Meets the following criteria: ___ ___ ___
   a. Tight on hose or appliance
   b. Undamaged threads
   c. Not out of round
   d. Free of burrs
   e. Clean

2. Inspect the female couplings. Meets the following criteria: ___ ___ ___
   a. Tight on hose or appliance
   b. Undamaged threads
   c. Not out of round
   d. Free of burrs
   e. Clean
   f. Free-spinning swivel
   g. Swivel gasket undamaged, pliable, and clean

Replace a Hose Gasket

3. Inspect the sexless couplings. Meets the following criteria: ___ ___ ___
      a. Tight on hose or appliance
      b. Not edged
      c. Free of burrs
      d. Clean
      e. Free-spinning swivel
      f. Swivel gasket undamaged
         and clean
      g. Swivel gasket in place
      h. Undamaged connecting lugs

                                        Time (Total)   ___ ___ ___

EVALUATOR'S COMMENTS

_____

_____

Select the Proper Nozzle and Hose for Given Fire Attack Situations

Worksheet 12A-1

Name_____ Date _____

Evaluator _____ Competency Rating _____

References NFPA® 1001, *Fireground Operations* 5.3.10A

Prerequisites None

Introduction Firefighters must know the different sizes and uses for the various hoses and nozzles used in the fire service. Just as a carpenter knows that a particular type of saw or screwdriver is right for a specific job, so too should the firefighter be able to choose the hose and nozzle type appropriate for the fire situation on hand.

Directions Select the correct nozzle and hose for each of the situations described below. Write your answers in the blanks.

Short Answer

Write the correct answers on the blanks provided.

Situation 1: Wildland fire

a. Nozzle selected _____

b. Hose size/type selected _____

Situation 2: Residential structure; fire confined to two bedrooms

a. Nozzle selected _____

b. Hose size/type selected _____

Situation 3: Large, fully involved warehouse

a. Nozzle selected _____

b. Hose size/type selected _____

Laying, Carrying, & Advancing Hose

Terms

Write the definition of the terms below on the blanks provided.

1. Forward Hose Lay vs. Reverse Hose Lay _____

   _____

2. Intake Hose vs. Supply Hose _____

   _____

3. Soft-Sleeve Hose vs. Hard Suction (Sleeve) Hose _____

   _____

4. Split Hose Lay _____

   _____

5. Standpipe _____

   _____

Short Answer

Write the correct answers on the blanks provided.

1. What are the usual basic causes of hose damage? _____

   _____

2. What is the most important factor affecting the life of fire hose? _____

   _____

3. Detail specific ways that fire hose may be damaged, and then list recommended practices to prevent these damages.

   Mechanical damage _____

   _____

   Prevention practices_____

   _____

Awareness-Level First Responder

Name_____ Date _____

References	NFPA® 472, 4.2.3; *Hazardous Materials for First Responders*, 3rd ed.; *Emergency Response Guidebook*
Prerequisites	None
Introduction	The Emergency Response Guidebook is primarily a guide to aid first responders in quickly identifying the specific or generic hazards of the materials involved in an emergency incident, so that they may protect themselves and the general public during the initial response phase of the incident.
	The ERG assists responders in making initial decisions upon arriving at the scene of a hazardous materials incident. It is designed primarily for use at a haz mat incident occurring on a highway or railroad, so there may be limited value in its application at fixed facility locations.
Directions	Using the current edition of the *ERG*, answer the following questions. Always refer to the current edition to ensure up-to-date information.

Short Answer

Write the correct answers on the blanks provided.

1. What is the definition of oxidizer?_____

   _____

2. On which orange-bordered Guide page will you find information for Titanium trichloride, pyrophoric? _____

   _____

3. What is the UN/NA identification number for nitrous oxide, compressed?_____

   _____

Appendix J
Risk-Management Formulas

The following formulas may be used to calculate the frequency or incident rate and the severity of incidents.

The Occupational Safety and Health Administration (OSHA) calculates the frequency (incident rate) as follows:

$$N/EH \times 200,000 = IR$$

Where:

> N = number of injuries and/or illnesses
> EH = total hours worked by all employees during the calendar year
> 200,000 = base for 100 full-time equivalent employees (provides *standardization between agencies and companies*)
> IR = incident rate

OSHA calculates the severity as follows:

$$LWD/EH \times 200,000 = S$$

Where:

> LWD = loss work days
> EH = total hours worked by all employees during the calendar year
> 200,000 = base for 100 full-time equivalent employees
> S = severity rate

Another method is to assign values to the frequency and severity in the following formula:

$$R = S \times IR$$

Where:

> R = risk
> S = severity rate
> IR = incident rate

Assessment of Severity

8. Extreme — Multiple deaths or widespread destruction may result from hazard.

7. Very High — Potential death or injury or severe financial loss may result.

6. High — Permanent disabling injury may result.

5. Serious — Loss time injury greater than 28 days or considerable financial loss.

4. Moderate — Loss time injury of 4 to 28 days or moderate financial loss.

3. Minor — Loss time injury up to 3 days.

2. Slight — Minor injury resulting in no loss of time or slight financial loss.

1. Minimal — No loss of time injury or financial loss to organization.

Assessment of Incident Rate

7. Frequent   Occurs weekly.

6. Very Likely   Occurs once every few months.

5. Likely   Occurs about once a year.

4. Occasional   Occurs annually in the United States.

3. Rare   Occurs every 10 to 30 years.

2. Exceptional Occurs every 10 to 30 years in the United States.

1. Unlikely   May occur less than once in 100 years within the global fire service.

Appendix K
NFPA® Standards Applicable to Training

NFPA® Standards that affect training are as follows:

- NFPA® 472, *Standard for Professional Competence of Responders to Hazardous Materials Incidents*
- NFPA® 473, *Standard for Competencies for EMS Personnel Responding to Hazardous Materials Incidents*
- NFPA® 600, *Standard on Industrial Fire Brigades*
- NFPA® 1001, *Standard for Fire Fighter Professional Qualifications*
- NFPA® 1002, *Standard for Fire Apparatus Driver/Operator Professional Qualifications*
- NFPA® 1003, *Standard for Airport Fire Fighter Professional Qualifications*
- NFPA® 1021, *Standard for Fire Officer Professional Qualifications*
- NFPA® 1031, *Standard for Professional Qualifications for Fire Inspector and Plan Examiner*
- NFPA® 1033, *Standard for Professional Qualifications for Fire Investigator*
- NFPA® 1035, *Standard for Professional Qualifications for Public Fire and Life Safety Educator*
- NFPA® 1041, *Standard for Fire Service Instructor Professional Qualifications*
- NFPA® 1051, *Standard for Wildland Fire Fighter Professional Qualifications*
- NFPA® 1061, *Standard for Professional Qualifications for Public Safety Telecommunicator*
- NFPA® 1201, *Standard for Providing Emergency Services to the Public*
- NFPA® 1401, *Recommended Practice for Fire Service Training Reports and Records*
- NFPA® 1403, *Standard on Live Fire Training Evolutions*
- NFPA® 1404, *Standard for Fire Service Respiratory Protection Training*
- NFPA® 1500, *Standard on Fire Department Occupational Safety and Health Program*
- NFPA® 1521, *Standard for Fire Department Safety Officer*
- NFPA® 1710, *Standard for the Organization and Deployment of Fire Suppression Operations, Emergency Medical Operations, and Special Operations to the Public by Career Fire Departments*
- NFPA® 1720, *Standard for the Organization and Deployment of Fire Suppression Operations, Emergency Medical Operations, and Special Operations to the Public by Volunteer Fire Departments*

Appendix L
Sample Request for Proposal

Introduction

The _____Department is pursuing the evaluation and subsequent purchase of SCBA. To accomplish this, the department is requesting SCBA meeting the specifications shown in this request for proposal.

Through each of the major steps of the evaluation process, the SCBA evaluated will be assigned points based on a point system in the categories as follows:

SCBA Provider Support	30 points
Actual and/or Simulated Use Conditions	35 points
Classroom/Maintenance	35 points

Throughout the evaluation process each evaluation team member will review the features of the SCBA submitted and complete an evaluation form. The forms will be tabulated and totaled in each category.

The evaluation process will begin with distributor presentations and training of firefighters who are assigned to evaluate the SCBA. At the time of the presentation, the supplier must submit _____ SCBA meeting the specifications shown in this request for proposal and at least one spare cylinder for each SCBA to be used by the department for the evaluation period.

Each supplier is requested to complete the attached questionnaire and return it to:

_____
(Department Contact Person and Address)

The completed questionnaire should be returned no later than_____.

Pre-Qualification Questionnaire

All questions will be answered in detail on a separate sheet.

1. Location of Corporate/Business Headquarters:

   Company Name:
   Street:
   City, State, Zip:
   Phone:
   FAX:
   SCBA Supplied:

2. Location of the nearest office or distribution center with repair capabilities. Prompt facilitation of repairs will be a critical factor in pre-qualification. Describe in this section your ability to effectively perform maintenance service and repair functions.

Company Name:
Name of Person in Charge:
Street:
City, State, Zip:
Phone:
FAX:

3. Provide contact individuals, titles, and phone numbers of persons within your organization who will be responsible for supporting the department through the evaluation process as well as subsequent use and maintenance of SCBA.

4. How long has your firm been in the business of supplying SCBA and service?

5. What major fire department or industrial SCBA owner does your firm currently support? How many SCBA does this department/company own? How long has your firm supported this customer?

6. Indicate the approximate number of self-contained breathing apparatus sold during each of the past two years.

7. Indicate the approximate number of self-contained breathing apparatus overhauled/serviced during each of the past two years.

8. Will you furnish a finance program for this purchase? If so, include details of the program.

9. Indicate if you will provide facepiece fit testing, equipment identification, and record format. Please provide details of how each process is conducted.

10. Will you furnish a written guarantee that sufficient replacement apparatus and/or replacement parts and components will be available at your facility if requested within a minimum 24-hour period?

11. Will your firm provide support including training and technical information for the evaluation units and subsequent purchased SCBA?

12. Will you provide a written copy of the manufacturer's warranty on the entire SCBA unit? State length of standard warranty and portions of unit covered as well as all requirements for the department to remain within warranty compliance.

13. Provider must state estimated ability to meet current and future NFPA® standards.

14. Include any information that may be of interest to the _____ Department in this process.

15. Prospective provider must submit "Current Customer Profile" to allow the _____ Department full range of communication with current distributor customers.

Glossary

A

Academic Misconduct — Any unethical behavior in which students present another student's work as their own, or gain an unfair advantage on a test by bringing answers into the testing area, copying another student's answers, or acquiring test questions in advance.

Acquired Structure — Structure acquired by the authority having jurisdiction from a property owner for the purpose of conducting live fire training or rescue training evolutions. *Also known as* Acquired Building.

Administration Classification — Test classification based on how a test is administered.

Affective — Descriptive of a person's attitudes, values, and habits.

Agenda-Based Process — Classroom discussion format in which an agenda of topics or key points is provided to students for them to research, report on, and discuss as a group.

Alternatives — Possible answers in a multiple-choice test item.

Ancillary Components — Supplemental written materials that help students meet the learning objectives; may include information sheets, study guides, skill sheets, work or activity sheets, and assignment sheets.

Andragogy — Educational term that refers to the art of teaching adults.

Authority Having Jurisdiction (AHJ) — Term used in codes and standards to identify the legal entity, such as a building or fire official, that has the statutory authority to enforce a code and to approve or require equipment; may be a unit of a local, state, or federal government, depending on where the work occurs. In the insurance industry, it may refer to an insurance rating bureau or an insurance company inspection department.

B

Block Grant — Annual government grant to help local authorities provide general services for the public good, with few restrictions.

Blog — Abbreviation for *web log*; refers to a list of journal entries or articles posted by a single author or group of authors. Includes comment sections where readers can engage in conversation about entries.

Burn Building — Structure designed to contain live fires for the purpose of fire suppression training.

C

Capital Budget — Budget intended to fund large, one-time expenditures, such as those for fire stations, fire apparatus, or major pieces of equipment.

Case Study — Description of a real or hypothetical problem that an organization or an individual has dealt with and may face in the future.

Class Continuity — Principle of instruction which states that all information throughout a course should be presented in a logical, understandable pattern.

Coaching — Process in which instructors direct the skills performance of individuals by observing, evaluating, and making suggestions for improvement.

Code of Ethics — Statement of behavior that is right and proper conduct for an individual functioning within an organization or society as a whole.

Codes — A body of laws arranged systematically, usually pertaining to one subject area such as a mechanical code, a building code, an electrical code, or a fire code.

Cognition — Concept that refers to all forms of knowing, including perceiving, imagining, reasoning, and judging.

Competency-Based Learning (CBL) — Training that emphasizes knowledge and skills that are required on the job. Course objectives involve specific, criteria-based competence in performing tasks or understanding concepts that learners will use in their daily work. *Also known as* Criterion-Referenced and Performance-Based Learning.

Computer-Based Training (CBT) — A variety of self-study in which the student completes work on a computer with minimal communication with an instructor. *Also known as* E-learning, Blended E-learning, or Online Instruction.

Computer-Generated Slide Presentations — Computer presentations that are sequenced and displayed like traditional slideshows that use a slide projector with a carousel. Popular software for creating and viewing these presentations include Microsoft PowerPoint® and Apple Keynote®.

Cone of Learning — Visual representation that depicts what percentage of information human beings retain using their senses alone and in combination.

Controlled Burning — Any burn that is safely set and controlled for the purposes of fire and emergency services training.

Cost/Benefit Analysis — Systematic methodology to compare costs and benefits to make cost-effective funding decisions on projects.

Counseling — Advising learners or program participants on their educational progress, career opportunities, personal anxieties, or sudden crises in their lives.

Course — Series of lessons that lead to the completion of a discipline or certification.

Course Consistency — Principle of instruction that states that information throughout a course should have the same level of accuracy, be presented with the same equipment and training aids, and maintain a similar level of learning.

Course Objectives — Specific identification of the planned results of a course of instruction.

Criterion — The standard against which learning is compared after instruction. Plural for the term is *criteria*.

Criterion-Referenced Assessment — Measurement of individual performance against a set standard or criteria, not against other students. Mastery learning is the key element to criterion-referenced testing.

Critical Criteria — Step or steps on a practical skills test that must be completed accurately in order for the student to pass the test.

Curriculum — Series of courses in which students are introduced to skills and knowledge required for a specific discipline.

Customer Approval Rating (CAR) — Organizational rating that adds a quantifiable raking to qualitative evaluations. *Also known as* Customer Satisfaction Rating (CSR).

D

Disclosure — Legal term referring to the act of giving out information either voluntarily or to meet legal requirements or agency policy requirements.

Distance Learning — Generic term for instruction that occurs when the student is remote from the instructor, and a medium such as the Internet or Interactive Television is used to maintain communication between the two.

Distractors — Possible answers in a multiple-choice test item that are incorrect but plausible.

Domains of Learning — Areas of learning and classification of learning objectives; often referred to as cognitive (knowledge), affective (attitude), and psychomotor (skill performance) learning.

Drill Tower — A tall training structure, typically more than three stories high, used to create realistic training situations, especially ladder and rope evolutions. *Also known as* Tower.

E

Education — The acquisition of knowledge, usually through academic means such as college or university courses.

Evaluation — Systematic and thoughtful collection of information for decision-making; consists of criteria, evidence, and judgment.

Evolution — (1) Sequential operation, or set or prescribed action that results in an effective fireground activity. (2) Operation of fire and emergency services training covering one or several aspects of fire fighting. *Also known as* Practical Training Evolution.

F

Fair Use — Doctrine of the Copyright Act that grants the privilege of copying materials to persons other than the owner of the copyright, without consent, when the material is used in a reasonable manner.

Family Educational Rights and Privacy Act (FERPA) — Legislation that provides that an individual's school records are confidential and that information contained in those records may not be released without the individual's prior written consent.

File Sharing — Practice of making files or documents on one computer or server available to the general public, or to a selected group of individuals who are given access to the files. Allows users at remote locations to have access to the same materials without the need to put those materials on CD-ROM, memory drives, or other media.

Flammable/Combustible Liquid Pit — Training prop designed to provide controlled burns of flammable or combustible liquids; used in training for the extinguishment of flammable/combustible liquid fires.

Formative Test — Ongoing, repeated assessment during a course to evaluate student progress; may also help determine any needed changes in instructional content, methods, training aids, and testing techniques.

Foreseeability — Legal concept that states that reasonable people should be able to foresee the consequences of their actions and take reasonable precautions.

Four-Step Method of Instruction — Teaching method based upon four steps: preparation, presentation, application, and evaluation. May be preceded by a pretest.

G

Grant — Donated funding from a government or private source, typically secured through a competitive application process; funds do not have to be repaid, and may be separate from an organization's operational or capital budget.

Guideline — Statement that identifies a general philosophy; may be included as part of a policy.

H

Harassment — A course of conduct directed at a specific person that causes substantial emotional distress in said person and serves no legitimate purpose.

Hazard or Risk Analysis — Identification of hazards or risks and the determination of an appropriate response; combines the hazard assessment with risk management concepts.

I

Illustrated Lecture — Instructional technique in which audiovisual training aids accompany a lecture, in order to clarify information and facilitate interaction with the students.

Incident Action Plan (IAP) — Written or unwritten plan for the disposition of an incident; contains the overall strategic goals, tactical objectives, and support requirements for a given operational period during an incident.

Incident Command System (ICS) — System by which facilities, equipment, personnel, procedures, and communications are organized to operate within a common organizational structure designed to aid in the management of resources at emergency incidents.

Individualized Instruction — Adapting teaching methods to suit individual students' specific learning styles, so that students will be better able to achieve learning objectives.

Invasion of Privacy — Wrongful intrusion into a person's private activities by the government or other individuals.

J

Job Performance Requirement (JPR) — Statement that describes the performance required for a specific job.

K

Key Point — Important cognitive information on a skill sheet that students need to know in order to perform a task or operational step; generally appears on the right-hand side of a skill sheet.

Keystoning — Distortion of the projected transparency image that happens when the projector and screen are not perpendicular to each other.

L

Learning Disability — Classification of a disorder in which a person has difficulty learning in a typical manner because of a problem with the brain's ability to receive and process information.

Learning Objective — Specific statement that describes the knowledge or skills that students should acquire by the end of a lesson.

Learning Outcome — Statement that broadly specifies what students will know or be able to do once learning is complete.

Learning Plateau — A break or leveling of a student's progress in a training course or class.

Learning Style — Learner's habitual manner of problem-solving, thinking, or learning, though the learner may not be conscious of his or her style and may adopt different styles for different learning tasks or circumstances.

Legal Precedent — The history of rulings made in courts of law that can be referenced and used to make court decisions in future cases or influence laws outside of the court system.

Liability — To be legally obligated or responsible for an act or physical condition; *opposite of* Immunity.

Live-Fire Exercises — Training exercises that involve the use of an unconfined open flame or fire or other combustibles in a structure to provide a controlled burning environment. *Also known as* Live-Burn Exercises.

Logistics — Process of managing the scheduling of limited materials and equipment to meet the multiple demands of training programs and instructors.

M

Model Release — Legal document that grants permission to use a person's image or voice in photos or recordings.

Moulage Kit — Makeup kit containing appliqué wounds and stage makeup; used during casualty simulations to simulate wounds on a manikin or actor.

N

National Institute for Occupational Safety and Health (NIOSH) — U.S. government agency that helps ensure workplace safety; investigates workplaces, recommends safety measures, and produces reports about on-the-job fire injuries. Operates as part of the Centers for Disease Control and Prevention, within the U.S. Department of Health and Human Services.

Needs Analysis — Assessment of the gap between the training an organization provides and the training it should provide, either currently or in the future.

Nominal Group Process — Classroom discussion format that requires students to follow a decision-making process similar to the processes that they will encounter in their professional duties.

Norm-Referenced Assessment — Form of assessment in which a student's performance is compared to that of other students. Grades are determined by comparing scores to the class average, and assigning grades based on how students scored compared to that average.

O

Occupational Safety and Health Administration (OSHA) — U.S. federal agency that develops and enforces standards and regulations for occupational safety in the workplace.

Operational Budget — Document that outlines operating expenses for any course, curriculum, or training program.

Operational Step — The smallest aspect of performing a task; to complete the task, students perform a series of operational steps in sequential order.

Ordinance — Local or municipal law that applies to persons and things of the local jurisdiction; a local agency act that has the force of a statute; different from law that is enacted by federal or state/provincial legislatures.

Outcome Objective — Desired student performance resulting from a lesson or presentation.

P

Pilot Course — First implementation of a newly developed course; intended to allow instructors to evaluate a new course and make changes for improvement.

Policy — Organizational principle that is developed and adopted as a basis for decision-making.

Post-Incident Analysis — Overview and critique of an incident by members of all responding agencies, including dispatchers. Typically takes place within two weeks of the incident. In the training environment it may be used to evaluate student and instructor performance during a training evolution.

Prescriptive Test — Test given at the beginning of instruction to determine what students already know; alternatively, a test that is given remedially.

Pretest/Posttest — Prescriptive evaluation instrument administered to students and used to compare knowledge or skills either before (pretest) or after (posttest) a presentation or program. Pretests check entry-level knowledge or abilities; pretest scores are compared with posttest scores to determine learners' progress.

Procedure — Outline of the steps that must be performed in order to properly follow an organizational policy.

Program — Collection of curricula and the resources necessary to deliver the instruction for those curricula.

Psychomotor Learning Domain — Learning that involves physical, hands-on activities, or actions that a students must be able to do or perform.

Public Domain — Works of artists, photographers, and authors that were published before 1923 or are no longer covered by any copyright ownership.

Purpose Classification — Means of classifying tests based on when the test occurs during a course.

Purpose-Built Structure — Building specially designed for live-fire training; fires can be ignited inside the building multiple times without major structural damage.

Q

Qualitative Evaluation — Evaluation based on nonnumerical analysis and intended to assess the quality of something.

Quantitative Evaluation — Evaluation based on numeric or statistical analysis and intended to discover quantifiable data.

R

Reasonable Accommodation — Changes or adjustments in a work or school site, program, or job that makes it possible for an otherwise qualified employee or student with a disability to perform the duties or tasks required.

Records — Permanent accounts of past events or of actions taken by an individual, unit, or organization.

Regulations — Rules or directives of administrative agencies that have authorization to issue them.

Reliability — A condition of validity; the extent to which a test or test item consistently and accurately produces the same results or scores when given to a set of learners on different occasions, marked by different assessors, or marked by the same assessors on different occasions.

Reports — Official accounts of an incident, response, or training event, either verbally or in writing.

Request for Proposal (RFP) — Public document that advertises an organizational need to manufacturers or individuals who may be able to meet that need.

Restrictive Bid — Bid that includes many specifications that only one manufacturer can meet; *also known as* Sole-Sourced Bid.

Risk-Management Plan — Written plan that identifies and analyzes the exposure to hazards, selects appropriate risk management techniques to handle exposures, implements those techniques, and monitors the results.

Rubric — Scoring tool that outlines criteria that must be present on exams that are more subjective such as short-answer tests, essay tests, or oral tests; the criteria should be tied to learning objectives.

S

Self-Directed Learning — Method of instruction in which individual students work at their own pace to accomplish course objectives in any way they choose. Course objectives may be determined by the instructor or chosen by the student, but course content is always determined by the instructor. *Also known as* Independent Learning.

Sensory Memory — Mental storage system for attention-getting sensory stimuli or input.

Sequential Training — Preferred training method, in which the student is taken step by step from simple to complex exercises when learning to use equipment such as a self-contained breathing apparatus (SCBA).

Sexual Harassment — Superior offering advancement or special treatment in return for sexual favors from a subordinate; also may refer to any situation in which an employee, regardless of gender, believes that the workplace is a hostile environment because of sexually offensive or sexist behavior.

Smokehouse — Specially designed fire training building that is filled with smoke to simulate working under live fire conditions; used for SCBA and search and rescue training. *Also known as* Smoke Building.

Social Networking — Websites that allow users to be part of a virtual community. Users can communicate through private messages or real-time chat, and share photos, video, and audio.

Standard — Criterion documents that are developed to serve as models or examples of desired performance or behaviors and that contains requirements and specifications outlining minimum levels of performance, protection, or construction. No one is required to meet the requirements set forth in standards unless those standards are legally adopted by the authority having jurisdiction, in which case they become law.

Standard Operating Procedure (SOP) — Rule for how personnel should perform routine functions or emergency operations. Procedures are typically written in a handbook, so that all firefighters can become familiar with them.

Stem — Introductory statement in a multiple-choice test item.

Summative Test — Evaluation that measures students' learning at the conclusion of a training session or course; the test results can also be used to measure the effects and effectiveness of a course or program.

T

Task Analysis — Systematic analysis of duties for a specific job or jobs, which identifies and describes all component tasks of that job; enables program developers to design appropriate training for personnel and trainees who must learn certain tasks to perform a job.

Teleconferencing — Telephone service that allows multiple individuals at remote locations to have an audio-only meeting.

Test Item — Single question on a testing instrument that elicits a student response and can be scored for accuracy.

Testing Instrument — Series of test items that are based on learning objectives and collectively measure student learning on a specific topic.

Training — The transfer of knowledge regarding vocational or technical skills.

Training Aids — Broad term referring to any audiovisual aids, reprinted materials, training props, or equipment used to supplement instruction.

V

Validity — Extent to which a test or other assessment technique measures the learner qualities (knowledge or skills) that it is meant to measure.

Vehicle Driving Course — Permanent or temporary training course used for training in apparatus and vehicle driving and operation.

Vicarious Liability — Liability imposed on one person for the conduct of another, based solely on the relationship between the two persons; indirect legal responsibility for the acts of another, such as the liability of an employer for acts of an employee.

W

Web Conferencing — Meeting service that combines teleconferencing with an Internet-based sharing service, enabling users to communicate in real time while viewing and interacting with a computer-based presentation.

Wiki — Website that allows users to update, edit, or comment on the original content using their own Internet browser; allows for the rapid creation and deployment of websites and collaborative work on documents.

Wildland Fire — Unplanned, unwanted, and uncontrolled fire in vegetative fuels such as grass, brush, or timberland involving uncultivated lands; requires suppression action and may threaten structures or other improvements.

Wildland/Urban Interface — Line, area, or zone where an undeveloped wildland area meets a human development area. *Also known as* Urban/Wildland Interface.

Index

A

Abstract instructional strategy, 45
Academic misconduct, 240
Acceptance of instructors, 12
Access to training sites, 119
Accident investigation at training evolutions, 292
Accrediting organizations, 198
Acquired structure, 206–212
    asbestos, 209
    checklists and forms, 458–464
    dangers of, 206, 208, 458–464
    defined, 206
    environmental conditions, 208–209
    fuel usage, 210–211
    instructor responsibilities, 209–210
    limits on types of training, 208
    NFPA® 1403 standards, 208–211, 458–464
    safety of live-fire training, 206, 208, 458–464
    structural conditions, 209
    training forms, 458–464
    training possibilities, 209
    as training site, 115
    water supply requirements, 211–212
Act of commission, 216
Act of omission, 216
ADA. See Americans with Disabilities Act (ADA)
Administration
    classification
        defined, 228
        oral tests, 228
        performance tests, 229–230
        written tests, 228–229
    training evolution support, 282–283
    of training programs. *See* Training program administration
Affective (attitude) domain of learning, 43–44, 264
Age of adult learners, 40
Agency level needs analysis, 413–414
Agency training history, 376
Agenda-based process, 151
Aggressive students, 176
AHJ. *See* Authority having jurisdiction (AHJ)
Aircraft hangars as training sites, 117
Aircraft incident props, 98
Airports as training site, 115
Alternative-response question, 304
American Council on Education, 347
American National Standards Institute (ANSI), 196
American Psychiatric Association (APA), 353
American Society of Safety Engineers (ASSE), 197
Americans with Disabilities Act (ADA)
    categories of learning disabilities, 172
    protection from discrimination, 173
    provisions, 21, 350, 435
    students' rights, 177
Analysis
    agency level needs analysis, 331, 413–414
    cognitive level of learning, 315
    cost/benefit analysis of curriculums, 379–380

    hazard and risk, 285–286, 472–473
    ICS-215A, Incident Action Safety Plan Analysis, 453
    post-incident, 289–290
    task analysis, 378
    test item analysis, 388–389
    test result analysis, 388
    training needs analysis, 376–377
Anatomical manikins, 96
Anatomical models as training aids, 88
Ancillary components, 269–273
    assignment sheet, 272–273
    defined, 269
    examples, 465–471
    information sheet, 270
    skill sheet, 270–271
    study sheet, 272
    worksheet, 271–272
Andragogy, 36
Animations, 139
ANSI (American National Standards Institute), 196
APA (American Psychiatric Association), 353
APA Style, 353
Application
    certification application records, 246
    cognitive level of learning, 315
    four-step instruction method, 142
Asbestos at acquired structures, 209
ASSE (American Society of Safety Engineers), 197
Assessment of students. *See also* Evaluation
    criterion-referenced, 226
    norm-referenced, 226
Assignment sheet, 272–273
Assignments of lesson plans, 73
Association of new and old information, 37, 256
Atmosphere, environmental issues at training evolutions, 290, 292
Attendance records, 246, 345
Attending as listening skill, 132
Attitude
    domain of learning, 43–44
    of supervisors, 330
    unsafe behavior, 285
Audio recordings as training aids, 88
Audiovisual components of lesson plans, 273–274
Audiovisual equipment in classrooms, 112–113
Audit of records, 347
Auditorium style seating arrangement, 108
Authority having jurisdiction (AHJ)
    computer-based training, 160
    defined, 22
    laws governing training activities, 22
    national codes and standards adopted by, 23

B

Baby boomer characteristics, 41
Behavioral reinforcement, 154–155
Bias
    grading, 239

development of, 412–413
  evaluation, 360
  ICS, 442–453
  sample model release form, 439–440
Foundations of learning, 34–38
  Cone of Learning, 34–35
  Knowles' assumptions of adult learners, 36
  sensory-stimulus theory, 34–35
  Thorndike's laws of learning, 36–38
Four-step development model, 374
Four-step method of instruction, 140–143
  application, 142
  defined, 140
  evaluation, 143
  preparation, 142
  presentation, 142
Freedom of Information Act, 349, 426
Fuel usage at acquired structure training, 210–211
Funding. *See* Budget

G

Gas fed props, 99
Gas storage and processing incident props, 99
Gender of adult learners, 40
Generational characteristics, 41
Gen-X characteristics, 41
Gen-Y characteristics, 41
Gestures as nonverbal communication, 131
Global instructional strategies, 45
Goals
  of courses, 381
  goal-based evaluations, 396
  of instructors, 327
Government-owned reservations as training site, 115
Grading tests
  bias, 239
  defined, 233
  fire and emergency services tests, 238–239
  grade reporting, 239
Grain elevators/silos as training site, 115
Grants
  block grants, 340–341
  defined, 340
Guided discussion, 149
Guideline
  adoption of, 419
  defined, 416
  need for new guideline, 416–417

H

Handouts, 86–87
Harassment, 21
Hazard and risk analysis, 285–286, 472–473
Hazard exposure training, 205–215
  examples of, 205
  increased hazard exposure training, 214–215
  live-fire training, 206–214
  overview, 205–206
Hazard vs. risk, 286
Hazardous materials, incident props, 99
Health Insurance Portability Accountability Act (HIPAA), 22

Heating, ventilating, and air conditioning (HVAC) systems for classrooms, 111
High-angle rescue props, 97
HIPAA (Health Insurance Portability Accountability Act), 22
Holistic instructional strategies, 45
Hollow square style seating arrangement, 110
Honesty of instructors, 15
Horseshoe style seating arrangement, 108
Human resources management, 426–428
  instructional staff selection, 426–427
  instructor qualifications, 427
  position advertising, 427–428
HVAC systems for classrooms, 111

I

IAFC (International Association of Fire Chiefs), 197, 347
IAFF (International Association of Fire Fighters), 197
IAP (incident action plan), 287–288
ICMA (International City/County Managers Association), 347
ICS. *See* Incident command system (ICS) model
IDEA (Individuals with Disabilities Education Act), 173
IFSAC (International Fire Service Accreditation Congress), 198, 347, 400
Illustrated lecture, 146–147
Illustration displays, 85–86
ILT. *See* Instructor-led training (ILT)
Incident action plan (IAP), 287–288
Incident command system (ICS) model, 287–290
  duties and functions, 287
  forms, 442–453
    ICS-201, Incident Briefing, 443–446
    ICS-202, Incident Objectives, 447
    ICS-203, Organization Assignment List, 448
    ICS-204, Assignment List, 449
    ICS-205, Incident Radio Communications Plan, 450
    ICS-206, Medical Plan, 451
    ICS-215, Operational Planning Worksheet, 452
    ICS-215A, Incident Action Safety Plan Analysis, 453
  incident action plan, 287–288
  NIMS-ICS
    evolution control, 202
    training safety guidelines, 198
  post-incident analysis, 289–290
  purpose of, 287
  training safety guidelines, 198
Incident/injury records, 246, 345
Independent learning, 163–164
Individual student needs, 171–177
  disruptive, nonparticipating students, 176–177
  gifted students, 173–174
  learning disabilities, 172–173
  low literacy level, 171–172
  nondisruptive, nonparticipating students, 175–176
  nondisruptive, participating, successful students, 177
  slow learners or slow students, 174–175
Individual-based teaching, 139
Individualized instruction, 164–165
Individuals with Disabilities Education Act (IDEA), 173
Industrial training sites, 116
Information sheet, 270
Information sources for research, 351–353
Ingenuity of instructors, 13

Medical records, privacy of, 22
Mentoring, 182–183
Message (the lesson) of information, 126
MFIPPA (Municipal Freedom of Information and Protection of Privacy Act), 348
Military reservations as training site, 115
Millenials, characteristics of, 41
Miniatures as training aids, 88
MiniDV/HDV video, 93
Model release, 83, 439–440
Models
    actual tools and equipment, 88
    anatomical models, 88
    cutaway models, 87
    four-step development model, 374
    ICS model, 287–290
        duties and functions, 287
        forms, 442–453
        incident action plan, 287–288
        post-incident analysis, 289–290
        purpose of, 287
        training safety guidelines, 198
    Kirkpatrick's Four-Level Training Evaluation Model, 397–398
    Mager Model, 74–75, 262, 272
    replicas or miniatures, 88
    sample model release form, 439–440
    tabletop miniatures, 87
Modules, 139
Motivation
    of adult learners, 39
    andragogy assumption, 36
    of instructors, 11
    of students, 45–46, 153–154
Moulage kits, 88–89
Multimedia projectors as training aids, 89–91, 139
Multiple-choice test
    alternatives, 302
    described, 228
    distractors, 302
    stem, 302
    test items, 302–303
    time requirements, 301
Municipal Freedom of Information and Protection of Privacy Act (MFIPPA), 348

N

NAFTD (North American Fire Training Directors), 197
National Board on Fire Service Professional Qualifications (ProBoard)
    accrediting and certifying, 198
    training program evaluations, 400
    training record, legal requirements, 347
National Fire Academy (NFA), 195, 398
National Fire Protection Association® (NFPA®). *See also specific NFPA® standard*
    purpose of, 196
    standards applicable to training, 474
National Institute for Occupational Safety and Health (NIOSH)
    live-fire training safety, 206
    resource materials, 81
    safe workplace policies, 194
    Workplace Solutions, 454–457

National Institute of Science and Technology (NIST)
    resource materials, 81
    safe workplace policies, 194
    study on fuel pallet size in training evolutions, 211
National Registry of Emergency Medical Technicians (NREMT), 198
National Volunteer Fire Council (NVFC), 197
National Wildland Coordinating Group (NWCG), 214
Needs analysis
    training program, 413–414
        committee meetings, 414
        data organization and interpretation, 414
        prerequisites for, 413
    training schedule, 331
Negative reinforcement, 155
New York, State of, v. Baird, 219
Nexters, characteristics of, 41
NFA (National Fire Academy), 195, 398
NFPA® 1021, *Standard for Fire Officer Professional Qualifications*, 1
NFPA® 1035, *Standard for Professional Qualifications for Fire and Life Safety Educator*, 420
NFPA® 1041, *Standard for Fire Service Instructor Professional Qualifications*
    chapter and page correlation, 433–434
    evaluation of Level I Instructors, 359
    fire service terminology and technical writing, 384
    hazard exposure training, 205
    instructor qualifications, 427
    job performance requirements compared to learning objectives, 75
    lesson plan development, 256
    Level III instructor, 373, 375
    live-fire training, 121
    purpose of, 1, 197
    record-keeping prerequisites, 412
    testing and evaluation duties, 225
    testing instruments, 297
NFPA® 1142, water supply requirements, 211
NFPA® 1201, *Standard for Providing Emergency Services to the Public*, 415
NFPA® 1401, *Recommended Practice for Fire Service Training Reports and Records*, 344–345, 411
NFPA® 1402, *Guide to Building Fire Service Training Centers*, 197
NFPA® 1403, *Standard on Live Fire Training Evolutions*
    acquired structure training safety, 208–211
    acquired structures, 115
    adoption of a standard, 421
    exterior fire training, 212
    instructor requirements, 121
    procedure development, 416
    purpose of, 197, 206
    purpose-built structure for training, 212
    requirements, 284
    training ground safety, 119
NFPA® 1410, *Standard on Training for Initial Emergency Scene Operations*, 197
NFPA® 1500, *Standard on Fire Department Occupational Safety and Health Program*
    live-fire training, 121
    policy development, 415
    purpose of, 197

Index by Nancy Kopper